THE HOME BOOK OF VERSE
FOR YOUNG FOLKS

The
HOME BOOK
of VERSE *for*
YOUNG FOLKS

Selected and arranged by
BURTON EGBERT STEVENSON

Decorations by
WILLY POGANY

Revised and Enlarged Edition

NEW YORK
HENRY HOLT AND COMPANY

672 p.

COPYRIGHT ACKNOWLEDGMENT

To
ELIZABETH, LIZZIE,
BETSY, AND BESS

THE ARGUMENT OF THIS BOOK

I sing of brooks, of blossoms, birds, and bowers,
Of April, May, of June, and July flowers;

.   .   .   .   .   .

I sing of dews, of rains, and, piece by piece,
Of balm, of oil, of spice, and ambergris.
I sing of times trans-shifting; and I write
How roses first came red, and lilies white;
I write of groves, of twilights, and I sing
The court of Mab, and of the Fairy King.

.   .   .   .   .   .

Robert Herrick

TABLE OF CONTENTS

THE DUTY OF CHILDREN

FAIRYLAND

THE GLAD EVANGEL

THIS WONDERFUL WORLD

STORIES IN RHYME

MY COUNTRY

A GARLAND OF GOLD

INDICES

I. In the Nursery

BABY-LAND

Which is the way to Baby-land?
  Any one can tell;
    Up one flight,
    To your right;
  Please to ring the bell.

What can you see in Baby-land?
  Little folks in white,
    Downy heads,
    Cradle-beds,
  Faces pure and bright.

What do they do in Baby-land?
  Dream and wake and play,
    Laugh and crow,
    Shout and grow,
  Jolly times have they.

What do they say in Baby-land?
  Why, the oddest things;
    Might as well
    Try to tell
  What a birdie sings.

Who is the Queen of Baby-land?
  Mother, kind and sweet;
    And her love,
    Born above,
  Guides the little feet.

George Cooper

IN THE NURSERY

MOTHER GOOSE'S MELODIES

Mistress Mary, quite contrary,
How does your garden grow?
With cockle-shells, and silver bells,
And pretty maids all in a row.

Peter, Peter, pumpkin eater,
Had a wife and couldn't keep her;
He put her in a pumpkin shell
And there he kept her very well.

Rub-a-dub-dub,
Three men in a tub,
And who do you think they be?
The butcher, the baker,
The candlestick-maker;
Turn 'em out, knaves all three!

Hickory, dickory, dock,
The mouse ran up the clock;
The clock struck one,
The mouse ran down,
Hickory, dickory, dock.

A dillar, a dollar, a ten o'clock scholar,
What makes you come so soon?
You used to come at ten o'clock,
But now you come at noon.

Three wise men of Gotham
Went to sea in a bowl;

If the bowl had been stronger,
My song had been longer.

There was an old woman lived under a hill
And if she's not gone, she lives there still.

One misty, moisty morning,
    When cloudy was the weather,
I met a little old man
    Clothed all in leather;
He began to bow and scrape,
    And I began to grin,—
How do you do, and how do you do,
    And how do you do again?

There was a little man, and he had a little gun,
    And his bullets were made of lead, lead, lead;
He shot Johnny Sprig through the middle of his wig,
    And knocked it right off his head, head, head.

There was an old woman who lived in a shoe,
She had so many children she didn't know what to do;
She gave them some broth without any bread,
Then whipped them all soundly and put them to bed.

Hey, diddle, diddle,
    The cat and the fiddle,
The cow jumped over the moon;
    The little dog laughed
    To see such sport,
And the dish ran away with the spoon.

Little Jack Horner
Sat in the corner
Eating a Christmas pie;

He put in his thumb,
And pulled out a plum,
And said, "What a good boy am I!"

Little Miss Muffet
Sat on a tuffet,
Eating of curds and whey;
There came a big spider
That sat down beside her,
And frightened Miss Muffet away.

Little Polly Flinders,
Sat among the cinders,
Warming her pretty little toes;
Her mother came and caught her,
And whipped her little daughter
For spoiling her nice new clothes.

There was a crooked man, and he went a crooked mile;
He found a crooked sixpence against a crooked stile:
He bought a crooked cat, which caught a crooked mouse,
And they all lived together in a little crooked house.

Barber, barber, shave a pig,
How many hairs will make a wig?
"Four-and-twenty, that's enough."
Give the barber a pinch of snuff.

Little Boy Blue, come blow your horn,
The sheep's in the meadow, the cow's in the corn;
But where is the boy that looks after the sheep?
He's under a hay-cock, fast asleep.
Will you awake him? No, not I;
For if I do, he'll be sure to cry.

There was a man of our town,
And he was wondrous wise,

He jumped into a bramble bush,
    And scratched out both his eyes;
But when he saw his eyes were out,
    With all his might and main,
He jumped into another bush,
    And scratched 'em in again.

———

Pussy-cat, pussy-cat, where have you been?
I've been to London to look at the Queen.
Pussy-cat, pussy-cat, what did you there?
I frightened a little mouse under the chair.

———

There were two blackbirds sitting on a hill,
The one named Jack, the other named Jill;
Fly away, Jack! Fly away, Jill!
Come again, Jack! Come again, Jill!

———

Little Tommy Tucker
    Sing for your supper.
What shall I sing?
    Brown bread and butter.
How shall I cut it
    Without any knife?
How shall I marry
    Without any wife?

———

Hark, hark! The dogs do bark,
    The beggars are coming to town,
Some in rags, some in tags,
    And one in a velvet gown.

———

Baa, baa, black sheep, have you any wool?
Yes, sir, yes, sir, three bags full.
One for my master, one for my dame,
And one for the little boy that lives in the lane.

Ride a cock-horse to Banbury Cross,
To see a fine lady upon a white horse,
Rings on her fingers, and bells on her toes,
She shall have music wherever she goes.

———

Hector Protector was dressed all in green;
Hector Protector was sent to the Queen.
The Queen did not like him, no more did the King;
So Hector Protector was sent back again.

———

Peter Piper picked a peck of pickled peppers;
A peck of pickled peppers Peter Piper picked;
If Peter Piper picked a peck of pickled peppers,
Where's the peck of pickled peppers Peter Piper picked?

———

Jack Sprat could eat no fat,
 His wife could eat no lean,
And so, betwixt them both,
 They licked the platter clean.

———

As Tommy Snooks and Bessy Brooks
 Were walking out one Sunday,
Says Tommy Snooks to Bessy Brooks,
 "To-morrow will be Monday."

———

To market, to market, to buy a fat pig,
Home again, home again, jiggety-jig;
To market, to market, to buy a fat hog,
Home again, home again, jiggety-jog;
To market, to market, to buy a plum bun,
Home again, home again, market is done.

———

Curly Locks, Curly Locks, wilt thou be mine?
Thou shalt not wash dishes, nor yet feed the swine,
But sit on a cushion and sew a fine seam,
And live upon strawberries, sugar, and cream.

JACK AND JILL

Jack and Jill went up the hill,
   To fetch a pail of water;
Jack fell down and broke his crown
   And Jill came tumbling after.

Up Jack got and home did trot
   As fast as he could caper,
And went to bed to mend his head
   With vinegar and brown paper.

SOLOMON GRUNDY

Solomon Grundy,
Born on a Monday,
Christened on Tuesday,
Married on Wednesday,
Took ill on Thursday,
Worse on Friday,
Died on Saturday,
Buried on Sunday,
This is the end of
Solomon Grundy.

THE QUEEN OF HEARTS

The Queen of Hearts
She made some tarts,
All on a summer's day;
The Knave of Hearts
He stole those tarts,
And with them ran away.

The King of Hearts
Called for those tarts,
And beat the Knave full sore;
The Knave of Hearts
Brought back the tarts,
And vowed he'd steal no more.

GOOD KING ARTHUR

When good King Arthur ruled this land,
He was a goodly King;
He stole three pecks of barley meal,
To make a bag-pudding.

A bag-pudding the Queen did make,
And stuffed it well with plums:
And in it put great lumps of fat,
As big as my two thumbs.

The King and Queen did eat thereof,
And noblemen beside;
And what they could not eat that night,
The Queen next morning fried.

OLD KING COLE

Old King Cole was a merry old soul,
And a merry old soul was he;
He called for his pipe, and he called for his bowl,
And he called for his fiddlers three.

Every fiddler, he had a fiddle,
And a very fine fiddle had he;
Twee tweedle dee, tweedle dee, went the fiddlers.
Oh, there's none so rare, as can compare
With King Cole and his fiddlers three!

LITTLE BO-PEEP

Little Bo-peep has lost her sheep,
  And can't tell where to find them;
Leave them alone, and they'll come home,
  Wagging their tails behind them.

Little Bo-peep fell fast asleep,
  And dreamed she heard them bleating;
But when she awoke, she found it a joke,
  For they were still a-fleeting.

Then up she took her little crook,
  Determined for to find them;
She found them indeed, but it made her heart bleed,
  For they'd left their tails behind them!

It happened one day, as Bo-peep did stray
  Into a meadow hard by,
There she espied their tails side by side,
  All hung on a tree to dry.

She heaved a sigh and wiped her eye,
  And over the hillocks she raced
And did what she could, as a shepherdess should,
  That each tail should be properly placed.

SIMPLE SIMON

Simple Simon met a pieman
  Going to the fair;
Says Simple Simon to the pieman,
  "Let me taste your ware."

Says the pieman to Simple Simon,
  "Show me first your penny;"

Says Simple Simon to the pieman,
"Indeed I have not any."

Simple Simon went a-fishing
For to catch a whale;
All the water he had got
Was in his mother's pail.

Simple Simon went to look
If plums grew on a thistle;
He pricked his fingers very much,
Which made poor Simon whistle.

I HAD A LITTLE HUSBAND

I had a little husband
No bigger than my thumb;
I put him in a pint pot,
And there I bid him drum.

I bought a little horse
That galloped up and down;
I bridled him and saddled him,
And sent him out of town.

I gave him some garters,
To garter up his hose,
And a little handkerchief,
To wipe his pretty nose.

SING A SONG OF SIXPENCE

Sing a song of sixpence,
A pocket full of rye;
Four-and-twenty blackbirds
Baked in a pie;

When the pie was opened,
  The birds began to sing:
Wasn't that a dainty dish
  To set before the King?

The King was in the parlor
  Counting out his money;
The Queen was in the kitchen
  Eating bread and honey;
The maid was in the garden
  Hanging out the clothes,
When down came a blackbird,
  And nipped off her nose.

JOHNNY SHALL HAVE A NEW BONNET

Johnny shall have a new bonnet,
  And Johnny shall go to the fair,
And Johnny shall have a blue ribbon
  To tie up his bonny brown hair.

And why may not I love Johnny,
  And why may not Johnny love me?
And why may not I love Johnny
  As well as another body?

And here's a leg for a stocking,
  And here's a foot for a shoe;
And he has a kiss for his daddy,
  And one for his mammy, too.

And why may not I love Johnny,
  And why may not Johnny love me?
And why may not I love Johnny,
  As well as another body?

COCK A DOODLE DOO

Cock a doodle doo!
My dame has lost her shoe;
My master's lost his fiddle-stick,
And don't know what to do.

Cock a doodle doo!
What is my dame to do?
Till master finds his fiddle-stick,
She'll dance without her shoe.

Cock a doodle doo!
My dame has found her shoe,
And master's found his fiddle-stick,
Sing doodle, doodle, doo!

Cock a doodle doo!
My dame will dance with you,
While master fiddles his fiddle-stick
For dame and doodle doo.

A PLEASANT SHIP

I saw a ship a-sailing,
A-sailing on the sea,
And oh! it was all laden
With pretty things for thee!

There were comfits in the cabin,
And apples in the hold;
The sails were made of silk,
And the masts were made of gold.

The four-and-twenty sailors
That stood between the decks
Were four-and-twenty white mice,
With chains about their necks.

The captain was a duck
With a packet on his back,
And when the ship began to move
The captain said "Quack! Quack!"

LITTLE ROBIN REDBREAST

Little Robin Redbreast sat upon a tree,
Up went pussy-cat, and down went he;
Down came pussy-cat, and away Robin ran;
Said little Robin Redbreast, "Catch me if you can."

Little Robin Redbreast jumped upon a wall,
Pussy-cat jumped after him, and almost got a fall;
Little Robin chirped and sang, and what did pussy say?
Pussy-cat said naught but "Mew," and Robin flew away.

A FARMER WENT TROTTING

A farmer went trotting upon his gray mare;
    Bumpety, bumpety, bump!
With his daughter behind him, so rosy and fair;
    Lumpety, lumpety, lump!

A raven cried croak! and they all tumbled down;
    Bumpety, bumpety, bump!
The mare broke her knees, and the farmer his crown;
    Lumpety, lumpety, lump!

The mischievous raven flew laughing away;
    Bumpety, bumpety, bump!

And vowed he would serve them the same the next day;
  Lumpety, lumpety, lump!

WHERE ARE YOU GOING, MY PRETTY MAID

"Where are you going, my pretty maid?"
"I'm going a-milking, sir," she said.

"May I go with you, my pretty maid?"
"You're kindly welcome, sir," she said.

"What is your father, my pretty maid?"
"My father's a farmer, sir," she said.

"What is your fortune, my pretty maid?"
"My face is my fortune, sir," she said.

"Then I can't marry you, my pretty maid."
"Nobody asked you, sir," she said.

MARY'S LAMB

Mary had a little lamb,
  Its fleece was white as snow,
And everywhere that Mary went
  The lamb was sure to go;
He followed her to school one day—
  That was against the rule.
It made the children laugh and play
  To see a lamb at school.

And so the Teacher turned him out,
  But still he lingered near,
And waited patiently about
  Till Mary did appear;

And then he ran to her, and laid
    His head upon her arm,
As if he said, "I'm not afraid—
    You'll keep me from all harm."

"What makes the lamb love Mary so?"
    The eager children cry.
"Oh, Mary loves the lamb, you know,"
    The Teacher did reply;
"And you each gentle animal
    In confidence may bind,
And make them follow at your call,
    If you are always kind."

Sarah Josepha Hale

WHEN MARY GOES WALKING

When Mary goes walking,
    The autumn winds blow,
The poplars they curtsey.
    The larches bend low,
The oaks and the beeches
    Their gold they fling down,
To make her a carpet,
    To make her a crown.

Patrick R. Chalmers

WISHES

What do you look for, what do you seek?
    A silver bird with a golden beak.

What do you long for, what do you crave?
    Golden gems in a silver cave.

What do you lack, and what do you need?
    A silver sword and a golden steed.

What do you want, of what do you dream?
  A golden ship on a silver stream.

What do you have, and what do you own?
  A silver robe and a golden crown.

What would you be?　Oh, what would you be?
  Only the king of the land and the sea.

Norman Ault

MINNIE AND WINNIE

Minnie and Winnie slept in a shell.
Sleep, little ladies!　And they slept well.

Pink was the shell within, silver without;
Sounds of the great sea wandered about.

Sleep, little ladies!　Wake not soon!
Echo on echo dies to the moon.

Two bright stars peeped into the shell.
"What are they dreaming of? Who can tell?"

Started a green linnet out of the croft;
Wake, little ladies!　The sun is aloft.

Alfred Tennyson

WHAT DOES LITTLE BIRDIE SAY

What does little birdie say
In her nest at peep of day?
Let me fly, says little birdie,
Mother, let me fly away.
Birdie, rest a little longer,
Till the little wings are stronger.
So she rests a little longer,
Then she flies away.

What does little baby say,
In her bed at peep of day?
Baby says, like little birdie,
Let me rise and fly away.
Baby, sleep a little longer,
Till the little limbs are stronger,
If she sleeps a little longer,
Baby too shall fly away.

Alfred Tennyson

THE TURTLE-DOVES' NEST

High in the pine-tree,
　The little turtle-dove
Made a little nursery
　To please her little love:
"Coo," said the turtle-dove,
　"Coo," said she,
In the long shady branches
　Of the dark pine-tree.

The young turtle-doves
　Never quarrelled in the nest,
For they loved each other dearly,
　Though they loved their mother best:
"Coo," said the little doves,
　"Coo!" said she,
And they played together kindly
　In the dark pine-tree.

THE STAR

Twinkle, twinkle, little star,
How I wonder what you are!
Up above the world so high,
Like a diamond in the sky.

When the blazing sun is set,
And the grass with dew is wet,
Then you show your little light,
Twinkle, twinkle, all the night.

Then the traveler in the dark
Thanks you for your tiny spark,
He could not see where to go
If you did not twinkle so.

In the dark blue sky you keep,
And often through my curtains peep,
For you never shut your eye
Till the sun is in the sky.

As your bright and tiny spark
Lights the traveler in the dark,
Though I know not what you are,
Twinkle, twinkle, little star.

Jane Taylor

MOON, SO ROUND AND YELLOW

Moon, so round and yellow,
    Looking from on high,
How I love to see you
    Shining in the sky.
Oft and oft I wonder,
    When I see you there,
How they get to light you,
    Hanging in the air;

Where you go at morning,
    When the night is past,
And the sun comes peeping
    O'er the hills at last.

Sometime I will watch you
    Slyly overhead,
When you think I'm sleeping
    Snugly in my bed.

Matthias Barr

THE MOON

O, look at the moon!
    She is shining up there;
O mother, she looks
    Like a lamp in the air.

Last week she was smaller,
    And shaped like a bow;
But now she's grown bigger,
    And round as an O.

Pretty moon, pretty moon,
    How you shine on the door,
And make it all bright
    On my nursery floor!

You shine on my playthings
    And show me their place,
And I love to look up
    At your pretty bright face.

And there is a star
    Close by you, and maybe
That small twinkling star
    Is your little baby.

Eliza Lee Follen

THE LOST PLAYMATE

All in the pleasant afternoon
I saw a pretty baby moon,

And oh, I loved her silver shine!
She was a little friend of mine.

Through rainy days and sunny weather
I thought we two should play together;
But, then, alas! I did not know
How fast a little moon can grow.

And now when I go out to play
I cannot find the moon all day;
But she has grown so big and bright,
They let her keep awake at night!

Though I may not sit up to see,
In bed she comes and shines at me;
But oh! I miss the little moon
Who played there in the afternoon.

Abbie Farwell Brown

THE EARLY MORNING

The moon on the one hand, the dawn on the other:
The moon is my sister, the dawn is my brother.
The moon on my left and the dawn on my right.
My brother, good morning: my sister, good night.

Hilaire Belloc

THE CLOCKING HEN

"Will you take a walk with me,
    My little wife, to-day?
There's barley in the barley-fields,
    And hay-seed in the hay."

"Thank you," said the clocking hen;
    "I've something else to do;
I'm busy sitting on my eggs,
    I cannot walk with you.

"Clock, clock, clock, clock,"
  Said the clocking hen;
"My little chicks will soon be hatched,
  I'll think about it then."

The clocking hen sat on her nest,
  She made it in the hay;
And warm and snug beneath her breast
  A dozen white eggs lay.

Crack, crack, went all the eggs;
  Out dropped the chickens small!
"Clock," said the clocking hen,
  "Now I have you all.

"Come along, my little chicks,
  I'll take a walk with *you*."
"Hallo!" said the barn-yard cock,
  "Cock-a-doodle-doo."

THE CITY MOUSE AND THE GARDEN MOUSE

The city mouse lives in a house;—
  The garden mouse lives in a bower,
He's friendly with the frogs and toads,
  And sees the pretty plants in flower.

The city mouse eats bread and cheese;—
  The garden mouse eats what he can;
We will not grudge him seeds and stocks,
  Poor little timid furry man.
                              Christina Georgina Rossetti

THE BELLS OF LONDON

*Gay go up and gay go down
To ring the bells of London town.*

Bulls' eyes and targets,
Say the bells of Saint Marg'ret's.

Brickbats and tiles,
Say the bells of Saint Giles'.

Half-pence and farthings,
Say the bells of Saint Martin's.

Oranges and lemons,
Say the bells of Saint Clement's.

Pancakes and fritters,
Say the bells of Saint Peter's.

Two sticks and an apple,
Say the bells of Whitechapel.

Old Father Baldpate,
Say the slow bells at Aldgate.

Pokers and tongs,
Say the bells of Saint John's.

Kettles and pans,
Say the bells of Saint Ann's.

You owe me ten shillings,
Say the bells of Saint Helen's.

When will you pay me?
Say the bells at Old Bailey.

When I grow rich,
Say the bells of Shoreditch.

Pray, when will that be?
Say the bells of Stepney.

I am sure I don't know,
Says the great bell at Bow.

MERRY ARE THE BELLS

Merry are the bells, and merry would they ring,
Merry was myself, and merry could I sing;
With a merry ding-dong, happy, gay, and free,
And a merry sing-song, happy let us be!

Waddle goes your gait, and hollow are your hose:
Noddle goes your pate, and purple is your nose:
Merry is your sing-song, happy, gay, and free;
With a merry ding-dong, happy let us be!

Merry have we met, and merry have we been;
Merry let us part, and merry meet again;
With our merry sing-song, happy, gay, and free,
With a merry ding-dong, happy let us be!

THE HOUSE THAT JACK BUILT

This is the house that Jack built.

This is the malt
That lay in the house that Jack built.

This is the rat
That ate the malt
That lay in the house that Jack built.

This is the cat
That killed the rat
That ate the malt
That lay in the house that Jack built.

This is the dog
That worried the cat
That killed the rat
That ate the malt
That lay in the house that Jack built.

This is the cow with the crumpled horn
That tossed the dog
That worried the cat
That killed the rat
That ate the malt
That lay in the house that Jack built.

This is the maiden all forlorn
That milked the cow with the crumpled horn
That tossed the dog
That worried the cat
That killed the rat
That ate the malt
That lay in the house that Jack built.

This is the man all tattered and torn
That kissed the maiden all forlorn
That milked the cow with the crumpled horn
That tossed the dog
That worried the cat
That killed the rat
That ate the malt
That lay in the house that Jack built.

This is the priest all shaven and shorn
That married the man all tattered and torn
That kissed the maiden all forlorn
That milked the cow with the crumpled horn
That tossed the dog
That worried the cat

That killed the rat
That ate the malt
That lay in the house that Jack built.

This is the cock that crowed in the morn
That waked the priest all shaven and shorn
That married the man all tattered and torn
That kissed the maiden all forlorn
That milked the cow with the crumpled horn
    That tossed the dog
    That worried the cat
    That killed the rat
    That ate the malt
That lay in the house that Jack built.

This is the farmer sowing his corn
That kept the cock that crowed in the morn
That waked the priest all shaven and shorn
That married the man all tattered and torn
That kissed the maiden all forlorn
That milked the cow with the crumpled horn
    That tossed the dog
    That worried the cat
    That killed the rat
    That ate the malt
That lay in the house that Jack built.

THE GREEN GRASS GROWING ALL AROUND

There was a tree stood in the ground,
The prettiest tree you ever did see;
The tree in the wood, and the wood in the ground,
And the green grass growing all around.

And on this tree there was a limb,
The prettiest limb you ever did see;

The limb on the tree, and the tree in the wood,
The tree in the wood, and the wood in the ground,
And the green grass growing all around.

And on this limb there was a bough,
The prettiest bough you ever did see;
The bough on the limb, and the limb on the tree,
The limb on the tree, and the tree in the wood,
The tree in the wood, and the wood in the ground,
And the green grass growing all around.

Now on this bough there was a nest,
The prettiest nest you ever did see;
The nest on the bough, and the bough on the limb,
The limb on the tree, and the tree in the wood,
The tree in the wood, and the wood in the ground,
And the green grass growing all around.

And in the nest there were some eggs,
The prettiest eggs you ever did see;
Eggs in the nest, and the nest on the bough,
The bough on the limb, and the limb on the tree,
The limb on the tree, and the tree in the wood,
The tree in the wood, and the wood in the ground,
And the green grass growing all around, around, around,
And the green grass growing all around!

OLD MOTHER HUBBARD

Old Mother Hubbard
Went to the cupboard,
To get her poor dog a bone;
But when she got there
The cupboard was bare,
And so the poor dog had none.

She went to the baker's
  To buy him some bread,
But when she came back
  The poor dog was dead.

She went to the joiner's
  To buy him a coffin,
But when she came back
  The poor dog was laughing.

She took a clean dish
  To get him some tripe,
But when she came back
  He was smoking a pipe.

She went to the fishmonger's
  To buy him some fish,
But when she came back
  He was licking the dish.

She went to the hatter's
  To buy him a hat,
But when she came back
  He was feeding the cat.

She went to the barber's
  To buy him a wig,
But when she came back
  He was dancing a jig.

She went to the fruiterer's
  To buy him some fruit,
But when she came back
  He was playing the flute.

She went to the tailor's
  To buy him a coat,
But when she came back
  He was riding a goat.

She went to the cobbler's
  To buy him some shoes,
But when she came back
  He was reading the news.

She went to the seamstress
  To buy him some linen,
But when she came back
  The dog was spinning.

She went to the hosier's
  To buy him some hose,
But when she came back
  He was dressed in his clothes.

The dame made a curtsey,
  The dog made a bow,
The dame said, "Your servant,"
  The dog said, "Bow-wow."

This wonderful dog
  Was Dame Hubbard's delight;
He could sing, he could dance,
  He could read, he could write.

She gave him rich dainties
  Whenever he fed,
And built him a monument
  When he was dead.

THE DEATH AND BURIAL OF COCK ROBIN

Who killed Cock Robin?
  "I," said the Sparrow,
  "With my bow and arrow,
I killed Cock Robin."

Who saw him die?
  "I," said the Fly,
  "With my little eye,
I saw him die."

Who caught his blood?
  "I," said the Fish,
  "With my little dish,
I caught his blood."

Who'll make his shroud?
  "I," said the Beetle,
  "With my thread and needle,
I'll make his shroud."

Who'll dig his grave?
  "I," said the Owl,
  "With my spade and trowel,
I'll dig his grave."

Who'll be the parson?
  "I," said the Rook,
  "With my little book.
I'll be the parson."

Who'll be the clerk?
  "I," said the Lark,
  "If it's not in the dark;
I'll be the clerk."

Who'll be chief mourner?
  "I," said the Dove,
  "I mourn for my love;
I'll be chief mourner."

Who'll bear the torch?
  "I," said the Linnet,
  "I'll come in a minute;
I'll bear the torch."

Who'll sing his dirge?
  "I," said the Thrush,
  As she sat in a bush,
"I'll sing his dirge."

Who'll bear the pall?
  "We," said the Wren,
  Both the Cock and the Hen;
"We'll bear the pall."

Who'll carry his coffin?
  "I," said the Kite,
  "If it's not in the night,
I'll carry his coffin."

Who'll toll the bell?
  "I," said the Bull,
  "Because I can pull,
I'll toll the bell."

All the birds of the air
  Fell to sighing and sobbing
When they heard the bell toll
  For poor Cock Robin.

THE SPIDER AND THE FLY

"Will you walk into my parlor?" said the Spider to the Fly.
" 'Tis the prettiest little parlor that ever you did spy;
The way into my parlor is up a winding stair,
And I have many curious things to show when you are
   there."
"Oh no, no," said the little Fly, "to ask me is in vain;
For who goes up your winding stair can ne'er come down
   again."

"I'm sure you must be weary, dear, with soaring up so
   high;
Will you rest upon my little bed?" said the Spider to the
   Fly.
"There are pretty curtains drawn around, the sheets are
   fine and thin;
And if you like to rest awhile, I'll snugly tuck you in!"
"Oh no, no," said the little Fly, "for I've often heard it
   said
They never, never wake again, who sleep upon your bed!"

Said the cunning Spider to the Fly, "Dear friend, what
   can I do
To prove the warm affection I've always felt for you?
I have, within my pantry, good store of all that's nice;
I'm sure you're very welcome—will you please to take a
   slice?"
"Oh no, no," said the little Fly, "kind sir, that cannot be,
I've heard what's in your pantry, and I do not wish to see!"

"Sweet creature," said the Spider, "you're witty and
   you're wise;
How handsome are your gauzy wings, how brilliant are
   your eyes!

I have a little looking-glass upon my parlor shelf;
If you'll step in one moment, dear, you shall behold your-
   self."
"I thank you, gentle sir," she said, "for what you're
   pleased to say,
And bidding you good-morning now, I'll call another day."

The Spider turned him round about, and went into his den,
For well he knew the silly Fly would soon be back again;
So he wove a subtle web in a little corner sly,
And set his table ready to dine upon the Fly.
Then he came out to his door again, and merrily did sing,
"Come hither, hither, pretty Fly, with the pearl and silver
   wing;
Your robes are green and purple, there's a crest upon your
   head;
Your eyes are like the diamond bright, but mine are dull
   as lead."

Alas, alas! how very soon this silly little Fly,
Hearing his wily, flattering words, came slowly flitting by;
With buzzing wings she hung aloft, then near and nearer
   drew,—
Thinking only of her brilliant eyes, and green and purple
   hue;
Thinking only of her crested head—poor foolish thing!
   At last,
Up jumped the cunning Spider, and fiercely held her fast.
He dragged her up his winding stair, into his dismal den
Within his little parlor—but she ne'er came out again!

And now, dear little children, who may this story read,
To idle, silly, flattering words, I pray you ne'er give heed;
Unto an evil counsellor close heart, and ear, and eye,
And take a lesson from this tale of the Spider and the Fly.

                                             Mary Howitt

THE BABES IN THE WOOD

Now ponder well, you parents dear,
　　These words, which I shall write;
A doleful story you shall hear,
　　In time brought forth to light.
A gentleman of good account
　　In Norfolk dwelt of late,
Who did in honor far surmount
　　Most men of his estate.

Sore sick was he, and like to die,
　　No help his life could save;
His wife by him as sick did lie,
　　And both possessed one grave.
No love between these two was lost,
　　Each was to other kind;
In love they lived, in love they died,
　　And left two babes behind:

The one a fine and pretty boy
　　Not passing three years old;
The other a girl more young than he,
　　And framed in beauty's mold.
The father left his little son,
　　As plainly does appear,
When he to perfect age should come,
　　Three hundred pounds a year.

And to his little daughter Jane
　　Five hundred pounds in gold,
To be paid down on marriage-day,
　　Which might not be controlled:
But if the children chance to die,
　　Ere they to age should come,

Their uncle should possess their wealth;
    For so the will did run.

"Now, brother," said the dying man,
    "Look to my children dear;
Be good unto my boy and girl,
    No friends else have they here:
To God and you I recommend
    My children dear this day;
But little while be sure we have
    Within this world to stay.

"You must be father and mother both,
    And uncle all in one;
God knows what will become of them,
    When I am dead and gone."
With that bespake their mother dear,
    "O brother kind," quoth she,
"You are the man must bring our babes
    To wealth or misery.

"And if you keep them carefully
    Then God will you reward;
But if you otherwise should deal,
    God will your deeds regard."
With lips as cold as any stone,
    They kissed their children small:
"God bless you both, my children dear;"
    With that the tears did fall.

These speeches then their brother spake
    To this sick couple there,
"The keeping of your little ones,
    Sweet sister, do not fear;
God never prosper me nor mine,
    Nor aught else that I have,

If I do wrong your children dear,
　When you are laid in grave."

The parents being dead and gone,
　The children home he takes,
And brings them straight into his house,
　Where much of them he makes.
He had not kept these pretty babes
　A twelvemonth and a day,
But, for their wealth, he did devise
　To make them both away.

He bargained with two ruffians strong,
　Which were of furious mood,
That they should take these children young,
　And slay them in a wood.
He told his wife an artful tale,
　He would the children send
To be brought up in fair London,
　With one that was his friend.

Away then went these pretty babes,
　Rejoicing at that tide,
Rejoicing with a merry mind,
　They should on cock-horse ride.
They prate and prattle pleasantly,
　As they rode on the way,
To those that should their butchers be,
　And work their lives' decay:

So that the pretty speech they had
　Made Murder's heart relent;
And they that undertook the deed,
　Full sore did now repent.
Yet one of them more hard of heart,
　Did vow to do his charge,

Because the wretch that hired him
Had paid him very large.

The other won't agree thereto,
So here they fall to strife;
With one another they did fight
About the children's life:
And he that was of mildest mood
Did slay the other there,
Within an unfrequented wood;
The babes did quake for fear!

He took the children by the hand,
Tears standing in their eye,
And bade them straightway follow him,
And look they did not cry:
And two long miles he led them on,
While they for food complain:
"Stay here," quoth he, "I'll bring you bread,
When I come back again."

These pretty babes, with hand in hand,
Went wandering up and down,
But never more could see the man
Approaching from the town;
Their pretty lips with black-berries
Were all besmeared and dyed,
And, when they saw the darksome night,
They sat them down and cried.

Thus wandered these poor innocents,
Till death did end their grief;
In one another's arms they died,
As wanting due relief:
No burial this pretty pair
Of any man receives,

Till Robin Redbreast piously
  Did cover them with leaves.

And now the heavy wrath of God
  Upon their uncle fell;
Yea, fearful fiends did haunt his house,
  His conscience felt an hell:
His barns were fired, his goods consumed,
  His lands were barren made,
His cattle died within the field,
  And nothing with him stayed.

And in a voyage to Portugal
  Two of his sons did die;
And, to conclude, himself was brought
  To want and misery:
He pawned and mortgaged all his land
  Ere seven years came about,
And now at length his wicked act
  Did by this means come out:

The fellow, that did take in hand
  These children for to kill,
Was for a robbery judged to die,
  Such was God's blessed will:
Who did confess the very truth
  As here hath been displayed:
Their uncle having died in jail,
  Where he for debt was laid.

You that executors be made,
  And overseers eke
Of children that be fatherless,
  And infants mild and meek,
Take your example by this thing,
  And yield to each his right,

Lest God with such like misery
    Your wicked minds requite.

THE COW

Thank you, pretty cow, that made
Pleasant milk to soak my bread,
Every day, and every night,
Warm, and fresh, and sweet, and white.

Do not chew the hemlock rank,
Growing on the weedy bank;
But the yellow cowslips eat,
They will make it very sweet.

Where the purple violet grows,
Where the bubbling water flows,
Where the grass is fresh and fine,
Pretty cow, go there and dine.

Ann Taylor

THE MILK JUG

THE KITTEŇ SPEAKS

The Gentle Milk Jug blue and white
    I love with all my soul;
She pours herself with all her might
    To fill my breakfast bowl.

All day she sits upon the shelf,
    She does not jump or climb—
She only waits to pour herself
    When 'tis my supper-time.

And when the jug is empty quite,
    I shall not mew in vain,
The Friendly Cow, all red and white,
    Will fill her up again.

Oliver Herford

THE BREAKFAST SONG

At five o'clock he milks the cow,
  The busy farmer's man.
At six o'clock he strains the milk
  And pours it in the can.

At seven o'clock the milkman's horse
  Must go to town—"get up!"
At eight o'clock Nurse Karen pours
  The milk in Baby's cup.

At five o'clock the Baby sleeps
  As sound as sound can be.
At six o'clock he laughs and shouts,
  So wide awake is he.

At seven o'clock he's in his bath,
  At eight o'clock he's dressed,
Just when the milk is ready, too,
  So you can guess the rest.

Emilie Poulsson

BABY'S BREAKFAST

Baby wants his breakfast,
  Oh! what shall I do?
Said the cow, "I'll give him
  Nice fresh milk—moo-*oo!*"

Said the hen, "Cut-*dah* cut!
  I have laid an egg
For the Baby's breakfast—
  Take it now, I beg!"

And the buzzing bee said,
  "Here is honey sweet.
Don't you think the Baby
  Would like that to eat?"

Then the baker kindly
  Brought the Baby's bread.
"Breakfast is all ready,"
  Baby's mother said;

"But before the Baby
  Eats his dainty food,
Will he not say 'Thank you!'
  To his friends so good?"

Then the bonny Baby
  Laughed and laughed away.
That was all the "Thank you"
  He knew how to say.

Emilie Poulsson

BABY AT PLAY

Brow bender,
Eye peeper,
Nose smeller,
Mouth eater,
Chin chopper,
Knock at the door—peep in,
Lift up the latch—walk in.

Here sits the Lord Mayor,   [Forehead.
Here sit his two men,   [Eyes.
Here sits the cock,   [Right cheek.

And here sits the hen;   [Left cheek.
Here sit the chickens,   [Tip of nose.
And here they go in,   [Mouth.
Chippety, chippety, chippety chin. [Chuck the chin.

Ring the bell!
Knock at the door!
Lift up the latch!
Walk in!

This little pig went to market;
This little pig stayed at home;
This little pig got roast beef;
This little pig got none;
This little pig cried wee, wee, all the way home.

One, two,
Buckle my shoe;
Three, four,
Shut the door;
Five, six,
Pick up sticks;
Seven, eight,
Lay them straight;
Nine, ten,
A good fat hen;
Eleven, twelve,
Who will delve?
Thirteen, fourteen,
Maids a-courting;
Fifteen, sixteen,
Maids a-kissing;
Seventeen, eighteen,
Maids a-waiting;
Nineteen, twenty,
My stomach's empty.

THE DIFFERENCE

Eight fingers,
　　Ten toes,
Two eyes,
　　And one nose.
Baby said
　　When she smelt the rose,
"Oh! what a pity
　　I've only one nose!"

Ten teeth
　　In even rows,
Three dimples,
　　And one nose.
Baby said
　　When she smelt the snuff,
"Deary me!
　　One nose is enough."

Laura E. Richards

THE FIVE LITTLE FAIRIES

FINGER-PLAY

Said this little fairy,
"I'm as thirsty as can be!"

Said this little fairy,
"I'm hungry, too! dear me!"

Said this little fairy,
"Who'll tell us where to go?"

Said this little fairy,
"I'm sure that I don't know!"

Said this little fairy,
  "Let's brew some Dew-drop Tea!"
So they sipped it and ate honey
  Beneath the maple tree.

Maud Burnham

FOOT SOLDIERS

'Tis all the way to Toe-town,
  Beyond the Knee-high hill,
That Baby has to travel down
  To see the soldiers drill.

One, two, three, four, five, a-row—
  A captain and his men—
And on the other side, you know,
  Are six, seven, eight, nine, ten.

John Banister Tabb

ONE AND ONE

Two little girls are better than one,
Two little boys can double the fun,
Two little birds can build a fine nest,
Two little arms can love mother best.
Two little ponies must go to a span;
Two little pockets has my little man;
Two little eyes to open and close,
Two little ears and one little nose,
Two little elbows, dimpled and sweet,
Two little shoes on two little feet,
Two little lips and one little chin,
Two little cheeks with a rose shut in;
Two little shoulders, chubby and strong,
Two little legs running all day long.
Two little prayers does my darling say,
Twice does he kneel by my side each day,

Two little folded hands, soft and brown,
Two little eyelids cast meekly down,
And two little angels guard him in bed,
"One at the foot, and one at the head."

Mary Mapes Dodge

THE ALPHABET

A was an apple pie;
B bit it;
C cut it;
D dealt it;
E eat it;
F fought for it;
G got it;
H had it;
J jumped for it;
K knelt for it;
L longed for it;
M mourned for it;
N nodded for it;
O opened it;
P peeped in it;
Q quartered it;
R ran for it;
S sang for it;
T took it;
U, V, W, X, Y, Z, all had a large
    slice and went off to bed.

Kate Greenaway

TOM THUMB'S ALPHABET

A was an Archer, who shot at a frog;
B was a Butcher, who had a great dog;

C was a Captain, all covered with lace;
D was a Drunkard, and had a red face;
E was an Esquire, with pride on his brow;
F was a Farmer, and followed the plow;
G was a Gamester, who had but ill luck;
H was a Hunter, who hunted a buck;
I was an Innkeeper, who loved to carouse;
J was a Joiner, who built up a house;
K was a King, so mighty and grand;
L was a Lady, who had a white hand;
M was a Miser, and hoarded up gold;
N was a Nobleman, gallant and bold;
O was an Oysterman, who went about town;
P was a Parson, and wore a black gown;
Q was a Quack, with a wonderful pill;
R was a Robber, who wanted to kill;
S was a Sailor, who spent all he got;
T was a Tinker, and mended a pot;
U was an Usurer, a miserable elf;
V was a Vintner, who drank all himself;
W was a Watchman, who guarded the door;
X was Expensive, and so became poor;
Y was a Youth, that did not love school;
Z was a Zany, a poor harmless fool.

GRAMMAR IN A NUTSHELL

Three little words you often see
Are Articles—A, An, and The.

A Noun's the name of anything,
As School or Garden, Hoop or Swing.

Adjectives tell the kind of Noun,
As Great, Small, Pretty, White, or Brown.

Instead of Nouns the Pronouns stand—
Her head, His face, Your arm, My hand.

Verbs tell something being done—
To Read, Count, Laugh, Sing, Jump, or Run.

How things are done the Adverbs tell,
As Slowly, Quickly, Ill, or Well.

Conjunctions join the words together,
As men And women, wind Or weather.

The Preposition stands before
A Noun, as In or Through a door.

The Interjection shows surprise,
As Oh! how pretty! Ah! how wise!

The Whole are called nine Parts of Speech,
Which reading, writing, speaking teach.

SIMILES

As wet as a fish—as dry as a bone;
As live as a bird—as dead as a stone;
As plump as a partridge—as poor as a rat;
As strong as a horse—as weak as a cat;
As hard as a flint—as soft as a mole;
As white as a lily—as black as a coal;
As plain as a pike-staff—as rough as a bear;
As tight as a drum—as free as the air;
As heavy as lead—as light as a feather;
As steady as time—uncertain as weather;
As hot as a furnace—as cold as a frog;
As gay as a lark—as sick as a dog;

As slow as a tortoise—as swift as the wind;
As true as the gospel—as false as mankind;
As thin as a herring—as fat as a pig;
As proud as a peacock—as blithe as a grig;
As fierce as a tiger—as mild as a dove;
As stiff as a poker—as limp as a glove;
As blind as a bat—as deaf as a post;
As cool as a cucumber—as warm as a toast;
As flat as a flounder—as round as a ball;
As blunt as a hammer—as sharp as an awl;
As red as a ferret—as safe as the stocks;
As bold as a thief—as sly as a fox;
As straight as an arrow—as bent as a bow;
As yellow as saffron—as black as a sloe;
As brittle as glass—as tough as gristle;
As neat as my nail—as clean as a whistle;
As good as a feast—as bad as a witch;
As light as is day—as dark as is pitch;
As brisk as a bee—as dull as an ass;
As full as a tick—as solid as brass.

DAYS OF THE MONTH

Thirty days hath September,
April, June, and November;
All the rest have thirty-one;
February twenty-eight alone,—
Save in leap year, at which time
February's days are twenty-nine.

THE GARDEN YEAR

January brings the snow,
Makes our feet and fingers glow.

February brings the rain,
Thaws the frozen lake again.

March brings breezes, loud and shrill,
To stir the dancing daffodil.

April brings the primrose sweet,
Scatters daisies at our feet.

May brings flocks of pretty lambs
Skipping by their fleecy dams.

June brings tulips, lilies, roses,
Fills the children's hands with posies.

Hot July brings cooling showers,
Apricots, and gillyflowers.

August brings the sheaves of corn,
Then the harvest home is borne.

Warm September brings the fruit;
Sportsmen then begin to shoot.

Fresh October brings the pheasant;
Then to gather nuts is pleasant.

Dull November brings the blast;
Then the leaves are whirling fast.

Chill December brings the sleet,
Blazing fire, and Christmas treat.

Sara Coleridge

RIDDLES

There was a girl in our town,
Silk an' satin was her gown,
Silk an' satin, gold an' velvet,
Guess her name, three times I've telled it. (Ann.)

As soft as silk, as white as milk,
As bitter as gall, a thick green wall,
And a brown coat covers me all. (A walnut.)

Make three fourths of a cross, and a circle complete;
And let two semicircles on a perpendicular meet;
Next add a triangle that stands on two feet;
Next two semicircles, and a circle complete. (TOBACCO.)

Flour of England, fruit of Spain,
Met together in a shower of rain;
Put in a bag tied round with a string,
If you'll tell me this riddle, I'll give you a ring.

(A plum-pudding.)

In marble walls as white as milk,
Lined with a skin as soft as silk;
Within a fountain crystal clear,
A golden apple doth appear.
No doors there are to this stronghold,
Yet thieves break in and steal the gold. (An egg.)

Little Nanny Netticoat,
In a white petticoat,
And a red nose;
The longer she stands,
The shorter she grows. (A candle.)

Long legs, crooked thighs,
Little head and no eyes. (A pair of tongs.)

Thirty white horses upon a red hill,
Now they tramp, now they champ, now they stand still.
                              (The teeth.)

Formed long ago, yet made to-day,
    Employed while others sleep;
What few would like to give away,
    Nor any wish to keep. (A bed.)

Elizabeth, Lizzy, Betsy and Bess,
All went together to seek a bird's nest;
They found a nest with five eggs in it;
They each took one and left four in it.   (One Girl.)

√ Thomas a Tattamus took two T's,
To tie two tups to two tall trees,
To frighten the terrible Thomas a Tattamus!
Tell me how many T's there are in all THAT!   (Two.)

Old Mother Twitchett had but one eye,
And a long tail which she let fly;
And every time she went over a gap,
She left a bit of her tail in a trap.
                              (A needle and thread.)

As I went through a garden gap,
Who should I meet but Dick Red-Cap!
A stick in his hand, a stone in his throat,
If you'll tell me this riddle, I'll give you a groat.
                              (A cherry.)

Humpty Dumpty sat on a wall,
Humpty Dumpty had a great fall;

All the king's horses and all the king's men
Cannot put Humpty Dumpty together again. (An egg.)

As I was going to St. Ives,
I met a man with seven wives,
Every wife had seven sacks,
Every sack had seven cats,
Every cat had seven kits—
Kits, cats, sacks, and wives,
How many were going to St. Ives? (One.)

Two legs sat upon three legs,
With one leg in his lap;
In comes four legs
And runs away with one leg;
Up jumps two legs
Catches up three legs,
Throws it after four legs,
And makes him drop one leg.
            (A man, a stool, a leg of mutton, and a dog.)

OLD SUPERSTITIONS

See a pin and pick it up,
All the day you'll have good luck.
See a pin and let it lay,
Bad luck you will have all day.

The maid who, on the first of May,
Goes to the fields at break of day,
And washes in dew from the hawthorn tree,
Will ever after handsome be.

Friday night's dream on a Saturday told,
Is sure to come true, be it never so old.

Monday's child is fair of face,
Tuesday's child is full of grace,
Wednesday's child is full of woe,
Thursday's child has far to go,
Friday's child is loving and giving,
Saturday's child works hard for its living,
And a child that is born on the Sabbath day
Is fair and wise and good and gay.

Marry Monday, marry for wealth;
Marry Tuesday, marry for health;
  Marry Wednesday, the best day of all;
Marry Thursday, marry for crosses;
Marry Friday, marry for losses;
  Marry Saturday, no luck at all.

They that wash on Monday
  Have all the week to dry;
They that wash on Tuesday
  Are not so much awry;
They that wash on Wednesday
  Are not so much to blame;
They that wash on Thursday
  Wash for shame;
They that wash on Friday
  Wash for need;
And they that wash on Saturday,
  Oh, slovens are indeed!

Sneeze on a Monday, you sneeze for danger;
Sneeze on a Tuesday, you'll kiss a stranger;
Sneeze on a Wednesday, you sneeze for a letter;
Sneeze on a Thursday, for something better;
Sneeze on a Friday, you sneeze for sorrow;
Sneeze on a Saturday, your sweetheart to-morrow;
Sneeze on a Sunday, your safety seek,
For you will have trouble the whole of the week.

WEATHER WISDOM

A sunshiny shower
Won't last half an hour

Rain before seven,
Fair by eleven.

The South wind brings wet weather,
The North wind wet and cold together;
The West wind always brings us rain,
The East wind blows it back again.

March winds and April showers
Bring forth May flowers.

Evening red and morning gray
Set the traveler on his way;
But evening gray and morning red
Bring the rain upon his head.

Rainbow at night is the sailor's delight;
Rainbow at morning, sailors, take warning.

If bees stay at home,
Rain will soon come;
If they fly away,
Fine will be the day.

When clouds appear like rocks and towers,
The earth's refreshed by frequent showers.

CLAPPING GAME

Pease-porridge hot,
Pease-porridge cold,

Pease-porridge in the pot,
  Nine days old.

Some like it hot,
  Some like it cold,
Some like it in the pot
  Nine days old.

THE PANCAKE

Mix a pancake,
Stir a pancake,
  Pop it in the pan;
Fry the pancake,
Toss the pancake,—
  Catch it if you can!

             Christina Georgina Rossetti

STAR WISH

Star light, star bright,
First star I see to-night,
I wish I may, I wish I might
Have the wish I wish to-night.

BED CHARM

Matthew, Mark, Luke and John
Bless the bed that I lie on!
Four corners to my bed,
Four angels round my head,
One at head and one at feet,
And two to guard my soul asleep.

NIGHT BLESSING

Good night,
Sleep tight,
Wake up bright
In the morning light
To do what's right
With all your might.

INFANT JOY

"I have no name;
I am but two days old."
What shall I call thee?
"I happy am,
Joy is my name."
Sweet joy befall thee!

Pretty joy!
Sweet joy, but two days old.
Sweet joy I call thee;
Thou dost smile,
I sing the while;
Sweet joy befall thee!

William Blake

ONLY A BABY SMALL

Only a baby small,
   Dropped from the skies,
Only a laughing face,
   Two sunny eyes;
Only two cherry lips,
   One chubby nose;
Only two little hands,
   Ten little toes.

Only a golden head,
   Curly and soft;
Only a tongue that wags
   Loudly and oft;
Only a little brain,
   Empty of thought;
Only a little heart,
   Troubled with naught.

Only a tender flower
   Sent us to rear;
Only a life to love
   While we are here;
Only a baby small,
   Never at rest;
Small, but how dear to us,
   God knoweth best.

Matthias Barr

STRANGE LANDS

Where do you come from, Mr. Jay?
"From the land of Play, from the land of Play."
And where can that be, Mr. Jay?
      "Far away—far away."

Where do you come from Mrs. Dove?
"From the land of Love, from the land of Love."
And how do you get there, Mrs. Dove?
      "Look above—look above."

Where do you come from, Baby Miss?
"From the land of Bliss, from the land of Bliss."
And what is the way there, Baby Miss?
      "Mother's kiss—Mother's kiss."

Laurence Alma-Tadema

BABY

Where did you come from, baby dear?
Out of the everywhere into the here.

Where did you get those eyes so blue?
Out of the sky as I came through.

What makes the light in them sparkle and spin?
Some of the starry spikes left in.

Where did you get that little tear?
I found it waiting when I got here.

What makes your forehead so smooth and high?
A soft hand stroked it as I went by.

What makes your cheek like a warm white rose?
I saw something better than any one knows.

Whence that three-cornered smile of bliss?
Three angels gave me at once a kiss.

Where did you get this pearly ear?
God spoke, and it came out to hear.

Where did you get those arms and hands?
Love made itself into bonds and bands.

Feet, whence did you come, you darling things?
From the same box as the cherubs' wings.

How did they all just come to be you?
God thought about me, and so I grew.

But how did you come to us, you dear?
God thought about you, and so I am here.

George Macdonald

BARTHOLOMEW

Bartholomew is very sweet,
From sandy hair to rosy feet.

Bartholomew is six months old,
And dearer far than pearls or gold.

Bartholomew has deep blue eyes,
Round pieces dropped from out the skies.

Bartholomew is hugged and kissed:
He loves a flower in either fist.

Bartholomew's my saucy son:
No mother has a sweeter one!

Norman Gale

A BUNCH OF ROSES

The rosy mouth and rosy toe
    Of little baby brother,
Until about a month ago
    Had never met each other;
But nowadays the neighbors sweet,
    In every sort of weather,
Half-way with rosy fingers meet,
    To kiss and play together.

John Banister Tabb

THE FIRST TOOTH

There once was a wood, and a very thick wood,
So thick that to walk was as much as you could;
But a sunbeam got in, and the trees understood.

I went to this wood, at the end of the snows,
And as I was walking I saw a primrose;
Only one! Shall I show you the place where it grows?

There once was a house, and a very dark house,
As dark, I believe, as the hole of a mouse,
Or a tree in my wood, at the thick of the boughs.

I went to this house, and I searched it aright,
I opened the chambers, and I found a light;
Only one! Shall I show you this little lamp bright?

There once was a cave, and this very dark cave
One day took a gift from an incoming wave;
And I made up my mind to know what the sea gave.

I took a lit torch, I walked round the ness
When the water was lowest; and in a recess
In my cave was a jewel. Will nobody guess?

O there was a baby, he sat on my knee,
With a pearl in his mouth that was precious to me,
His little dark mouth like my cave of the sea!

I said to my heart, "And my jewel is bright!
He blooms like a primrose! He shines like a light!"
Put your hand in his mouth! Do you feel? He can bite!

William Brighty Rands

A LETTER TO ELSA

Rose-red, russet-brown,
Were there elves in your town?
When you breathed little words
Would they flock in like birds?

Did you eat magic fruit
For your supper to suit
The spiced garden, the dew,
And the sweetness of you?
Had the elf-mother spread
A low table with bread
And milk white as the moon?
Did you find very soon
A bed white as the milk,
Smooth and tender with silk,
Where you laid your tired head,
Russet-brown, rose-red?

Russet-eyes, rose-mouth,
When the wind's from the south,
When he rustles and stirs
In the plumed junipers,
Does he bring coaxing words
From the sly mocking-birds?
Do they call you to come
Where the wind is at home
When he rests from his trips?
Elf-locks, scarlet-lips,
I am wiser than they.
Hearken now what *I* say!

I will build you a house
Velvet-gray like a mouse,
Snug and shy among trees.
There shall be if you please
Peacocks pacing the walks,
And a fountain that talks,
And a playmate for you,
And a green cockatoo.
Bees shall dwell in the phlox
And the gay hollyhocks,

And their honey will be
In the sycamore tree.
Every dusk I will spread
A low table with bread
And a brown honey-comb
(When the bees have gone home),
And heaped mulberry-fruit,
(While the thrush tries his flute),
And milk white as the moon.
Then if bed-time come soon,
You shall lay your dear head
On a smooth silken bed
To the thrush-lullabies,
Russet-brown, rose-red,
Rose-mouth, russet-eyes!

Grace Hazard Conkling

BEDTIME

'Tis bedtime; say your hymn, and bid "Good-night;
God bless Mamma, Papa, and dear ones all."
Your half-shut eyes beneath your eyelids fall,
Another minute, you will shut them quite.
Yes, I will carry you, put out the light,
And tuck you up, although you are so tall!
What will you give me, Sleepy One, and call
My wages, if I settle you all right?

I laid her golden curls upon my arm,
I drew her little feet within my hand,
Her rosy palms were joined in trustful bliss,
Her heart next mine beat gently, soft and warm
She nestled to me, and, by Love's command,
Paid me my precious wages—"Baby's kiss."

Francis Robert St. Clair Erskine

NIGHT

The sun descending in the west,
The evening star does shine;
The birds are silent in their nest,
And I must seek for mine.
　　The moon, like a flower
　　In heaven's high bower,
　　With silent delight
　　Sits and smiles on the night.

Farewell, green fields and happy grove,
Where flocks have ta'en delight;
Where lambs have nibbled, silent move
The feet of angels bright:
　　Unseen, they pour blessing
　　And joy without ceasing,
　　On each bud and blossom,
　　On each sleeping bosom.

They look in every thoughtless nest,
Where birds are covered warm;
They visit caves of every beast,
To keep them all from harm.
　　If they see any weeping
　　That should have been sleeping,
　　They pour sleep on their head,
　　And sit down by their bed.

When wolves and tigers howl for prey
They pitying stand and weep,
Seeking to drive their thirst away,
And keep them from the sheep.
　　But, if they rush dreadful,
　　The angels, most heedful,
　　Receive each mild spirit
　　New worlds to inherit.

And there the lion's ruddy eyes
Shall flow with tears of gold:
And pitying the tender cries,
And walking round the fold,
    Saying: "Wrath by His meekness,
    And, by His health, sickness,
    Are driven away
    From our immortal day.

"And now beside thee, bleating lamb,
I can lie down and sleep,
Or think on Him who bore thy name,
Graze after thee, and weep.
    For, washed in life's river,
    My bright mane for ever
    Shall shine like the gold,
    As I guard o'er the fold."

William Blake

MY BED IS A BOAT

My bed is like a little boat;
    Nurse helps me in when I embark;
She girds me in my sailor's coat
    And starts me in the dark.

At night, I go on board and say
    Good-night to all my friends on shore;
I shut my eyes and sail away
    And see and hear no more.

And sometimes things to bed I take,
    As prudent sailors have to do;
Perhaps a slice of wedding-cake,
    Perhaps a toy or two.

All night across the dark we steer;
    But when the day returns at last,
Safe in my room, beside the pier,
    I find my vessel fast.

Robert Louis Stevenson

ESCAPE AT BEDTIME

The lights from the parlor and kitchen shone out
    Through the blinds and the windows and bars;
And high overhead and all moving about,
    There were thousands of millions of stars.
There ne'er were such thousands of leaves on a tree,
    Nor of people in church or the Park,
As the crowds of the stars that looked down upon me,
    And that glittered and winked in the dark.

The Dog, and the Plow, and the Hunter, and all,
    And the star of the sailor, and Mars,
These shone in the sky, and the pail by the wall
    Would be half full of water and stars.
They saw me at last, and they chased me with cries,
    And they soon had me packed into bed;
But the glory kept shining and bright in my eyes,
    And the stars going round in my head.

Robert Louis Stevenson

HUSH-A-BYES

Hush-a-bye, baby, on the tree-top,
When the wind blows, the cradle will rock,
When the bough breaks, the cradle will fall,
Down will come baby, bough, cradle, and all.

Bye, baby bunting, daddy's gone a-hunting
To get a little rabbit-skin to wrap his baby bunting in.

Rock-a-bye, baby, thy cradle is green;
Father's a nobleman, mother's a Queen,
Betty's a lady and wears a gold ring,
And Johnny's a drummer and drums for the King.

TROT, TROT!

Every evening Baby goes
   Trot, trot, to town,
Across the river, through the fields,
   Up hill and down.

Trot, trot, the Baby goes,
   Up hill and down,
To buy a feather for her hat,
   To buy a woolen gown.

Trot, trot, the Baby goes;
   The birds fly down, alack!
"You cannot have our feathers, dear,"
   They say, "so please trot back."

Trot, trot, the Baby goes;
   The lambs come bleating near.
"You cannot have our wool," they say,
   "But we are sorry, dear."

Trot, trot, the Baby goes,
   Trot, trot, to town;
She buys a red rose for her hat,
   She buys a cotton gown.

Mary F. Butts

BED-TIME SONG

Sleep, my baby, while I sing
Bed-time news of everything.
Chickens run to mother hen;
Piggy curls up in the pen.
In the field, all tired with play,
Quiet now the lambkins stay.
Kittens cuddle in a heap—
Baby, too, must go to sleep!

Sleep, my baby, while I sing
Bed-time news of everything.
Now the cows from pasture come;
Bees fly home with drowsy hum.
Little birds are in the nest,
Under mother-bird's soft breast.
Over all soft shadows creep—
Baby now must go to sleep.

Sleep, my baby, while I sing
Bed-time news of everything.
Sleepy flowers seem to nod,
Drooping toward the dewy sod;
While the big sun's fading light
Bids my baby dear good-night.
Mother loving watch will keep;
Baby now must go to sleep.

Emilie Poulsson

GOOD-NIGHT

Little baby, lay your head
On your pretty cradle-bed;
Shut your eye-peeps, now the day
And the light are gone away;

All the clothes are tucked in tight;
Little baby dear, good-night.

Yes, my darling, well I know
How the bitter wind doth blow;
And the winter's snow and rain
Patter on the window-pane:
But they cannot come in here,
To my little baby dear;

For the window shutteth fast,
Till the stormy night is past;
And the curtains warm are spread
Round about her cradle-bed:
So till morning shineth bright,
Little baby dear, good-night.

Jane Taylor

HOLY INNOCENTS

Sleep, little Baby, sleep;
  The holy Angels love thee,
And guard thy bed, and keep
  A blessed watch above thee.
No spirit can come near
  Nor evil beast to harm thee:
Sleep, Sweet, devoid of fear
  Where nothing need alarm thee.

The Love which doth not sleep,
  The eternal Arms surround thee:
The Shepherd of the sheep
  In perfect love hath found thee.
Sleep through the holy night,
  Christ-kept from snare and sorrow,
Until thou wake to light
  And love and warmth to-morrow.

Christina Georgina Rossetti

CRADLE SONG

Sleep, sleep, beauty bright,
Dreaming in the joys of night;
Sleep, sleep; in thy sleep
Little sorrows sit and weep.

Sweet babe, in thy face
Soft desires I can trace,
Secret joys and secret smiles,
Little pretty infant wiles.

As thy softest limbs I feel,
Smiles as of the morning steal
O'er thy cheek, and o'er thy breast
Where thy little heart doth rest.

O the cunning wiles that creep
In thy little heart asleep!
When thy little heart doth wake,
Then the dreadful night shall break.

William Blake

LULLABY

Sweet and low, sweet and low,
    Wind of the western sea,
Low, low, breathe and blow,
    Wind of the western sea!
Over the rolling waters go,
Come from the dying moon, and blow,
    Blow him again to me;
While my little one, while my pretty one, sleeps.

Sleep and rest, sleep and rest,
　　Father will come to thee soon;
Rest, rest, on mother's breast,
　　Father will come to thee soon;
Father will come to his babe in the nest,
Silver sails all out of the west
　　Under the silver moon;
Sleep, my little one, sleep, my pretty one, sleep.

Alfred Tennyson

WHEN THE SLEEPY MAN COMES

When the Sleepy Man comes with the dust on his eyes,
　　(Oh, weary, my Dearie, so weary!)
He shuts up the earth, and he opens the skies.
　　(So hush-a-by, weary my Dearie!)

He smiles through his fingers, and shuts up the sun;
　　(Oh, weary, my Dearie, so weary!)
The stars that he loves he lets out one by one.
　　(So hush-a-by, weary my Dearie!)

He comes from the castles of Drowsy-boy Town;
　　(Oh, weary, my Dearie, so weary!)
At the touch of his hand the tired eyelids fall down.
　　(So hush-a-by, weary my Dearie!)

He comes with a murmur of dream in his wings;
　　(Oh, weary, my Dearie, so weary!)
And whispers of mermaids and wonderful things.
　　(So hush-a-by, weary my Dearie!)

Then the top is a burden, the bugle a bane;
　　(Oh, weary, my Dearie, so weary!)
When one would be faring down Dream-a-way Lane.
　　(So hush-a-by, weary my Dearie!)

When one would be wending in Lullaby Wherry,
   (Oh, weary, my Dearie, so weary!)
To Sleepy Man's Castle, by Comforting Ferry.
   (So hush-a-by, weary my Dearie!)

Charles G. D. Roberts

WILLIE WINKIE

Wee Willie Winkie rins through the town,
Upstairs and doonstairs, in his nicht-gown,
Tirlin' at the window, cryin' at the lock,
"Are the weans in their bed?—for it's noo ten o'clock."

Hey, Willie Winkie! are ye comin' ben?
The cat's singin' gay thrums to the sleepin' hen,
The doug's speldered on the floor, and disna gie a cheep;
But here's a waukrife laddie, that winna fa' asleep.

Onything but sleep, ye rogue!—glowrin' like the moon.
Rattlin' in an airn jug wi' an airn spoon,
Rumblin', tumblin' roun' about, crawin' like a cock,
Skirlin' like a kenna-what—wauknin' sleepin' folk!

Hey, Willie Winkie! the wean's in a creel!
Waumblin' aff a bodie's knee like a vera eel,
Ruggin' at the cat's lug, and ravellin' a' her thrums:
Hey, Willie Winkie!—See, there he comes!

William Miller

AULD DADDY DARKNESS

Auld Daddy Darkness creeps frae his hole,
Black as a blackamoor, blin' as a mole:
Stir the fire till it lowes, let the bairnie sit,
Auld Daddy Darkness is no wantit yit.

See him in the corners hidin' frae the licht,
See him at the window gloomin' at the nicht;
Turn up the gas licht, close the shutters a',
An' Auld Daddy Darkness will flee far awa'.

Awa' to hide the birdie within its cosy nest,
Awa' to lap the wee flooers on their mither's breast,
Awa' to loosen Gaffer Toil frae his daily ca',
For Auld Daddy Darkness is kindly to a'.

He comes when we're weary to wean's frae oor waes,
He comes when the bairnies are getting aff their claes;
To cover them sae cosy, an' bring bonnie dreams,
So Auld Daddy Darkness is better than he seems.

Steek yer een, my wee tot, ye'll see Daddy then;
He's in below the bed claes, to cuddle ye he's fain;
Noo nestle to his bosie, sleep and dream yer fill,
Till Wee Davie Daylicht comes keekin' ower the hill.

James Ferguson

THE SANDMAN

The rosy clouds float overhead,
　　The sun is going down;
And now the sandman's gentle tread
　　Comes stealing through the town.
"White sand, white sand," he softly cries,
　　And as he shakes his hand,
Straightway there lies on babies' eyes
　　His gift of shining sand.
Blue eyes, gray eyes, black eyes, and brown,
　　As shuts the rose, they softly close,
When he goes through the town.

From sunny beaches far away—
    Yes, in another land—
He gathers up at break of day
    His store of shining sand.
No tempests beat that shore remote,
    No ships may sail that way;
His little boat alone may float
    Within that lovely bay.
Blue eyes, gray eyes, black eyes, and brown,
    As shuts the rose, they softly close,
When he goes through the town.

He smiles to see the eyelids close
    Above the happy eyes;
And every child right well he knows,—
    Oh, he is very wise!
But if, as he goes through the land,
    A naughty baby cries,
His other hand takes dull gray sand
    To close the wakeful eyes.
Blue eyes, gray eyes, black eyes, and brown,
    As shuts the rose, they softly close,
When he goes through the town.

So when you hear the sandman's song
    Sound through the twilight sweet,
Be sure you do not keep him long
    A-waiting in the street.
Lie softly down, dear little head,
    Rest quiet, busy hands,
Till, by your bed his good-night said,
    He strews the shining sands.
Blue eyes, gray eyes, black eyes, and brown,
    As shuts the rose, they softly close,
When he goes through the town.

Margaret Thomson Janvier

THE ROCK-A-BY LADY

The Rock-a-By Lady from Hushaby street
   Comes stealing; comes creeping;
The poppies they hang from her head to her feet,
And each hath a dream that is tiny and fleet—
She bringeth her poppies to you, my sweet,
   When she findeth you sleeping!

There is one little dream of a beautiful drum—
   "Rub-a-dub!" it goeth;
There is one little dream of a big sugar-plum,
And lo! thick and fast the other dreams come
Of popguns that bang, and tin tops that hum,
   And a trumpet that bloweth!

And dollies peep out of those wee little dreams
   With laughter and singing;
And boats go a-floating on silvery streams,
And the stars peek-a-boo with their own misty gleams,
And up, up, and up, where the Mother Moon beams,
   The fairies go winging!

Would you dream all these dreams that are tiny and fleet?
   They'll come to you sleeping;
So shut the two eyes that are weary, my sweet,
For the Rock-a-By Lady from Hushaby street,
With poppies that hang from her head to her feet,
   Comes stealing; comes creeping.   *Eugene Field*

THE SUGAR-PLUM TREE

Have you ever heard of the Sugar-Plum Tree?
   'Tis a marvel of great renown!

It blooms on the shore of the Lollypop Sea
    In the garden of Shut-Eye Town;
The fruit that it bears is so wondrously sweet
    (As those who have tasted it say)
That good little children have only to eat
    Of that fruit to be happy next day.

When you've got to the tree, you would have a hard time
    To capture the fruit which I sing;
The tree is so tall that no person could climb
    To the boughs where the sugar-plums swing!
But up in that tree sits a chocolate cat,
    And a gingerbread dog prowls below—
And this is the way you contrive to get at
    Those sugar-plums tempting you so:

You say but the word to that gingerbread dog
    And he barks with such terrible zest
That the chocolate cat is at once all agog,
    As her swelling proportions attest.
And the chocolate cat goes cavorting around
    From this leafy limb unto that,
And the sugar-plums tumble, of course, to the ground—
    Hurrah for that chocolate cat!

There are marshmallows, gumdrops, and peppermint canes
    With stripings of scarlet or gold,
And you carry away of the treasure that rains,
    As much as your apron can hold!
So come, little child, cuddle closer to me
    In your dainty white nightcap and gown,
And I'll rock you away to that Sugar-Plum Tree
    In the garden of Shut-Eye Town.

Eugene Field

WYNKEN, BLYNKEN, AND NOD

DUTCH LULLABY

Wynken, Blynken, and Nod one night
 Sailed off in a wooden shoe,—
Sailed on a river of crystal light
 Into a sea of dew.
"Where are you going, and what do you wish?"
 The old moon asked the three.
"We have come to fish for the herring fish
 That live in this beautiful sea;
 Nets of silver and gold have we!"
   Said Wynken,
   Blynken,
   And Nod.

The old moon laughed and sang a song,
 As they rocked in the wooden shoe;
And the wind that sped them all night long
 Ruffled the waves of dew.
The little stars were the herring fish
 That lived in that beautiful sea—
"Now cast your nets wherever you wish,—
 Never afeard are we!"
 So cried the stars to the fishermen three,
   Wynken,
   Blynken,
   And Nod.

All night long their nets they threw
 To the stars in the twinkling foam,—
Then down from the skies came the wooden shoe,
 Bringing the fishermen home:
'Twas all so pretty a sail, it seemed
 As if it could not be;

And some folk thought 'twas a dream they'd dreamed
  Of sailing that beautiful sea;
  But I shall name you the fishermen three:
      Wynken,
      Blynken,
      And Nod.

Wynken and Blynken are two little eyes,
  And Nod is a little head,
And the wooden shoe that sailed the skies
  Is a wee one's trundle-bed;
So shut your eyes while Mother sings
  Of wonderful sights that be,
And you shall see the beautiful things
  As you rock in the misty sea
  Where the old shoe rocked the fishermen three:—
      Wynken,
      Blynken,
      And Nod.

Eugene Field

JJ. The Duty of Children

DEDICATION ON THE GIFT OF
A BOOK TO A CHILD

Child! do not throw this book about!
    Refrain from the unholy pleasure
Of cutting all the pictures out!
    Preserve it as your chiefest treasure.

Child, have you never heard it said
    That you are heir to all the ages?
Why, then, your hands were never made
    To tear these beautiful thick pages!

Your little hands were made to take
    The better things and leave the worse ones:
They also may be used to shake
    The Massive Paws of Elder Persons.

And when your prayers complete the day,
    Darling, your little tiny hands
Were also made, I think, to pray
    For men that lose their fairylands.
                  Hilaire Belloc

THE DUTY OF CHILDREN

RULES OF BEHAVIOR

Hearts, like doors, will ope with ease
To very, very little keys,
And don't forget that two of these
Are "I thank you" and "If you please."

Come when you're called,
  Do what you're bid,
Close the door after you,
  Never be chid.

Seldom "can't,"
  Seldom "don't;"
Never "sha'n't,"
  Never "won't."

Tommy's tears and Mary's fears
Will make them old before their years.

For every evil under the sun,
There is a remedy, or there is none;
If there be one, try to find it;
If there be none, never mind it.

He that would thrive must rise at five;
He that hath thriven may lie till seven.

Cock crows in the morning to tell us to rise,
And he who lies late will never be wise;
For early to bed and early to rise
Is the way to be healthy and wealthy and wise.

POLITENESS

Good little boys should never say,
  "I will," and "Give me these;"
O, no! that never is the way,
  But, "Mother, if you please."

And, "If you please," to Sister Ann
  Good boys to say are ready;
And, "Yes, sir," to a Gentleman,
  And, "Yes, ma'am," to a Lady.

Elizabeth Turner

LITTLE FRED

  When little Fred
  Was called to bed,
He always acted right;
  He kissed Mama,
  And then Papa,
And wished them all good-night.

  He made no noise,
  Like naughty boys,
But gently up the stairs
  Directly went,
  When he was sent,
And always said his prayers.

KINDNESS TO ANIMALS

Little children, never give
Pain to things that feel and live;
Let the gentle robin come
For the crumbs you save at home,—
As his food you throw along
He'll repay you with a song;

Never hurt the timid hare
Peeping from her green grass lair,
Let her come and sport and play
On the lawn at close of day;
The little lark goes soaring high
To the bright windows of the sky,
Singing as if 'twere always spring,
And fluttering on an untired wing,—
Oh! let him sing his happy song,
Nor do these gentle creatures wrong

A RULE FOR BIRDS' NESTERS

The robin and the red-breast,
    The sparrow and the wren,
If ye take out o' their nest,
    Ye'll never thrive again!

The robin and the red-breast,
    The martin and the swallow,
If ye touch one o' their eggs,
    Bad luck will surely follow!

THE BROWN THRUSH

There's a merry brown thrush sitting up in the tree.
"He's singing to me! He's singing to me!"
    And what does he say, little girl, little boy?
    "Oh, the world's running over with joy!
        Don't you hear? Don't you see?
        Hush! Look! In my tree,
        I'm as happy as happy can be!"

And the brown thrush keeps singing, "A nest do you see
And five eggs hid by me in the juniper tree?

Don't meddle! Don't touch! little girl, little boy,
Or the world will lose some of its joy!
   Now I'm glad! Now I'm free!
   And I always shall be,
   If you never bring sorrow to me."

So the merry brown thrush sings away in the tree,
To you and to me, to you and to me;
   And he sings all the day, little girl, little boy,
   "Oh, the world's running over with joy!
   But long it won't be,
   Don't you know? Don't you see?
   Unless we're as good as can be."

Lucy Larcom

SING ON, BLITHE BIRD

I've plucked the berry from the bush,
   The brown nut from the tree,
But heart of happy little bird
   Ne'er broken was by me.
I saw them in their curious nests,
   Close crouching, slyly peer
With their wild eyes, like glittering beads,
   To note if harm were near;
I passed them by, and blessed them all;
   I felt that it was good
To leave unmoved the creatures small,
   Whose home was in the wood.

And here, even now, above my head,
   A lusty rogue doth sing;
He pecks his swelling breast and neck,
   And trims his little wing.
He will not fly; he knows full well,
   While chirping on that spray,

I would not harm him for the world,
  Or interrupt his lay.
Sing on, sing on, blithe bird! and fill
  My heart with summer gladness;
It has been aching many a day,
  With measures full of sadness!

William Motherwell

I LIKE LITTLE PUSSY

I like little Pussy,
  Her coat is so warm;
And if I don't hurt her
  She'll do me no harm.
So I'll not pull her tail,
  Nor drive her away,
But Pussy and I
  Very gently will play;
She shall sit by my side,
  And I'll give her some food;
And she'll love me because
  I am gentle and good.

I'll pat little Pussy,
  And then she will purr,
And thus show her thanks
  For my kindness to her;
I'll not pinch her ears,
  Nor tread on her paw,
Lest I should provoke her
  To use her sharp claw;
I never will vex her,
  Nor make her displeased,
For Pussy can't bear
  To be worried or teased.

Jane Taylor

THE LOVABLE CHILD

Frisky as a lambkin,
    Busy as a bee—
That's the kind of little girl
    People like to see.

Modest as a violet,
    As a rosebud sweet—
That's the kind of little girl
    People like to meet.

Bright as is a diamond,
    Pure as any pearl—
Everyone rejoices in
    Such a little girl.

Happy as a robin,
    Gentle as a dove—
That's the kind of little girl
    Everyone will love.

Fly away and seek her,
    Little song of mine,
For I choose that very girl
    As my Valentine.

Emilie Poulsson

THE LITTLE GENTLEMAN

Take your meals, my little man,
Always like a gentleman;
Wash your face and hands with care,
Change your shoes, and brush your hair;
Then so fresh, and clean and neat,
Come and take your proper seat;

Do not loiter and be late,
Making other people wait;
Do not rudely point or touch:
Do not eat and drink too much:
Finish what you have before
You even ask or send for more:
Never crumble or destroy
Food that others might enjoy;
They who idly *crumbs* will waste
Often want a loaf to taste!
Never spill your milk or tea,
Never rude or noisy be;
Never choose the daintiest food,
Be content with what is good:
Seek in all things that you can
To be a little gentleman.

WHOLE DUTY OF CHILDREN

A child should always say what's true
And speak when he is spoken to,
And behave mannerly at table;
At least as far as he is able.

Robert Louis Stevenson

THE VULTURE

The Vulture eats between his meals,
    And that's the reason why
He very, very rarely feels
    As well as you or I.
His eye is dull, his head is bald,
    His neck is growing thinner.
Oh, what a lesson for us all
    To only eat at dinner.

Hilaire Belloc

GREEDY JANE

"Pudding *and* pie,"
Said Jane; "O my!"
"Which would you rather?"
Said her father.
"Both!" cried Jane,
Quite bold and plain.

THE PLUM-CAKE

"Oh! I've got a plum-cake, and a fine feast I'll make,
    So nice to have all to myself!
I can eat every day while the rest are at play,
    And then put it by on the shelf."

Thus said little John, and how soon it was gone!
    For with zeal to his cake he applied,
While fingers and thumbs, for the sweetmeats and plums,
    Were hunting and digging beside.

But, woeful to tell, a misfortune befell,
    That shortly his folly revealed:
After eating his fill, he was taken so ill,
    That the cause could not now be concealed.

As he grew worse and worse, the doctor and nurse
    To cure his disorder were sent;
And rightly, you'll think, he had physic to drink,
    Which made him sincerely repent.

And while on the bed he rolled his hot head,
    Impatient with sickness and pain,
He could not but take this reproof from his cake:
    "Do not be such a glutton again."

Ann Taylor

THE CRUST OF BREAD

I must not throw upon the floor
    The crust I cannot eat;
For many little hungry ones
    Would think it quite a treat.

My parents labor very hard
    To get me wholesome food;
Then I must never waste a bit
    That would do others good.

For wilful waste makes woeful want,
    And I may live to say,
Oh! how I wish I had the bread
    That once I threw away!

THE STORY OF AUGUSTUS, WHO WOULD NOT HAVE ANY SOUP

Augustus was a chubby lad;
Fat, ruddy cheeks Augustus had;
And everybody saw with joy
The plump and hearty, healthy boy.
He ate and drank as he was told,
And never let his soup get cold.

But one day, one cold winter's day,
He screamed out—"Take the soup away!
O take the nasty soup away!
I won't have any soup to-day."

Next day begins his tale of woes;
Quite lank and lean Augustus grows.
Yet, though he feels so weak and ill,
The naughty fellow cries out still—

"Not any soup for me, I say:
O take the nasty soup away!
I won't have any soup to-day."

The third day comes; O what a sin!
To make himself so pale and thin.
Yet, when the soup is put on table,
He screams, as loud as he is able,—
"Not any soup for me, I say:
O take the nasty soup away!
I won't have any soup to-day."

Look at him, now the fourth day's come!
He scarcely weighs a sugar-plum;
He's like a little bit of thread,
And on the fifth day, he was—dead!

From the German of Heinrich Hoffmann

LET DOGS DELIGHT TO BARK AND BITE

Let dogs delight to bark and bite,
    For God hath made them so;
Let bears and lions growl and fight,
    For 'tis their nature, too.

But, children, you should never let
    Such angry passions rise;
Your little hands were never made
    To tear each other's eyes.

Isaac Watts

ANGER

Anger in its time and place
May assume a kind of grace.
It must have some reason in it,
And not last beyond a minute.

If to further lengths it go,
It does into malice grow.
'Tis the difference that we see
'Twixt the serpent and the bee.
If the latter you provoke,
It inflicts a hasty stroke,
Puts you to some little pain,
But it *never stings again*.
Close in tufted bush or brake
Lurks the poison-swellèd snake
Nursing up his cherished wrath;
In the purlieus of his path,
In the cold, or in the warm,
Mean him good, or mean him harm,
Wheresoever fate may bring you,
The vile snake will *always sting you*.

Charles and Mary Lamb

HOW DOTH THE LITTLE BUSY BEE

How doth the little busy bee
    Improve each shining hour,
And gather honey all the day
    From every opening flower!

How skilfully she builds her cell!
    How neat she spreads the wax!
And labors hard to store it well
    With the sweet food she makes.

In works of labor or of skill
    I would be busy too;
For Satan finds some mischief still
    For idle hands to do.

In books, or work, or healthful play,
   Let my first years be passed,
That I may give for every day
   Some good account at last.

Isaac Watts

THE ANT AND THE CRICKET

A silly young cricket, accustomed to sing
Through the warm, sunny months of gay summer and spring,
Began to complain, when he found that at home
His cupboard was empty and winter was come.
   Not a crumb to be found
   On the snow-covered ground;
   Not a flower could he see,
   Not a leaf on a tree:
"Oh, what will become," says the cricket, "of me?"

At last by starvation and famine made bold,
All dripping with wet and all trembling with cold,
Away he set off to a miserly ant,
To see if, to keep him alive, he would grant
   Him shelter from rain:
   A mouthful of grain
   He wished only to borrow,
   He'd repay it to-morrow:
If not, he must die of starvation and sorrow.

Says the ant to the cricket, "I'm your servant and friend,
But we ants never borrow, we ants never lend;
But tell me, dear sir, did you lay nothing by
When the weather was warm?" Said the cricket, "Not I.
   My heart was so light
   That I sang day and night,
   For all nature looked gay."
   "You sang, sir, you say?
Go then," said the ant, "and dance winter away."

Thus ending, he hastily lifted the wicket
And out of the door turned the poor little cricket.
Though this is a fable, the moral is good:
If you live without work, you must live without food.

THE SLUGGARD

'Tis the voice of a sluggard; I heard him complain,
"You have waked me too soon; I must slumber again."
As the door on its hinges, so he on his bed
Turns his sides, and his shoulders, and his heavy head.

"A little more sleep, and a little more slumber."
Thus he wastes half his days, and his hours without
    number;
And when he gets up, he sits folding his hands
Or walks about sauntering, or trifling he stands.

I passed by his garden, and saw the wild brier,
The thorn and the thistle grow broader and higher;
The clothes that hang on him are turning to rags;
And his money still wastes till he starves or he begs.

I made him a visit, still hoping to find
That he took better care for improving his mind;
He told me his dreams, talked of eating and drinking,
But he scarce reads his Bible, and never loves thinking.

Said I then to my heart, "Here's a lesson for me;
That man's but a picture of what I might be;
But thanks to my friends for their care in my breeding,
Who taught me betimes to love working and reading."

                                        Isaac Watts

THE BUTTERFLY

The butterfly, an idle thing,
Nor honey makes, nor yet can sing,
  As do the bee and bird;
Nor does it, like the prudent ant,
Lay up the grain for times of want,
  A wise and cautious hoard.

My youth is but a summer's day:
Then like the bee and ant I'll lay
  A store of learning by;
And though from flower to flower I rove,
My stock of wisdom I'll improve,
  Nor be a butterfly.

Adelaide O'Keefe

THE BUTTERFLY AND THE BEE

Methought I heard a butterfly
  Say to a laboring bee,
"Thou hast no colors of the sky
  On painted wings like me."

"Poor child of vanity! those dyes,
  And colors bright and rare,"
With mild reproof, the bee replies,
  "Are all beneath my care.

"Content I toil from morn till eve,
  And, scorning idleness,
To tribes of gaudy sloth I leave
  The vanity of dress."

William Lisle Bowles

DIRTY JIM

There was one little Jim,
'Tis reported of him,
   And must be to his lasting disgrace,
That he never was seen
With hands at all clean,
   Nor yet ever clean was his face.

His friends were much hurt
To see so much dirt,
   And often they made him quite clean;
But all was in vain,
He got dirty again,
   And not at all fit to be seen.

It gave him no pain
To hear them complain,
   Nor his own dirty clothes to survey;
His indolent mind
No pleasure could find
   In tidy and wholesome array.

The idle and bad,
Like this little lad,
   May love dirty ways, to be sure;
But good boys are seen,
To be decent and clean,
   Although they are ever so poor.

Jane Taylor

GODFREY GORDON GUSTAVUS GORE

Godfrey Gordon Gustavus Gore—
No doubt you have heard the name before—
Was a boy who never would shut a door!

The wind might whistle, the wind might roar,
And teeth be aching and throats be sore,
But still he never would shut the door.

His father would beg, his mother implore,
"Godfrey Gordon Gustavus Gore,
We really *do* wish you would shut the door!"

Their hands they wrung, their hair they tore;
But Godfrey Gordon Gustavus Gore
Was deaf as a buoy out at the Nore.

When he walked forth the folks would roar,
"Godfrey Gordon Gustavus Gore,
Why don't you think to shut the door?"

They rigged out a Shutter with sail and oar,
And threatened to pack off Gustavus Gore
On a voyage of penance to Singapore.

But he begged for mercy, and said, "No more!
Pray do not send me to Singapore
On a Shutter, and then I will shut the door!"

"You will?" said his parents; "then keep on shore!
But mind you do! For the plague is sore
Of a fellow that never will shut the door,
Godfrey Gordon Gustavus Gore!"

William Brighty Rands

THE STORY OF LITTLE SUCK-A-THUMB

One day, mamma said: "Conrad dear,
I must go out and leave you here.
But mind now, Conrad, what I say,
Don't suck your thumb while I'm away.

The great tall tailor always comes
To little boys that suck their thumbs;
And ere they dream what he's about,
He takes his great sharp scissors out
And cuts their thumbs clean off,—and then,
You know, they never grow again."

Mamma had scarcely turned her back,
The thumb was in, alack! alack!
The door flew open, in he ran,
The great, long, red-legged scissors-man.
Oh, children, see! the tailor's come
And caught our little Suck-a-Thumb.
Snip! snap! snip! the scissors go;
And Conrad cries out—"Oh! oh! oh!"

Snip! snap! snip! They go so fast,
That both his thumbs are off at last.
Mamma comes home; there Conrad stands,
And looks quite sad, and shows his hands;—
"Ah!" said mamma, "I knew he'd come
To naughty little Suck-a-Thumb."

From the German of Heinrich Hoffmann

GOOD AND BAD CHILDREN

Children, you are very little,
And your bones are very brittle;
If you would grow great and stately,
You must try to walk sedately.

You must still be bright and quiet,
And content with simple diet;
And remain, through all bewild'ring,
Innocent and honest children.

Happy hearts and happy faces,
Happy play in grassy places—
That was how, in ancient ages,
Children grew to kings and sages.

But the unkind and the unruly,
And the sort who eat unduly,
They must never hope for glory—
Theirs is quite a different story!

Cruel children, crying babies,
All grow up as geese and gabies,
Hated, as their age increases,
By their nephews and their nieces.

Robert Louis Stevenson

THERE WAS A LITTLE GIRL

There was a little girl, who had a little curl
   Right in the middle of her forehead,
And when she was good, she was very, very good,
   But when she was bad she was horrid.

She stood on her head, on her little trundle-bed,
   With nobody by for to hinder;
She screamed and she squalled, she yelled and she bawled,
   And drummed her little heels against the winder.

Her mother heard the noise, and thought it was the boys
   Playing in the empty attic,
She rushed upstairs, and caught her unawares,
   And spanked her, most emphatic.

A NURSERY SONG

Oh, Peterkin Pout and Gregory Grout
   Are two little goblins black.

Full oft from my house I've driven them out,
  But somehow they still come back.
They clamber up to the baby's mouth,
  And pull the corners down;
They perch aloft on the baby's brow,
  And twist it into a frown.

And one says "Must!" and t'other says "Can't!"
And one says "Shall!" and t'other says "Shan't!"
Oh, Peterkin Pout and Gregory Grout,
I pray you now from my house keep out!

But Samuel Smile and Lemuel Laugh
  Are two little fairies bright;
They're always ready for fun and chaff,
  And sunshine is their delight.
And when they creep into Baby's eyes,
  Why, there the sunbeams are;
And when they peep through her rosy lips,
  Her laughter rings near and far.

And one says "Please!" and t'other says "Do!"
And both together say "I love you!"
So, Lemuel Laugh and Samuel Smile,
Come in, my dears, and tarry awhile!

Laura E. Richards

MY LADY WIND

My Lady Wind, my Lady Wind,
Went round about the house to find
  A chink to set her foot in;
She tried the keyhole in the door,
She tried the crevice in the floor,
  And drove the chimney soot in.

And then one night when it was dark
She blew up such a tiny spark
　　That all the town was bothered;
From it she raised such flame and smoke
That many in great terror woke,
　　And many more were smothered.

And thus when once, my little dears,
A whisper reaches itching ears—
　　The same will come, you'll find:
Take my advice, restrain the tongue,
Remember what old nurse has sung
　　Of busy Lady Wind.

THE NAUGHTY BLACKBIRD

The King and the Queen were riding
　　Upon a summer's day,
And a Blackbird flew above them
　　To hear what they might say.

The King said he liked apples,
　　The Queen said she liked pears;
And what shall we do to the Blackbird
　　Who listens unawares?
　　　　　　　　　　Kate Greenaway

A HINT TO THE WISE

I know a little garden path
　　That leads you through the trees,
Past flower-beds and hollyhocks
　　And by the homes of bees,
Until at last it brings you to
　　A little fountain bath

Where tiny birds may wash themselves.
  If you go down that path,
Remember to be careful what
  You say. A little bird
May cause a lot of trouble by
  Repeating what he's heard.

Pringle Barret

JOHN WESLEY'S RULE

Do all the good you can,
In all the ways you can,
In all the places you can,
At all the times you can,
To all the people you can,
As long as ever you can.

A BAKER'S DUZZEN UV WIZE SAWZ

Them ez wants, must choose.
Them ez hez, must lose.
Them ez knows, won't blab.
Them ez guesses, will gab.
Them ez borrows, sorrows.
Them ez lends, spends.
Them ez gives, lives.
Them ez keeps dark, is deep.
Them ez kin earn, kin keep.
Them ez aims, hits.
Them ez hez, gits.
Them ez waits, win.
Them ez *will*, *kin*.

Edward Rowland Sill

THE BEST FIRM

A pretty good firm is "Watch & Waite,"
And another is "Attit, Early & Layte;"
And still another is "Doo & Dairet;"
But the best is probably "Grinn & Barrett."

Walter G. Doty.

JOG ON, JOG ON

Jog on, jog on the foot-path way
  And merrily hent the stile-a;
A merry heart goes all the day,
  Your sad tires in a mile-a.

William Shakespeare

HAPPY THOUGHT

The world is so full of a number of things,
I'm sure we should all be as happy as kings.

Robert Louis Stevenson

LITTLE THINGS

Little drops of water,
  Little grains of sand,
Make the mighty ocean
  And the pleasant land.

So the little moments,
  Humble though they be,
Make the mighty ages
  Of eternity.

So our little errors
  Lead the soul away

From the path of virtue,
    Far in sin to stray.

Little deeds of kindness,
    Little words of love,
Help to make earth happy
    Like the heaven above.
                        Julia Fletcher Carney

A TERNARIE OF LITTLES, UPON A PIPKIN OF JELLY SENT TO A LADY

A little Saint best fits a little Shrine,
A little Prop best fits a little Vine,
As my small Cruse best fits my little Wine.

A little Seed best fits a little Soil,
A little Trade best fits a little Toil,
As my small Jar best fits my little Oil.

A little Bin best fits a little Bread,
A little Garland fits a little Head,
As my small Stuff best fits my little Shed.

A little Hearth best fits a little Fire,
A little Chapel fits a little Quire,
As my small Bell best fits my little Spire.

A little Stream best fits a little Boat,
A little Lead best fits a little Float,
As my small Pipe best fits my little Note.

A little Meat best fits a little Belly,
As sweetly, lady, give me leave to tell ye,
This little Pipkin fits this little Jelly.
                        Robert Herrick

THE TUMBLE

Tumble down, tumble up, never mind it, my sweet;
   No, no, never beat the poor floor:
'Twas your fault, that could not stand straight on your
     feet;
   Beat yourself, if you beat any more.

Oh dear! what a noise: will a noise make it well?
   Will crying wash bruises away?
Suppose that it should bleed a little and swell.
   'Twill all be gone down in a day.

That's right, be a man, love, and dry up your tears.
   Come, smile, and I'll give you a kiss:
If you live in the world but a very few years,
   You must bear greater troubles than this.

Ah! there's the last tear dropping down from your cheek!
   All the dimples are coming again!
And your round little face looks as ruddy and meek
   As a rose that's been washed in the rain.

Ann Taylor

THINK BEFORE YOU ACT

   Elizabeth her frock has torn,
      And pricked her finger too;
   Why did she meddle with the thorn,
      Until its use she knew?

   Because Elizabeth will touch
      Whate'er comes in her way;
   I've seen her suffer quite as much,
      A dozen times a day.

Yet, though so oft she feels the pain,
  The habit is so strong,
That all her caution is in vain,
  And seldom heeded long.

I should not wonder if, at last,
  She meet some dreadful fate;
And then, perhaps, regret the past,
  When sorrow comes too late.

Mary Elliott

REBECCA'S AFTER-THOUGHT

Yesterday, Rebecca Mason,
  In the parlor by herself,
Broke a handsome china basin,
  Placed upon the mantel-shelf.

Quite alarmed, she thought of going
  Very quietly away,
Not a single person knowing,
  Of her being there that day.

But Rebecca recollected
  She was taught deceit to shun;
And the moment she reflected,
  Told her mother what was done;

Who commended her behavior,
Loved her better, and forgave her.

Elizabeth Turner

THE PIN

"Dear me! what signifies a pin,
  Wedged in a rotten board?

I'm certain that I won't begin,
    At ten years old, to hoard;
I never will be called a miser,
That I'm determined," said Eliza.

So onward tripped the little maid,
    And left the pin behind,
Which very snug and quiet lay,
    To its hard fate resigned;
Nor did she think (a careless chit)
'Twas worth her while to stoop for it.

Next day a party was to ride,
    To see an air balloon;
And all the company beside
    Were dressed and ready soon;
But she a woeful case was in,
For want of just a single pin.

In vain her eager eyes she brings,
    To every darksome crack;
There was not one, and yet her things
    Were dropping off her back.
She cut her pincushion in two,
But no, not one had fallen through.

At last, as hunting on the floor,
    Over a crack she lay,
The carriage rattled to the door,
    Then rattled fast away;
But poor Eliza was not in,
For want of just—a single pin!

There's hardly anything so small,
    So trifling or so mean,
That we may never want at all,
    For service unforeseen;

And wilful waste, depend upon't,
Brings, almost always, woeful want!

Ann Taylor

JANE AND ELIZA

There were two little girls, neither handsome nor plain,
One's name was Eliza, the other's was Jane;
They were both of one height, as I've heard people say,
And both of one age, I believe, to a day.

'Twas fancied by some who but slightly had seen them,
There was not a pin to be chosen between them;
But no one for long in this notion persisted,
So great a distinction there *really* existed.

Eliza knew well that she could not be pleasing
While fretting and fuming, while sulking or teasing;
And therefore in company artfully tried,
Not to *break* her bad habits, but only to *hide*.

So, when she was out, with much labor and pain,
She contrived to look *almost* as pleasant as Jane;
But then you might see that, in forcing a smile,
Her mouth was uneasy, and ached all the while.

And in spite of her care it would sometimes befall
That some cross event happened to ruin it all;
And because it might chance that her share was the worst,
Her temper broke loose, and her dimples dispersed.

But Jane, who had nothing she wanted to hide,
And therefore these troublesome arts never tried,
Had none of the care and fatigue of concealing,
But her face always showed what her bosom was feeling.

At home or abroad there was peace in her smile,
A cheerful good nature that needed no guile.
And Eliza worked hard, but could never obtain
The affection that freely was given to Jane.

Ann Taylor

MEDDLESOME MATTY

One ugly trick has often spoiled
   The sweetest and the best;
Matilda, though a pleasant child,
   One ugly trick possessed,
Which, like a cloud before the skies,
Hid all her better qualities.

Sometimes she'd lift the tea-pot lid,
   To peep at what was in it;
Or tilt the kettle, if you did
   But turn your back a minute.
In vain you told her not to touch,
Her trick of meddling grew so much.

Her grandmamma went out one day,
   And by mistake she laid
Her spectacles and snuff-box gay
   Too near the little maid;
"Ah! well," thought she, "I'll try them on,
As soon as grandmamma is gone."

Forthwith she placed upon her nose
   The glasses large and wide;
And looking round, as I suppose,
   The snuff-box too she spied:
"Oh! what a pretty box is that;
I'll open it," said little Matt.

"I know that grandmamma would say,
   'Don't meddle with it, dear';
But then, she's far enough away,
   And no one else is near:
Besides, what can there be amiss
In opening such a box as this?"

So thumb and finger went to work
   To move the stubborn lid,
And presently a mighty jerk
   The mighty mischief did;
For all at once, ah! woeful case,
The snuff came puffing in her face.

Poor eyes, and nose, and mouth, beside,
   A dismal sight presented;
In vain, as bitterly she cried,
   Her folly she repented.
In vain she ran about for ease;
She could do nothing now but sneeze.

She dashed the spectacles away,
   To wipe her tingling eyes,
And as in twenty bits they lay,
   Her grandmamma she spies.
"Heydey! and what's the matter now?"
Says grandmamma, with lifted brow.

Matilda, smarting with the pain,
   And tingling still, and sore,
Made many a promise to refrain
   From meddling evermore.
And 'tis a fact, as I have heard,
She ever since has kept her word.

Ann Taylor

CONTENTED JOHN

One honest John Tomkins, a hedger and ditcher,
Although he was poor, did not want to be richer;
For all such vain wishes in him were prevented
By a fortunate habit of being contented.

Though cold were the weather, or dear were the food,
John never was found in a murmuring mood;
For this he was constantly heard to declare,—
What he could not prevent he would cheerfully bear.

"For why should I grumble and murmur?" he said;
"If I cannot get meat, I'll be thankful for bread;
And, though fretting may make my calamities deeper,
It can never cause bread and cheese to be cheaper."

If John was afflicted with sickness or pain,
He wished himself better, but did not complain,
Nor lie down to fret in despondence and sorrow,
But said that he hoped to be better to-morrow.

If any one wronged him or treated him ill,
Why, John was good-natured and sociable still;
For he said that revenging the injury done
Would be making two rogues where there need be but one.

And thus honest John, though his station was humble,
Passed through this sad world without even a grumble;
And I wish that some folks, who are greater and richer,
Would copy John Tomkins, the hedger and ditcher.

Jane Taylor

THE VIOLET

Down in a green and shady bed
A modest violet grew;

Its stalk was bent, it hung its head,
  As if to hide from view.

And yet it was a lovely flower,
  Its color bright and fair;
It might have graced a rosy bower,
  Instead of hiding there.

Yet there it was content to bloom,
  In modest tints arrayed;
And there diffused a sweet perfume,
  Within the silent shade.

Then let me to the valley go,
  This pretty flower to see,
That I may also learn to grow
  In sweet humility.

Jane Taylor

DEEDS OF KINDNESS

Suppose the little Cowslip
  Should hang its golden cup
And say, "I'm such a little flower
  I'd better not grow up!"
How many a weary traveler
  Would miss its fragrant smell,
How many a little child would grieve
  To lose it from the dell!

Suppose the glistening Dewdrop
  Upon the grass should say,
"What can a little dewdrop do?
  I'd better roll away!"

The blade on which it rested,
  Before the day was done,
Without a drop to moisten it,
  Would wither in the sun.

Suppose the little Breezes,
  Upon a summer's day,
Should think themselves too small to cool
  The traveler on his way:
Who would not miss the smallest
  And softest ones that blow,
And think they made a great mistake
  If they were acting so?

How many deeds of kindness
  A little child can do,
Although it has but little strength
  And little wisdom too!
It wants a loving spirit,
  Much more than strength, to prove
How many things a child may do
  For others by its love.

BUTTERCUPS AND DAISIES

  Buttercups and daisies,
    Oh, the pretty flowers;
  Coming ere the springtime,
    To tell of sunny hours,
  While the trees are leafless,
    While the fields are bare,
  Buttercups and daisies
    Spring up here and there.

  Ere the snow-drop peepeth,
    Ere the crocus bold,

Ere the early primrose
  Opes its paly gold,—
Somewhere on the sunny bank
  Buttercups are bright;
Somewhere midst the frozen grass
  Peeps the daisy white.

Little hardy flowers,
  Like to children poor,
Playing in their sturdy health
  By their mother's door.
Purple with the north-wind,
  Yet alert and bold;
Fearing not, and caring not,
  Though they be a-cold!

What to them is winter!
  What are stormy showers!
Buttercups and daisies
  Are these human flowers!
He who gave them hardships
  And a life of care,
Gave them likewise hardy strength
  And patient hearts to bear.

Mary Howitt

THE BOY AND THE WOLF

A little Boy was set to keep
A little flock of goats or sheep;
He thought the task too solitary,
And took a strange perverse vagary;
To call the people out of fun,
To see them leave their work and run,
He cried and screamed with all his might,—
"Wolf! wolf!" in a pretended fright.

Some people, working at a distance,
Came running in to his assistance.
They searched the fields and bushes round:
The Wolf was nowhere to be found.
The Boy, delighted with his game,
A few days after did the same,
And once again the people came.
The trick was many times repeated:
At last they found that they were cheated.
One day the Wolf appeared in sight,
The Boy was in a real fright,
He cried, "Wolf! wolf!"—the neighbors heard,
But not a single creature stirred.
"We need not go from our employ,—
'Tis nothing but that idle boy."
The little Boy cried out again,
"Help, help! the Wolf!" He cried in vain.
At last his master came to beat him.
He came too late, the Wolf had eat him.
This shows the bad effect of lying,
And likewise of continual crying.
If I had heard you scream and roar,
For nothing, twenty times before,
Although you might have broke your arm,
Or met with any serious harm,
Your cries could give me no alarm;
They would not make me move the faster,
Nor apprehend the least disaster;
I should be sorry when I came,
But you yourself would be to blame.

John Hookham Frere

THE LION AND THE MOUSE

A lion with the heat oppressed,
One day composed himself to rest:

But while he dozed as he intended,
A mouse, his royal back ascended;
Nor thought of harm, as Æsop tells,
Mistaking him for someone else;
And traveled over him, and round him,
And might have left him as she found him
Had she not—tremble when you hear—
Tried to explore the monarch's ear!
Who straightway woke, with wrath immense,
And shook his head to cast her thence.
"You rascal, what are you about?"
Said he, when he had turned her out,
"I'll teach you soon," the lion said,
"To make a mouse-hole in my head!"
So saying, he prepared his foot
To crush the trembling tiny brute:
But she (the mouse) with tearful eye,
Implored the lion's clemency,
Who thought it best at last to give
His little prisoner a reprieve.

'Twas nearly twelve months after this,
The lion chanced his way to miss;
When pressing forward, heedless yet,
He got entangled in a net.
With dreadful rage, he stamped and tore,
And straight commenced a lordly roar;
When the poor mouse, who heard the noise,
Attended, for she knew his voice.
Then what the lion's utmost strength
Could not effect, she did at length;
With patient labor she applied
Her teeth, the network to divide;
And so at last forth issued he,
A *lion*, by a mouse set free.

Few are so small or weak, I guess,
But may assist us in distress,
Nor shall we ever, if we're wise,
The meanest, or the least despise.

Jeffreys Taylor

SOME MURMUR WHEN THEIR SKY IS CLEAR

Some murmur when their sky is clear,
   And wholly bright to view,
If one small speck of dark appear
   In their great heaven of blue.
And some with thankful love are filled,
   If but one streak of light,
One ray of God's good mercy, gild
   The darkness of their night.

In palaces are hearts that ask,
   In discontent and pride,
Why life is such a dreary task,
   And all good things denied.
And hearts in poorest huts admire
   How love has in their aid
(Love that not ever seems to tire)
   Such rich provision made.

Richard Chevenix Trench

TO A CHILD

Small service is true service while it lasts:
Of humblest friends, bright creature! scorn not one:
The daisy, by the shadow that it casts,
Protects the lingering dewdrop from the sun.

William Wordsworth

WRITTEN IN A LITTLE LADY'S LITTLE ALBUM

Hearts good and true
Have wishes few
In narrow circles bounded,
And hope that lives
On what God gives
Is Christian hope well founded.

Small things are best;
Grief and unrest
To rank and wealth are given;
But little things
On little wings
Bear little souls to heaven.

Frederick William Faber

A FAREWELL

My fairest child, I have no song to give you;
No lark could pipe to skies so dull and gray:
Yet, if you will, one quiet hint I'll leave you
For every day.

I'll tell you how to sing a clearer carol
Than lark who hails the dawn on breezy down:
To earn yourself a purer poet's laurel
Than Shakespeare's crown.

Be good, sweet maid, and let who will be clever;
Do noble things, not dream them, all day long:
And so make Life, Death, and that vast For Ever
One grand sweet song.

Charles Kingsley

III. Rhymes of Childhood

REEDS OF INNOCENCE

Piping down the valleys wild,
   Piping songs of pleasant glee,
On a cloud I saw a child,
   And he laughing said to me:

"Pipe a song about a lamb!"
   So I piped with merry cheer.
"Piper, pipe that song again;"
   So I piped: he wept to hear.

"Drop thy pipe, thy happy pipe;
   Sing thy songs of happy cheer!"
So I sang the same again,
   While he wept with joy to hear.

"Piper, sit thee down and write
   In a book that all may read."
So he vanished from my sight;
   And I plucked a hollow reed,

And I made a rural pen,
   And I stained the water clear,
And I wrote my happy songs
   Every child may joy to hear.

William Blake

RHYMES OF CHILDHOOD

FOREIGN LANDS

Up into the cherry tree
Who should climb but little me?
I held the trunk with both my hands
And looked abroad on foreign lands.

I saw the next door garden lie,
Adorned with flowers, before my eye,
And many pleasant places more
That I had never seen before.

I saw the dimpling river pass
And be the sky's blue looking-glass;
The dusty roads go up and down
With people tramping in to town.

If I could find a higher tree
Farther and farther I should see,
To where the grown-up river slips
Into the sea among the ships.

To where the roads on either hand
Lead onward into fairy land,
Where all the children dine at five,
And all the playthings come alive.

Robert Louis Stevenson

THE GARDENER

The gardener does not love to talk,
He makes me keep the gravel walk;
And when he puts his tools away,
He locks the door and takes the key.

Away behind the currant row
Where no one else but cook may go,
Far in the plots, I see him dig,
Old and serious, brown and big.

He digs the flowers, green, red, and blue,
Nor wishes to be spoken to.
He digs the flowers and cuts the hay,
And never seems to want to play.

Silly gardener! summer goes,
And winter comes with pinching toes,
When in the garden bare and brown
You must lay your barrow down.

Well now, and while the summer stays,
To profit by these garden days
O how much wiser you would be
To play at Indian wars with me!

Robert Louis Stevenson

MY SHADOW

I have a little shadow that goes in and out with me,
And what can be the use of him is more than I can see.
He is very, very like me from the heels up to the head;
And I see him jump before me, when I jump into my bed.

The funniest thing about him is the way he likes to grow—
Not at all like proper children, which is always very slow;
For he sometimes shoots up taller like an India-rubber ball,
And he sometimes gets so little that there's none of him
    at all.

He hasn't got a notion of how children ought to play,
And can only make a fool of me in every sort of way.

He stays so close beside me, he's a coward you can see;
I'd think shame to stick to nursie as that shadow sticks to
    me!

One morning, very early, before the sun was up,
I rose and found the shining dew on every buttercup;
But my lazy little shadow, like an arrant sleepy-head,
Had stayed at home behind me and was fast asleep in bed.

Robert Louis Stevenson

THE LAND OF COUNTERPANE

When I was sick and lay a-bed,
I had two pillows at my head,
And all my toys beside me lay
To keep me happy all the day.

And sometimes for an hour or so
I watched my leaden soldiers go,
With different uniforms and drills,
Among the bed-clothes, through the hills;

And sometimes sent my ships in fleets
All up and down among the sheets;
Or brought my trees and houses out,
And planted cities all about.

I was the giant great and still
That sits upon the pillow-hill,
And sees before him, dale and plain,
The pleasant land of counterpane.

Robert Louis Stevenson

PLAYGROUNDS

In summer I am very glad
We children are so small,

For we can see a thousand things
　　That men can't see at all.

They don't know much about the moss
　　And all the stones they pass:
They never lie and play among
　　The forests in the grass:

They walk about a long way off;
　　And, when we're at the sea,
Let father stoop as best he can,
　　He can't find things like me.

But, when the snow is on the ground
　　And all the puddles freeze,
I wish that I were very tall,
　　High up above the trees.

Laurence Alma-Tadema

THE PEDDLER'S CARAVAN

I wish I lived in a caravan
With a horse to drive, like a peddler-man!
Where he comes from nobody knows,
Or where he goes to, but on he goes!

His caravan has windows two,
And a chimney of tin, that the smoke comes through;
He has a wife, with a baby brown,
And they go riding from town to town.

Chairs to mend, and delf to sell!
He clashes the basins like a bell;
Tea-trays, baskets ranged in order,
Plates, with alphabets round the border!

The roads are brown, and the sea is green,
But his house is like a bathing-machine;
The world is round, and he can ride,
Rumble and slash, to the other side!

With the peddler-man I should like to roam,
And write a book when I came home;
All the people would read my book,
Just like the Travels of Captain Cook!

William Brighty Rands

MR. COGGS

A watch will tell the time of day,
Or tell it nearly, any way,
Excepting when it's overwound,
Or when you drop it on the ground.

If any of our watches stop,
We haste to Mr. Coggs's shop;
For though to scold us he pretends,
He's quite among our special friends.

He fits a dice-box in his eye,
And takes a long and thoughtful spy,
And prods the wheels, and says, "Dear, dear!
More carelessness, I greatly fear."

And then he lays the dice-box down
And frowns a most prodigious frown;
But if we ask him what's the time,
He'll make his gold repeater chime.

Edward Verrall Lucas

MR. WELLS

On Sunday morning, then he comes
   To church, and everybody smells
The blacking and the toilet soap
   And camphor balls from Mr. Wells.

He wears his whiskers in a bunch,
   And wears his glasses on his head.
I mustn't call him Old Man Wells—
   No matter—that's what father said.

And when the little blacking smells
   And camphor balls and soap begin,
I do not have to look to know
   That Mr. Wells is coming in.

Elizabeth Madox Roberts

MR. MINNITT

Mr. Minnitt mends my soles
When I have walked them into holes.
He works in such a funny place
And has a wrinkly, twinkly face.
His hands are brown and hard and thin,
His thread goes slowly out and in.
He cannot walk without a crutch—
I like him very, very much.

Rose Fyleman

THE SHOPMAN

The Shopman sells inside his shops
Safety-pins and acid drops,
And the Shopman has as well
Many other things to sell;

But these are the things that I
And my mother mostly buy.

Behind the counter where he lives
Lots of change the Shopman gives,
Does up parcels by the score,
Bows and asks you, "Nothing more?"
"Nothing more to-day," we say.
"Isn't it a lovely day?"

Eleanor Farjeon

MR. NOBODY

I know a funny little man,
    As quiet as a mouse,
Who does the mischief that is done
    In everybody's house!
There's no one ever sees his face,
    And yet we all agree
That every plate we break was cracked
    By Mr. Nobody.

'Tis he who always tears our books,
    Who leaves the door ajar,
He pulls the buttons from our shirts,
    And scatters pins afar;
That squeaking door will always squeak
    For, prithee, don't you see,
We leave the oiling to be done
    By Mr. Nobody.

He puts damp wood upon the fire,
    That kettles cannot boil;
His are the feet that bring in mud,
    And all the carpets soil.

The papers always are mislaid,
    Who had them last but he?
There's no one tosses them about
    But Mr. Nobody.

The finger-marks upon the door
    By none of us are made;
We never leave the blinds unclosed,
    To let the curtains fade.
The ink we never spill, the boots
    That lying round you see
Are not our boots; they all belong
    To Mr. Nobody.

IN THE GARDEN

I spied beside the garden bed
    A tiny lass of ours,
Who stopped and bent her sunny head
    Above the red June flowers.

Pushing the leaves and thorns apart,
    She singled out a rose,
And in its inmost crimson heart,
    Enraptured, plunged her nose.

"O dear, dear rose, come, tell me true—
    Come, tell me true," said she,
"If I smell just as sweet to you
    As you smell sweet to me!"
                                        Ernest Crosby

LITTLE RAINDROPS

Oh, where do you come from,
    You little drops of rain,

Pitter patter, pitter patter,
  Down the window-pane?

They won't let me walk,
  And they won't let me play,
And they won't let me go
  Out of doors at all to-day.

They put away my playthings
  Because I broke them all,
And then they locked up all my bricks,
  And took away my ball.

Tell me, little raindrops,
  Is that the way you play,
Pitter patter, pitter patter,
  All the rainy day?

They say I'm very naughty,
  But I've nothing else to do
But sit here at the window;
  I should like to play with you.

The little raindrops cannot speak,
  But "pitter, patter pat"
Means, "We can play on *this* side:
  Why can't you play on *that?*"

Anne Hawkshaw

WISHING

Ring-ting! I wish I were a Primrose,
A bright yellow Primrose, blowing in the Spring!
  The stooping bough above me,
  The wandering bee to love me,
The fern and moss to creep across,
  And the Elm-tree for our King!

Nay,—stay! I wish I were an Elm-tree,
A great lofty Elm-tree, with green leaves gay!
　The winds would set them dancing,
　The sun and moonshine glance in,
The Birds would house among the boughs,
　　And sweetly sing!

O—no! I wish I were a Robin,
A Robin or a little Wren, everywhere to go;
　Through forest, field, or garden,
　And ask no leave or pardon,
Till Winter comes with icy thumbs
　　To ruffle up our wing.

Well—tell! Where should I fly to,
Where go to sleep in the dark wood or dell?
　Before a day was over,
　Home comes the rover,
For Mother's kiss,—sweeter this
　　Than any other thing!

William Allingham

THE DUCK

If I were in a fairy tale,
And it were my good luck
To have a wish, I'd choose to be
A lovely snow-white duck.

When she puts off into the pond
And leaves me on the brink,
She wags her stumpy tail at me,
And gives a saucy wink,

Which says as plain as words could say
I'm safe as safe can be:

Stay there, or you will drown yourself,
The pond was made for me.

She goes a-sailing to and fro,
Just like a fishing-boat,
And steers and paddles all herself,
And never wets her coat.

Then in the water, upside down,
I've often seen her stand,
More neatly than the little boys
Who do it on the land.

And, best of all, her children are
The ducklings, bright as gold,
Who swim about the pond with her
And do as they are told.

Edith King

BUNCHES OF GRAPES

"Bunches of grapes," says Timothy;
"Pomegranates pink," says Elaine;
"A junket of cream and a cranberry tart
  For me," says Jane.

"Love-in-a-mist," says Timothy;
"Primroses pale," says Elaine;
"A nosegay of pinks and mignonette
  For me," says Jane.

"Chariots of gold," says Timothy;
"Silvery wings," says Elaine;
"A bumpity ride in a wagon of hay
  For me," says Jane.

Walter de la Mare

PRINCE TATTERS

Little Prince Tatters has lost his cap!
   Over the hedge he threw it;
Into the river it fell "kerslap!"
   Stupid old thing to do it!
Now Mother may sigh and Nurse may fume
For the gay little cap with its eagle plume.
"One cannot be thinking all day of such matters!
Trifles are trifles!" says little Prince Tatters.

Little Prince Tatters has lost his coat!
   Playing, he did not need it;
"Left it *right there*, by the nanny-goat,
   And nobody never seed it!"
Now Mother and Nurse may search till night
For the little new coat with its buttons bright;
But—"Coat-sleeves or shirt-sleeves, how little it matters!
Trifles are trifles!" says little Prince Tatters.

Little Prince Tatters has LOST HIS BALL!
   Rolled away down the street!
Somebody'll *have to find it*, that's all,
   Before he can sleep or eat.
Now raise the neighborhood, quickly, do!
And send for the crier and constable too!
"Trifles are trifles; but serious matters,
They must be *seen to*," says little Prince Tatters.

Laura E. Richards

SEEIN' THINGS

I ain't afeard uv snakes, or toads, or bugs, or worms, or
    mice,
An' things 'at girls are skeered uv I think are awful nice!

I'm pretty brave, I guess; an' yet I hate to go to bed,
For when I'm tucked up warm an' snug an' when my
    prayers are said,
Mother tells me, "Happy Dreams!" an' takes away the
    light,
An' leaves me lyin' all alone an' seein' things at night!

Sometimes they're in the corner, sometimes they're by the
    door,
Sometimes they're all a-standin' in the middle uv the floor;
Sometimes they are a-sittin' down, sometimes they're
    walkin' round
So softly and so creepylike they never make a sound!
Sometimes they are as black as ink, an' other times they're
    white—
But the color ain't no difference when you see things at
    night!

Once, when I licked a feller 'at had just moved on our
    street,
An' father sent me up to bed without a bite to eat,
I woke up in the dark an' saw things standin' in a row,
A-lookin' at me cross-eyed an' p'intin' at me—so!
Oh, my! I wuz so skeered that time I never slep' a mite—
It's almost alluz when I'm bad I see things at night!

Lucky thing I ain't a girl, or I'd be skeered to death!
Bein' I'm a boy, I duck my head an' hold my breath;
An' I am, oh, *so* sorry I'm a naughty boy, an' then
I promise to be better an' I say my prayers again!
Gran'ma tells me that's the only way to make it right
When a feller has been wicked an' sees things at night!

An' so, when other naughty boys would coax me into sin,
I try to skwush the Tempter's voice 'at urges me within;

An' when they's pie for supper, or cakes 'at's big an' nice,
I want to—but I do not pass my plate f'r them things
    twice!
No, ruther let Starvation wipe me slowly out o' sight
Than I should keep a-livin' on an' seein' things at night!
                           Eugene Field

THE RAGGEDY MAN *

O The Raggedy Man! He works fer Pa;
An' he's the goodest man ever you saw!
He comes to our house every day,
An' waters the horses, an' feeds 'em hay;
An' he opens the shed—an' we all ist laugh
When he drives out our little old wobble-ly calf;
An' nen—ef our hired girl says he can—
He milks the cow fer 'Lizabuth Ann.—
    Ain't he a' awful good Raggedy Man?
      Raggedy! Raggedy! Raggedy Man!

W'y The Raggedy Man—he's ist so good,
He splits the kindlin' an' chops the wood;
An' nen he spades in our garden, too,
An' does most things 'at *boys* can't do.—
He clumbed clean up in our big tree
An' shooked a' apple down fer me—
An' nother 'n', too, fer 'Lizabuth Ann—
An' nother 'n', too, fer The Raggedy Man.—
    Ain't he a' awful kind Raggedy Man?
      Raggedy! Raggedy! Raggedy Man!

An' The Raggedy Man, he knows most rhymes,
An' tells 'em, ef I be good, sometimes:

* This and the following poems by James Whitcomb Riley are from the
Biographical Edition of his complete works, copyright 1913, and are used
by special permission of the publishers, The Bobbs-Merrill Company.

Knows 'bout Giunts, an' Griffuns, an' Elves,
An' the Squidgicum-Squees 'at swallers the'rselves!
An', wite by the pump in our pasture-lot,
He showed me the hole 'at the Wunks is got,
'At lives 'way deep in the ground, an' can
Turn into me, 'er 'Lizabuth Ann!
Er Ma, er Pa, er The Raggedy Man!
 Ain't he a funny old Raggedy Man?
  Raggedy! Raggedy! Raggedy Man!

The Raggedy Man—one time, when he
Was makin' a little bow-'n'-orry fer me,
Says, "When you're big like your Pa is,
Air *you* go' to keep a fine store like his—
An' be a rich merchunt—an' wear fine clothes?—
Er what *air* you go' to be, goodness knows?"
An' nen he laughed at 'Lizabuth Ann,
An' I says, " 'M go' to be a Raggedy Man!
 I'm ist go' to be a nice Raggedy Man!"
  Raggedy! Raggedy! Raggedy Man!
     James Whitcomb Riley

THE MAN IN THE MOON

Said The Raggedy Man, on a hot afternoon:
 My!
  Sakes!
   What a lot o' mistakes
Some little folks makes on The Man in the Moon!
But people that's b'en up to *see* him, like *me*,
And calls on him frequent and intimuttly,
Might drop a few facts that would interest you
 Clean!
  Through!—
   If you wanted 'em to—
Some *actual* facts that might interest you!

O The Man in the Moon has a crick in his back;
   Whee!
      Whimm!
         Ain't you sorry for him?
And a mole on his nose that is purple and black;
And his eyes are so weak that they water and run
If he dares to *dream* even he looks at the sun,—
So he jes' dreams of stars, as the doctors advise—
   My!
      Eyes!
         But isn't he wise—
To jes' dream of stars, as the doctors advise?

And The Man in the Moon has a boil on his ear,—
   Whee!
      Whing!
         What a singular thing!
I know! but these facts are authentic, my dear,—
There's a boil on his ear; and a corn on his chin,—
He calls it a dimple—but dimples stick in—
Yet it might be a dimple turned over, you know!
   Whang!
      Ho!
         Why, certainly so!—
It might be a dimple turned over, you know!

And The Man in the Moon has a rheumatic knee,—
   Gee!
      Whizz!
         What a pity that is!
And his toes have worked round where his heels ought
   to be.—
So whenever he wants to go North he goes *South*,
And comes back with porridge-crumbs all round his
   mouth,

And he brushes them off with a Japanese fan,
    Whing!
        Whann!
            What a marvelous man!
What a very remarkably marvelous man!

And The Man in the Moon, sighed The Raggedy Man,
    Gits!
        So!
            Sullonesome, you know,—
Up there by hisse'f sence creation began!—
That when I call on him and then come away,
He grabs me and holds me and begs me to stay,—
Till—*Well!* if it wasn't fer *Jimmy-cum-jim*,
    Dadd!
        Limb!
            I'd go pardners with him—
Jes' jump my job here and be pardners with *him!*
                    James Whitcomb Riley

OUR HIRED GIRL

Our hired girl, she's 'Lizabuth Ann;
  An' she can cook best things to eat!
She ist puts dough in our pie-pan,
  An' pours in somepin' 'at's good an' sweet;
An' nen she salts it all on top
With cinnamon; an' nen she'll stop
  An' stoop an' slide it, ist as slow,
In th' old cook-stove, so's 'twon't slop
  An' git all spilled; nen bakes it, so
    It's custard-pie, first thing you know!
      An' nen she'll say,
      "Clear out o' my way!
They's time fer work, an' time fer play!

Take yer dough, an' run, child, run!
Er I cain't git no cookin' done!"

When our hired girl 'tends like she's mad,
   An' says folks got to walk the chalk
When *she's* around, er wisht they had!
   I play out on our porch an' talk
To Th' Raggedy Man 'at mows our lawn;
An' he says, "*Whew!*" an' nen leans on
   His old crook-scythe, and blinks his eyes,
An' sniffs all 'round an' says, "I swawn!
   Ef my old nose don't tell me lies,
   It 'pears like I smell custard-pies!"
      An' nen *he'll* say,
      "Clear out o' my way!
   They's time fer work, an' time fer play!
      Take yer dough, an' run, child, run!
      Er she cain't git no cookin' done!"

Wunst our hired girl, when she
   Got the supper, an' we all et,
An' it wuz night, an' Ma an' me
   An' Pa went wher' the "Social" met,—
An' nen when we come home, an' see
A light in the kitchen door, an' we
   Heerd a maccordeun, Pa says, "Lan'-
O'-Gracious, who can *her* beau be?"
   An' I marched in, an' 'Lizabuth Ann
   Wuz parchin' corn fer The Raggedy Man!
      Better say,
      "Clear out o' the way!
   They's time fer work, an' time fer play!
      Take the hint, an' run, child, run!
      Er we cain't git no courtin' done!"

                              James Whitcomb Riley

LITTLE ORPHANT ANNIE

Little Orphant Annie's come to our house to stay,
An' wash the cups an' saucers up, an' brush the crumbs
      away,
An' shoo the chickens off the porch, an' dust the hearth,
      an' sweep,
An' make the fire, an' bake the bread, an' earn her board-
      an'-keep;
An' all us other childern, when the supper-things is done,
We set around the kitchen fire an' has the mostest fun
A-list'nin' to the witch-tales 'at Annie tells about,
An' the Gobble-uns 'at gits you
            Ef you
                  Don't
                        Watch
                              Out!

Wunst they wuz a little boy wouldn't say his prayers,—
An' when he went to bed at night, away up-stairs,
His Mammy heerd him holler, an' his Daddy heerd him
      bawl,
An' when they turn't the kivvers down, he wuzn't there at
      all!
An' they seeked him in the rafter-room, an' cubby-hole,
      an' press,
An' seeked him up the chimbly-flue, an' ever'wheres, I
      guess;
But all they ever found wuz thist his pants an' round-
      about:—
An' the Gobble-uns'll git you
            Ef you
                  Don't
                        Watch
                              Out!

An' one time a little girl 'ud allus laugh an' grin,
An' make fun of ever' one, an' all her blood-an'-kin;
An' wunst, when they wuz "company," an' ole folks wuz
        there,
She mocked 'em an' shocked 'em, an' said she didn't care!
An' thist as she kicked her heels, an' turn't to run an' hide,
They wuz two great big Black Things a-standin' by her
        side,
An' they snatched her through the ceilin' 'fore she knowed
        what she's about!
An' the Gobble-uns'll git you
        Ef you
            Don't
                Watch
                Out!

An' little Orphant Annie says, when the blaze is blue,
An' the lamp-wick sputters, an' the wind goes *woo-oo!*
An' you hear the crickets quit, an' the moon is gray,
An' the lightnin'-bugs in dew is all squenched away,—
You better mind yer parunts, an' yer teachurs fond an'
        dear,
An' churish them 'at loves you, an' dry the orphant's tear,
An' he'p the pore an' needy ones 'at clusters all about,
Er the Gobble-uns'll git you
        Ef you
            Don't
                Watch
                Out!   *James Whitcomb Riley*

EXTREMES

A little boy once played so loud
That the Thunder, up in a thunder-cloud,
Said, "Since *I* can't be heard, why, then,
I'll never, never thunder again!"

And a little girl once kept so still
That she heard a fly on the window-sill
Whisper and say to a lady-bird,
"She's the stilliest child I ever heard!"

James Whitcomb Riley

A BOY'S MOTHER

My mother she's so good to me,
Ef I was good as I could be,
I couldn't be as good—no, sir!—
Can't any boy be good as her.

She loves me when I'm glad er sad;
She loves me when I'm good er bad;
An', what's a funniest thing, she says
She loves me when she punishes.

I don't like her to punish me,—
That don't hurt—but it hurts to see
Her cryin'.—Nen *I* cry; an' nen
We both cry an' be good again.

She loves me when she cuts an' sews
My little cloak an' Sund'y clothes;
An' when my Pa comes home to tea,
She loves him most as much as me.

She laughs an' tells him all I said,
An' grabs me up an' pats my head;
An' I hug *her*, an' hug my Pa,
An' love him purt' nigh as much as Ma.

James Whitcomb Riley

MY SORE THUMB

I jabbed a jack-knife in my thumb—
Th' blood just *spurted* when it come!

The cook got faint, an' nurse she yelled
And showed me how it should be held,
An' Gran'ma went to get a rag,
An' couldn't find one in th' bag;
   An' all the rest was just struck *dumb*
   To see my thumb!

Since I went an' jabbed my thumb
I go around a-lookin' glum,
   And Aunt, she pats me on the head
   An' gives me extra ginger-bread;
But brother's *mad*, an' says he'll go
An' take an axe, an' chop his toe:
   An' *then* he guesses I'll keep mum
   About my *thumb!*

At school they as't to see my thumb,
But I just showed it to my chum,
   An' any else that wants to see
   Must divvy up their cake with me!
It's gettin' well so fast, I think
I'll fix it up with crimson ink,
   An' that'll keep up *int'rest* some
   In my poor thumb!

                                   Burges Johnson

A MORTIFYING MISTAKE

I studied my tables over and over, and backward and for-
      ward, too;
But I couldn't remember six times nine, and I didn't know
      what to do,
Till sister told me to play with my doll, and not to bother
      my head.
"If you call her 'Fifty-four' for a while, you'll learn it by
      heart," she said.

So I took my favorite, Mary Ann (though I thought 'twas
    a dreadful shame
To give such a perfectly lovely child such a perfectly horrid
    name),
And I called her my dear little "Fifty-four" a hundred
    times, till I knew
The answer of six times nine as well as the answer of two
    times two.

Next day Elizabeth Wigglesworth, who always acts so
    proud,
Said, "Six times nine is fifty-two," and I nearly laughed
    aloud!
But I wished I hadn't when teacher said, "Now, Dorothy,
    tell if you can."
For I thought of my doll and—sakes alive!—I answered,
    "*Mary Ann!*"

Anna Maria Pratt

MANNERS

I have an uncle I don't like,
    An aunt I cannot bear:
She chucks me underneath the chin,
    He ruffles up my hair.

Another uncle I adore,
    Another aunty, too:
She shakes me kindly by the hand,
    He says, How do you do?

Mrs. Schuyler Van Rensselaer

AUNT SELINA

When Aunt Selina comes to tea
She always makes them send for me,

And I must be polite and clean
And seldom heard, but always seen.
I must sit stiffly in my chair
As long as Aunt Selina's there.

But there are certain things I would
Ask Aunt Selina if I could.
I'd ask when she was small, like me,
If she had ever climbed a tree.
Or if she's ever, ever gone
Without her shoes and stockings on
Where lovely puddles lay in rows
To let the mud squeege through her toes.
Or if she's coasted on a sled,
Or learned to stand upon her head
And wave her feet—and after that
I'd ask her how she got so fat.

These things I'd like to ask, and then—
I hope she would not come again!

Carol Haynes

LITTLE GUSTAVA

Little Gustava sits in the sun,
Safe in the porch, and the little drops run
From the icicles under the eaves so fast,
For the bright spring sun shines warm at last,
    And glad is little Gustava.

She wears a quaint little scarlet cap,
And a little green bowl she holds in her lap,
Filled with bread and milk to the brim,
And a wreath of marigolds round the rim:
    "Ha! ha!" laughs little Gustava.

Up comes her little gray coaxing cat
With her little pink nose, and she mews, "What's that?"
Gustava feeds her,—she begs for more;
And a little brown hen walks in at the door:
    "Good day!" cries little Gustava.

She scatters crumbs for the little brown hen.
There comes a rush and a flutter, and then
Down fly her little white doves so sweet,
With their snowy wings and crimson feet:
    "Welcome!" cries little Gustava.

So, dainty and eager, they pick up the crumbs.
But who is this through the doorway comes?
Little Scotch terrier, little dog Rags,
Looks in her face, and his funny tail wags:
    "Ha! ha!" laughs little Gustava.

"You want some breakfast too?" and down
She sets her bowl on the brick floor brown;
And little dog Rags drinks up her milk,
While she strokes his shaggy locks like silk:
    "Dear Rags!" says little Gustava.

Waiting without stood sparrow and crow,
Cooling their feet in the melting snow:
"Won't you come in, good folk?" she cried.
But they were too bashful, and stood outside
    Though "Pray come in!" cried Gustava.

So the last she threw them, and knelt on the mat
With doves and biddy and dog and cat.
And her mother came to the open house-door:
"Dear little daughter, I bring you some more.
    My merry little Gustava!"

Kitty and terrier, biddy and doves,
All things harmless Gustava loves.
The shy, kind creatures 'tis joy to feed,
And oh, her breakfast is sweet indeed
    To happy little Gustava!

Celia Thaxter

MILK FOR THE CAT

When the tea is brought at five o'clock,
And all the neat curtains are drawn with care,
The little black cat with bright green eyes
Is suddenly purring there.

At first she pretends, having nothing to do,
She has come in merely to blink by the grate,
But, though tea may be late or the milk may be sour,
She is never late.

And presently her agate eyes
Take a soft large milky haze,
And her independent casual glance
Becomes a stiff hard gaze.

Then she stamps her claws or lifts her ears
Or twists her tail and begins to stir,
Till suddenly all her lithe body becomes
One breathing trembling purr.

The children eat and wriggle and laugh;
The two old ladies stroke their silk:
But the cat is grown small and thin with desire,
Transformed to a creeping lust for milk.

The white saucer like some full moon descends
At last from the clouds of the table above;
She sighs and dreams and thrills and glows,
Transfigured with love.

She nestles over the shining rim,
Buries her chin in the creamy sea;
Her tail hangs loose; each drowsy paw
Is doubled under each bending knee.

A long dim ecstasy holds her life;
Her world is an infinite shapeless white.
Till her tongue has curled the last holy drop,
Then she sinks back into the night,

Draws and dips her body to heap
Her sleepy nerves in the great arm-chair,
Lies defeated and buried deep
Three or four hours unconscious there.

Harold Monro

THE GARDENER'S CAT

The gardener's cat's called Mignonette,
She hates the cold, she hates the wet,
She sits among the hothouse flowers
And sleeps for hours and hours and hours.

She dreams she is a tiger fierce
With great majestic claws that pierce,
She sits by the hot-water pipes
And dreams about a coat of stripes;

And in her slumbers she will go
And stalk the sullen buffalo,
And when he roars across the brake
She does not wink, she does not wake.

It must be perfectly immense
To dream with such magnificence,
And pass the most inclement day
In this indeed stupendous way.

She dreams of India's sunny clime,
And only wakes at dinner-time,
But even then she does not stir
But waits till milk is brought to her.

How nice to be the gardener's cat,
She troubles not for mouse or rat,
But, when it's coming down in streams,
She sits among the flowers and dreams.

The gardener's cat would be the thing,
Her dreams are so encouraging;
She dreams that she's a tiger, yet
She's just a cat called Mignonette!

.   .   .   .

The moral's this, my little man—
Sleep 'neath life's hailstones when you can,
And if you're humble in estate,
Dream splendidly, at any rate!

                              Patrick R. Chalmers

NICHOLAS NYE

Thistle and darnell and dock grew there,
    And a bush, in the corner, of may,
On the orchard wall I used to sprawl
    In the blazing heat of the day;
Half asleep and half awake,
    While the birds went twittering by,
And nobody there my lone to share
    But Nicholas Nye.

Nicholas Nye was lean and gray,
    Lame of a leg and old,
More than a score of donkey's years
    He had seen since he was foaled;

He munched the thistles, purple and spiked,
  Would sometimes stoop and sigh,
And turn to his head, as if he said,
  "Poor Nicholas Nye!"

Alone with his shadow he'd drowse in the meadow,
  Lazily swinging his tail,
At break of day he used to bray,—
  Not much too hearty and hale;
But a wonderful gumption was under his skin,
  And a clear calm light in his eye,
And once in a while: he'd smile:—
  Would Nicholas Nye.

Seem to be smiling at me, he would,
  From his bush in the corner, of may,—
Bony and ownerless, widowed and worn,
  Knobble-kneed, lonely and gray;
And over the grass would seem to pass
  'Neath the deep dark blue of the sky,
Something much better than words between me
  And Nicholas Nye.

But dusk would come in the apple boughs,
  The green of the glow-worm shine,
The birds in nest would crouch to rest,
  And home I'd trudge to mine;
And there, in the moonlight, dark with dew,
  Asking not wherefore nor why,
Would brood like a ghost, and as still as a post,
  Old Nicholas Nye.

Walter de la Mare

NURSE'S SONG

When the voices of children are heard on the green
  And laughing is heard on the hill,

My heart is at rest within my breast,
   And everything else is still.

"Then come home, my children, the sun is gone down,
   And the dews of the night arise;
Come, come, leave off play, and let us away
   Till the morning appears in the skies."

"No, no, let us play, for it is yet day,
   And we cannot go to sleep;
Besides, in the sky the little birds fly,
   And the hills are all covered with sheep."

"Well, well, go and play till the light fades away,
   And then go home to bed."
The little ones leaped, and shouted, and laughed,
   And all the hills echoèd.

William Blake

UNDER MY WINDOW

Under my window, under my window,
   All in the Midsummer weather,
Three little girls with fluttering curls
   Flit to and fro together:—
There's Bell with her bonnet of satin sheen,
And Maud with her mantle of silver-green,
   And Kate with her scarlet feather.

Under my window, under my window,
   Leaning stealthily over,
Merry and clear, the voice I hear
   Of each glad-hearted rover.
Ah! sly little Kate, she steals my roses;
And Maud and Bell twine wreaths and posies,
   As merry as bees in clover.

Under my window, under my window,
  In the blue Midsummer weather,
Stealing slow, on a hushed tiptoe,
  I catch them all together:—
Bell with her bonnet of satin sheen,
And Maud with her mantle of silver-green,
  And Kate with her scarlet feather.

Under my window, under my window,
  And off through the orchard closes;
While Maud she flouts, and Bell she pouts,
  They scamper and drop their posies;
But dear little Kate takes naught amiss,
And leaps in my arms with a loving kiss,
  And I give her all my roses.

Thomas Westwood

THE BAREFOOT BOY

Blessings on thee, little man,
Barefoot boy, with cheek of tan!
With thy turned-up pantaloons,
And thy merry whistled tunes;
With thy red lip, redder still
Kissed by strawberries on the hill;
With the sunshine on thy face,
Through thy torn brim's jaunty grace;
From my heart I give thee joy,—
I was once a barefoot boy!
Prince thou art,—the grown-up man
Only is republican,
Let the million-dollared ride!
Barefoot, trudging at his side,
Thou hast more than he can buy
In the reach of ear and eye,—
Outward sunshine, inward joy:
Blessings on thee, barefoot boy!

Oh for boyhood's painless play,
Sleep that wakes in laughing day,
Health that mocks the doctor's rules,
Knowledge never learned of schools,
Of the wild bee's morning chase,
Of the wild-flower's time and place,
Flight of fowl and habitude
Of the tenants of the wood;
How the tortoise bears his shell,
How the woodchuck digs his cell,
And the ground-mole sinks his well;
How the robin feeds her young,
How the oriole's nest is hung;
Where the whitest lilies blow,
Where the freshest berries grow,
Where the ground-nut trails its vine,
Where the wood-grape's clusters shine;
Of the black wasp's cunning way,
Mason of his walls of clay,
And the architectural plans
Of gray hornet artisans!
For, eschewing books and tasks,
Nature answers all he asks;
Hand in hand with her he walks,
Face to face with her he talks,
Part and parcel of her joy,—
Blessings on the barefoot boy!

Oh for boyhood's time of June,
Crowding years in one brief moon,
When all things I heard or saw,
Me, their master, waited for.
I was rich in flowers and trees,
Humming-birds and honey-bees;
For my sport the squirrel played,
Plied the snouted mole his spade;

For my taste the blackberry cone
Purpled over hedge and stone;
Laughed the brook for my delight
Through the day and through the night,
Whispering at the garden wall,
Talked with me from fall to fall;
Mine the sand-rimmed pickerel pond,
Mine the walnut slopes beyond,
Mine, on bending orchard trees,
Apples of Hesperides!
Still as my horizon grew,
Larger grew my riches too;
All the world I saw or knew
Seemed a complex Chinese toy,
Fashioned for a barefoot boy!

Oh for festal dainties spread,
Like my bowl of milk and bread;
Pewter spoon and bowl of wood,
On the door-stone, gray and rude!
O'er me, like a regal tent,
Cloudy-ribbed, the sunset bent,
Purple-curtained, fringed with gold,
Looped in many a wind-swung fold;
While for music came the play
Of the pied frogs' orchestra;
And, to light the noisy choir,
Lit the fly his lamp of fire.
I was monarch: pomp and joy
Waited on the barefoot boy!

Cheerily, then, my little man,
Live and laugh, as boyhood can!
Though the flinty slopes be hard,
Stubble-speared the new-mown sward,

Every morn shall lead thee through
Fresh baptisms of the dew;
Every evening from thy feet
Shall the cool wind kiss the heat:
All too soon these feet must hide
In the prison cells of pride,
Lose the freedom of the sod,
Like a colt's for work be shod,
Made to tread the mills of toil,
Up and down in ceaseless moil:
Happy if their track be found
Never on forbidden ground;
Happy if they sink not in
Quick and treacherous sands of sin.
Ah! that thou couldst know thy joy,
Ere it passes, barefoot boy!

John Greenleaf Whittier

WIND'S WORK

Kate rose up early as fresh as a lark,
Almost in time to see vanish the dark;
Jack, rather later, bouncing from bed,
Saw fade on the dawn's cheek the last flush of red:
Yet who knows
When the wind rose?

Kate went to watch the new lambs at their play
And stroke the white calf born yesterday;
Jack sought the woods where trees grow tall
As who would learn to swarm them all:
Yet who knows
Where the wind goes?

Kate has sown candy-tuft, lupins and peas,
Carnations, forget-me-nots and heart's-ease;

Jack has sown cherry-pie, marigold,
Love-that-lies-bleeding and snap-dragons bold;
But who knows
What the wind sows?

Kate knows a thing or two useful at home,
Darns like a fairy, and churns like a gnome;
Jack is a wise man at shaping a stick,
Once he's in the saddle the pony may kick.

But hark to the wind how it blows!
None comes, none goes,
None reaps or mows,
No friends turn foes,
No hedge bears sloes,
And no cock crows,
But the wind knows!

T. Sturge Moore

FATHER TIME

Father Time lives afar in the sky, so they say,
    And he's busy as busy can be;
For he always is making to-morrow to-day,
And to-day was made yesterday just the same way;
    So he makes a day daily, you see.

First some minutes he pours from a sack, then he shakes
    A few tears over all, and some fun;
Next he puts in some quarrels, and laughter, and aches,
And he mixes them well, like a cook making cakes;
    And he sends it to us when it's done.

But some days that he sends us are happy with song,
    And those days are the shortest, I know;
There are some that are tearful, and dreary, and long,
And some others just right, and yet others all wrong,
    And it seems very strange that it's so.

Now I think Father Time tries to make them one size,
  And alike as are peas in a pod;
But with many long years he's as old as he's wise,
He's so old that he's losing the sight of his eyes:
  That is why all the days are so odd.

For he cannot see how many minutes he takes,
  Or what tears, or what laughter to add.
That's the reason, I think, why he makes these mistakes—
Why the long days are nothing but grumbles and aches,
  And why only the short ones are glad.

Norman Ault

THE SHIPS OF YULE

When I was just a little boy,
  Before I went to school,
I had a fleet of forty sail
  I called the Ships of Yule;

Of every rig, from rakish brig
  And gallant barkentine
To little Fundy fishing-boats
  With gunwales painted green.

They used to go on trading trips
  Around the world for me,
For though I had to stay at home
  My heart was on the sea.

They stopped at every port of call
  From Babylon to Rome,
To load with all the lovely things
  We never had at home;

With elephants and ivory
    Bought from the King of Tyre,
And shells and silk and sandal-wood
    That sailor men admire;

With figs and dates from Samarkand,
    And squatty ginger-jars,
And scented silver amulets,
    From Indian bazaars;

With sugar-cane from Port of Spain,
    And monkeys from Ceylon,
And paper lanterns from Pekin
    With painted dragons on;

With coconuts from Zanzibar,
    And pines from Singapore;
And when they had unloaded these
    They could go back for more.

And even after I was big
    And had to go to school,
My mind was often far away
    Aboard the Ships of Yule.

                              Bliss Carman

ROMANCE

When I was but thirteen or so
    I went into a golden land,
Chimborazo, Cotopaxi
    Took me by the hand.

My father died, my brother too,
    They passed like fleeting dreams,
I stood where Popocatapetl
    In the sunlight gleams.

I dimly heard the master's voice
  And boys far-off at play,
Chimborazo, Cotopaxi
  Had stolen me away.

I walked in a great golden dream
  The town streets, to and fro—
Shining Popocatapetl
  Gleamed with his cap of snow.

I walked home with a gold dark boy
  And never a word I'd say,
Chimborazo, Cotapaxi
  Had taken my breath away:

I gazed entranced upon his face
  Fairer than any flower—
O shining Popocatapetl,
  It was thy magic hour:

The houses, people, traffic seemed
  Thin fading dreams by day,
Chimborazo, Cotopaxi,
  They had stolen my soul away!

                  W. J. Turner

TRUTH

The world is hollow like a pumpkin-shell—
We know it well—
And warm and full of true delightful things,
Hop-o'-my-thumbs and flittermice with wings,
And frequent beanstalks reaching to the sky,
And giants nine feet high.

When with your button nose against the pane
You say, watching the rain,

"The clouds are elephants with ears like sails
And trunks to match their tails"—
Oh that is true, oh that is very true!
I see them too.

Now stop your little ears with both your thumbs,
For here the Doubter comes;
And up and down he shortly will declare
The world is dirt and skies are made of air.

Never believe him though he looks so wise.
I marvel that his skies,
Like Chicken Little's, do not tumble down
And crash upon his crown.

Jessica Nelson North

THE CHILDREN'S HOUR

Between the dark and the daylight,
    When the night is beginning to lower,
Comes a pause in the day's occupations,
    That is known as the Children's Hour.

I hear in the chamber above me
    The patter of little feet,
The sound of a door that is opened,
    And voices soft and sweet.

From my study I see in the lamplight,
    Descending the broad hall stair,
Grave Alice, and laughing Allegra,
    And Edith with golden hair.

A whisper, and then a silence:
    Yet I know by their merry eyes
They are plotting and planning together
    To take me by surprise.

A sudden rush from the stairway,
   A sudden raid from the hall!
By three doors left unguarded
   They enter my castle wall!

They climb up into my turret
   O'er the arms and back of my chair;
If I try to escape, they surround me;
   They seem to be everywhere.

They almost devour me with kisses,
   Their arms about me entwine,
Till I think of the Bishop of Bingen
   In his Mouse-Tower on the Rhine!

Do you think, O blue-eyed banditti,
   Because you have scaled the wall,
Such an old mustache as I am
   Is not a match for you all!

I have you fast in my fortress,
   And will not let you depart,
But put you down into the dungeon
   In the round-tower of my heart.

And there will I keep you forever,
   Yes, forever and a day,
Till the walls shall crumble to ruin,
   And moulder in dust away!

Henry Wadsworth Longfellow

IV. Just Nonsense

MY RECOLLECTEST THOUGHTS

From "Davy and the Goblin"

My recollectest thoughts are those
    Which I remember yet;
And bearing on, as you'd suppose,
    The things I don't forget.

But my resemblest thoughts are less
    Alike than they should be;
A state of things, as you'll confess,
    You very seldom see.

And yet the mostest thought I love
    Is what no one believes—
That I'm the sole survivor of
    The famous Forty Thieves!

Charles Edward Carryl

JUST NONSENSE

MR. FINNEY'S TURNIP

Mr. Finney had a turnip
   And it grew behind the barn;
And it grew and it grew,
   And that turnip did no harm.

There it grew and it grew
   Till it could grow no longer;
Then his daughter Lizzie picked it
   And put it in the cellar.

There it lay and it lay
   Till it began to rot;
And his daughter Susie took it
   And put it in the pot.

And they boiled it and boiled it
   As long as they were able;
And then his daughters took it
   And put it on the table.

Mr. Finney and his wife
   They sat them down to sup;
And they ate and they ate
   And they ate that turnip up.

THE THREE JOVIAL WELSHMEN

There were three jovial Welshmen,
   As I have heard them say,
And they would go a-hunting
   Upon St. David's day.

All the day they hunted,
  And nothing could they find,
But a ship a-sailing,
  A-sailing with the wind.

One said it was a ship,
  The other he said, nay;
The third said it was a house
  With the chimney blown away.

And all night they hunted,
  And nothing could they find,
But the moon a-gliding,
  A-gliding with the wind.

One said it was the moon,
  The other he said, nay;
The third said it was a cheese,
  With half of it cut away.

And all day they hunted,
  And nothing could they find,
But a hedgehog in a bramble-bush,
  And that they left behind.

The first said 'twas a hedgehog,
  The second he said, nay;
The third it was a pin-cushion,
  With the pins stuck in wrong way.

And all night they hunted,
  And nothing could they find,
But a hare in a turnip field,
  And that they left behind.

The first said it was a hare,
    The second he said, nay;
The third said it was a calf,
    And the cow had run away.

And all day they hunted,
    And nothing could they find,
But an owl in a holly-tree,
    And that they left behind.

The first said it was an owl,
    The second he said, nay;
The third said 'twas an old man,
    And his beard was growing gray.

THE JUMBLIES

They went to sea in a sieve, they did;
    In a sieve they went to sea;
In spite of all their friends could say,
On a winter's morn, on a stormy day,
    In a sieve they went to sea.
And when the sieve turned round and round,
And every one cried, "You'll all be drowned!"
They called aloud, "Our sieve ain't big;
But we don't care a button; we don't care a fig:
    In a sieve we'll go to sea!"
        Far and few, far and few,
            Are the lands where the Jumblies live:
            Their heads are green, and their hands are blue;
                And they went to sea in a sieve.

They sailed away in a sieve, they did,
    In a sieve they sailed so fast,
With only a beautiful pea-green veil
Tied with a ribbon, by way of a sail,
    To a small tobacco-pipe mast.

And every one said who saw them go,
"Oh! won't they be soon upset, you know?
For the sky is dark, and the voyage is long;
And, happen what may, it's extremely wrong
   In a sieve to sail so fast."

The water it soon came in, it did;
   The water it soon came in;
So, to keep them dry, they wrapped their feet
In a pinky paper all folded neat:
   And they fastened it down with a pin.
And they passed the night in a crockery-jar;
And each of them said, "How wise we are!
Though the sky be dark, and the voyage be long.
Yet we never can think we were rash or wrong,
   While round in our sieve we spin."

And all night long they sailed away;
   And, when the sun went down,
They whistled and warbled a moony song
To the echoing sound of a coppery gong,
   In the shade of the mountains brown:
"O Timballoo! How happy we are
When we live in a sieve and a crockery-jar!
And all night long, in the moonlight pale,
We sail away with a pea-green sail
   In the shade of the mountains brown."

They sailed to the Western Sea, they did,—
   To a land all covered with trees:
And they bought an owl, and a useful cart,
And a pound of rice, and a cranberry-tart,
   And a hive of silvery bees;
And they bought a pig, and some green jackdaws,
And a lovely monkey with lollipop paws,
And forty bottles of ring-bo-ree,
   And no end of Stilton cheese.

And in twenty years they all came back,—
    In twenty years or more;
And every one said, "How tall they've grown!
For they've been to the Lakes, and the Torrible Zone,
    And the hills of the Chankly Bore."
And they drank their health, and gave them a feast
Of dumplings made of beautiful yeast;
And every one said, "If we only live,
We, too, will go to sea in a sieve,
    To the hills of the Chankly Bore."
      Far and few, far and few,
        Are the lands where the Jumblies live:
        Their heads are green, and their hands are blue;
        And they went to sea in a sieve.

Edward Lear

THE OWL AND THE PUSSY-CAT

The Owl and the Pussy-cat went to sea
    In a beautiful pea-green boat:
They took some honey, and plenty of money
    Wrapped up in a five-pound note.
The Owl looked up to the stars above,
    And sang to a small guitar,
"O lovely Pussy, O Pussy, my love,
    What a beautiful Pussy you are!"

Pussy said to the Owl, "You elegant fowl,
    How charmingly sweet you sing!
Oh! let us be married; too long we have tarried:
    But what shall we do for a ring?"
They sailed away, for a year and a day,
    To the land where the bong-tree grows;
And there in a wood a Piggy-wig stood,
    With a ring at the end of his nose.

"Dear Pig, are you willing to sell for one shilling
   Your ring?" Said the Piggy, "I will."
So they took it away, and were married next day
   By the turkey who lives on the hill.
They dined on mince and slices of quince,
   Which they ate with a runcible spoon;
And hand in hand, on the edge of the sand,
   They danced by the light of the moon.

Edward Lear

THE POBBLE WHO HAS NO TOES

The Pobble who has no toes
   Had once as many as we;
When they said, "Some day you may lose them all,"
   He replied, "Fish fiddle-de-dee!"
And his Aunt Jobiska made him drink
Lavender water tinged with pink,
For she said, "The World in general knows
There's nothing so good for a Pobble's toes!"

The Pobble who has no toes
   Swam across the Bristol Channel;
But before he set out he wrapped his nose
   In a piece of scarlet flannel.
For his Aunt Jobiska said, "No harm
Can come to his toes if his nose is warm;
And it's perfectly known that a Pobble's toes
Are safe,—provided he minds his nose."

The Pobble swam fast and well,
   And when boats or ships came near him,
He tinkledy-binkledy-winkled a bell,
   So that all the world could hear him.
And all the Sailors and Admirals cried,
When they saw him nearing the further side,—

"He has gone to fish for his Aunt Jobiska's
Runcible Cat with crimson whiskers!"

But before he touched the shore,—
  The shore of the Bristol Channel,—
A sea-green Porpoise carried away
  His wrapper of scarlet flannel.
And when he came to observe his feet,
Formerly garnished with toes so neat,
His face at once became forlorn
On perceiving that all his toes were gone!

And nobody ever knew,
  From that dark day to the present,
Whoso had taken the Pobble's toes,
  In a manner so far from pleasant.
Whether the shrimps or crawfish gray,
Or crafty Mermaids stole them away—
Nobody knew; and nobody knows
How the Pobble was robbed of his twice five toes!

The Pobble who has no toes
  Was placed in a friendly Bark,
And they rowed him back, and carried him up
  To his Aunt Jobiska's Park.
And she made him a feast, at his earnest wish,
Of eggs and buttercups fried with fish;
And she said, "It's a fact the whole world knows,
That Pobbles are happier without their toes."

                         Edward Lear

THE TABLE AND THE CHAIR

    Said the Table to the Chair,
    "You can hardly be aware
    How I suffer from the heat
    And from chilblains on my feet.

If we took a little walk,
We might have a little talk;
Pray let us take the air,"
Said the Table to the Chair.

Said the Chair unto the Table,
"Now, you *know* we are not able:
How foolishly you talk,
When you know we *cannot* walk!"
Said the Table with a sigh,
"It can do no harm to try.
I've as many legs as you:
Why can't we walk on two?"

So they both went slowly down,
And walked about the town
With a cheerful bumpy sound
As they toddled round and round;
And everybody cried,
As they hastened to their side,
"See! the Table and the Chair
Have come out to take the air!"

But in going down an alley
To a castle in a valley,
They completely lost their way,
And wandered all the day;
Till, to see them safely back,
They paid a Ducky-quack,
And a Beetle, and a Mouse,
Who took them to their house.

Then they whispered to each other,
"O delightful little brother,
What a lovely walk we've taken!
Let us dine on beans and bacon!"

So the Ducky and the leetle
Browny-Mousy and the Beetle
Dined, and danced upon their heads
Till they toddled to their beds.

Edward Lear

THE WHITING AND THE SNAIL

From "Alice's Adventures in Wonderland"

"Will you walk a little faster?" said a whiting to a snail,
"There's a porpoise close behind us, and he's treading on
    my tail,
See how eagerly the lobsters and the turtles all advance!
They are waiting on the shingle—will you come and join
    the dance?
  Will you, won't you, will you, won't you, will you join
    the dance?
  Will you, won't you, will you, won't you, won't you join
    the dance?

"You can really have no notion how delightful it will be
When they take us up and throw us, with the lobsters, out
    to sea!"
But the snail replied, "Too far, too far!" and gave a look
    askance—
Said he thanked the whiting kindly, but he would not join
    the dance,
  Would not, could not, would not, could not, would not
    join the dance.
  Would not, could not, would not, could not, could not
    join the dance.

"What matters it how far we go?" his scaly friend replied.
"There is another shore, you know, upon the other side.

The further off from England the nearer is to France—
Then turn not pale, belovèd snail, but come and join the
    dance.
    Will you, won't you, will you, won't you, will you join
      the dance?
    Will you, won't you, will you, won't you, won't you join
      the dance?"

Lewis Carroll

THE WALRUS AND THE CARPENTER

From "Through the Looking-Glass"

The sun was shining on the sea,
    Shining with all his might:
He did his very best to make
    The billows smooth and bright—
And this was odd, because it was
    The middle of the night.

The Walrus and the Carpenter
    Were walking close at hand:
They wept like anything to see
    Such quantities of sand:
"If this were only cleared away,"
    They said, "it *would* be grand!"

"If seven maids with seven mops
    Swept it for half a year,
Do you suppose," the Walrus said,
    "That they could get it clear?"
"I doubt it," said the Carpenter,
    And shed a bitter tear.

"O Oysters, come and walk with us!"
    The Walrus did beseech.

"A pleasant talk, a pleasant walk,
    Along the briny beach:
We cannot do with more than four,
    To give a hand to each."

The eldest Oyster looked at him,
    But never a word he said:
The eldest Oyster winked his eye,
    And shook his heavy head—
Meaning to say he did not choose
    To leave the oyster-bed.

But four young Oysters hurried up,
    All eager for the treat:
Their coats were brushed, their faces washed,
    Their shoes were clean and neat—
And this was odd, because, you know,
    They hadn't any feet.

Four other Oysters followed them,
    And yet another four;
And thick and fast they came at last,
    And more, and more, and more—
All hopping through the frothy waves,
    And scrambling to the shore.

The Walrus and the Carpenter
    Walked on a mile or so,
And then they rested on a rock
    Conveniently low:
And all the little Oysters stood
    And waited in a row.

"The time has come," the Walrus said,
    "To talk of many things:
Of shoes—and ships—and sealing wax—
    Of cabbages—and kings—

And why the sea is boiling hot—
    And whether pigs have wings."

"But wait a bit," the Oysters cried,
    "Before we have our chat;
For some of us are out of breath,
    And all of us are fat!"
"No hurry!" said the Carpenter.
    They thanked him much for that.

"A loaf of bread," the Walrus said,
    "Is what we chiefly need:
Pepper and vinegar besides
    Are very good indeed—
Now, if you're ready, Oysters dear,
    We can begin to feed."

"But not on us!" the Oysters cried,
    Turning a little blue.
"After such kindness, that would be
    A dismal thing to do!"
"The night is fine," the Walrus said.
    "Do you admire the view?

"It was so kind of you to come!
    And you are very nice!"
The Carpenter said nothing but
    "Cut us another slice.
I wish you were not quite so deaf—
    I've had to ask you twice!"

"It seems a shame," the Walrus said,
    "To play them such a trick,
After we've brought them out so far,
    And made them trot so quick!"
The Carpenter said nothing but
    "The butter's spread too thick!"

"I weep for you," the Walrus said:
  "I deeply sympathize."
With sobs and tears he sorted out
  Those of the largest size,
Holding his pocket-handkerchief
  Before his streaming eyes.

"O Oysters," said the Carpenter,
  "You've had a pleasant run!
Shall we be trotting home again?"
  But answer came there none—
And this was scarcely odd, because
  They'd eaten every one.

                  Lewis Carroll

HE THOUGHT HE SAW

From "Sylvie and Bruno"

He thought he saw a Buffalo
  Upon the chimney-piece:
He looked again, and found it was
  His Sister's Husband's Niece.
"Unless you leave this house," he said,
  "I'll send for the Police!"

He thought he saw a Rattlesnake
  That questioned him in Greek:
He looked again, and found it was
  The Middle of Next Week.
"The one thing I regret," he said,
  "Is that it cannot speak!"

He thought he saw a Banker's Clerk
  Decending from the 'bus:
He looked again, and found it was
  A Hippopotamus.

"If this should stay to dine," he said,
"There won't be much for us!"

He thought he saw a Kangaroo
    That worked a coffee-mill:
He looked again, and found it was
    A Vegetable-Pill.
"Were I to swallow this," he said,
    "I should be very ill!"

He thought he saw a Coach-and-Four
    That stood beside his bed:
He looked again, and found it was
    A Bear without a Head.
"Poor thing," he said, "poor silly thing!
    It's waiting to be fed!"

He thought he saw an Albatross
    That fluttered round the lamp:
He looked again, and found it was
    A Penny-Postage-Stamp.
"You'd best be getting home," he said:
    "The nights are very damp!"

Lewis Carroll

AN ELEGY ON THE DEATH OF A MAD DOG

Good people all, of every sort,
    Give ear unto my song;
And if you find it wondrous short,—
    It cannot hold you long.

In Islington there was a man
    Of whom the world might say.
That still a godly race he ran,—
    When'er he went to pray.

A kind and gentle heart he had,
   To comfort friends and foes:
The naked every day he clad,—
   When he put on his clothes.

And in that town a dog was found,
   As many dogs there be,
Both mongrel, puppy, whelp, and hound,
   And curs of low degree.

This dog and man at first were friends;
   But when a pique began,
The dog, to gain some private ends,
   Went mad, and bit the man.

Around from all the neighboring streets
   The wondering neighbors ran,
And swore the dog had lost his wits,
   To bite so good a man.

The wound it seemed both sore and sad
   To every Christian eye:
And while they swore the dog was mad,
   They swore the man would die.

But soon a wonder came to light,
   That showed the rogues they lied:—
The man recovered of the bite,
   The dog it was that died.

Oliver Goldsmith

OLD GRIMES

Old Grimes is dead; that good old man
   We never shall see more:
He used to wear a long black coat,
   All buttoned down before.

His heart was open as the day,
  His feelings all were true;
His hair was some inclined to gray—
  He wore it in a queue.

Whene'er he heard the voice of pain,
  His breast with pity burned;
The large, round head upon his cane
  From ivory was turned.

Kind words he ever had for all;
  He knew no base design:
His eyes were dark and rather small,
  His nose was aquiline.

He lived at peace with all mankind,
  In friendship he was true;
His coat had pocket-holes behind,
  His pantaloons were blue.

Unharmed, the sin which earth pollutes
  He passed securely o'er,
And never wore a pair of boots
  For thirty years or more.

But good old Grimes is now at rest,
  Nor fears misfortune's frown:
He wore a double-breasted vest—
  The stripes ran up and down.

He modest merit sought to find,
  And pay it its desert:
He had no malice in his mind,
  No ruffles on his shirt.

His neighbors he did not abuse—
  Was sociable and gay:

He wore large buckles on his shoes,
   And changed them every day.

His knowledge, hid from public gaze,
   He did not bring to view,
Nor made a noise, town-meeting days,
   As many people do.

His worldly goods he never threw
   In trust to fortune's chances,
But lived (as all his brothers do)
   In easy circumstances.

Thus undisturbed by anxious cares,
   His peaceful moments ran;
And everybody said he was
   A fine old gentleman.

Albert Gorton Greene

A TRAGIC STORY

There lived a sage in days of yore,
And he a handsome pigtail wore;
But wondered much and sorrowed more,
   Because it hung behind him.

He mused upon this curious case,
And swore he'd change the pigtail's place,
And have it hanging at his face,
   Not dangling there behind him.

Says he, "The mystery I've found,—
I'll turn me round,"—he turned him round;
   But still it hung behind him.

Then round and round, and out and in,
All day the puzzled sage did spin;
In vain—it mattered not a pin,—
    The pigtail hung behind him.

And right, and left, and round about,
And up, and down, and in, and out
He turned; but still the pigtail stout
    Hung steadily behind him.

And though his efforts never slack,
And though he twist, and twirl, and tack,
Alas! still faithful to his back,
    The pigtail hangs behind him.
                        William Makepeace Thackeray

THE BLIND MEN AND THE ELEPHANT

A HINDOO FABLE

It was six men of Indostan
    To learning much inclined,
Who went to see the Elephant
    (Though all of them were blind),
That each by observation
    Might satisfy his mind.

The *First* approached the Elephant,
    And happening to fall
Against his broad and sturdy side,
    At once began to bawl:
"God bless me! but the Elephant
    Is very like a wall!"

The *Second*, feeling of the tusk,
    Cried, "Ho! what have we here

So very round and smooth and sharp?
  To me 'tis mighty clear
This wonder of an Elephant
  Is very like a spear!"

The *Third* approached the animal,
  And happening to take
The squirming trunk within his hands,
  Thus boldly up and spake:
"I see," quoth he, "the Elephant
  Is very like a snake!"

The *Fourth* reached out an eager hand,
  And felt about the knee.
"What most this wondrous beast is like
  Is mighty plain," quoth he;
" 'Tis clear enough the Elephant
  Is very like a tree!"

The *Fifth* who chanced to touch the ear,
  Said: "E'en the blindest man
Can tell what this resembles most;
  Deny the fact who can,
This marvel of an Elephant
  Is very like a fan!"

The *Sixth* no sooner had begun
  About the beast to grope,
Than, seizing on the swinging tail
  That fell within his scope,
"I see," quoth he, "the Elephant
  Is very like a rope!"

And so these men of Indostan
  Disputed loud and long,

Each in his own opinion
   Exceeding stiff and strong,
Though each was partly in the right,
   And all were in the wrong!

Moral

So oft in theologic wars,
   The disputants, I ween,
Rail on in utter ignorance
   Of what each other mean,
And prate about an Elephant
   Not one of them has seen!

                         John Godfrey Saxe

LITTLE BILLEE

There were three sailors of Bristol city
Who took a boat and went to sea.
But first with beef and captain's biscuits
And pickled pork they loaded she.

There was gorging Jack and guzzling Jimmy,
And the youngest he was little Billee.
Now when they got as far as the Equator
They'd nothing left but one split pea.

Says gorging Jack to guzzling Jimmy,
"I am extremely hungaree."
To gorging Jack says guzzling Jimmy,
"We've nothing left, us must eat we."

Says gorging Jack to guzzling Jimmy,
"With one another we shouldn't agree!
There's little Bill, he's young and tender,
We're old and tough, so let's eat he.

"Oh! Billy, we're going to kill and eat you,
So undo the button of your chemie."
When Bill received this information
He used his pocket handkerchie.

"First let me say my catechism,
Which my poor mammy taught to me."
"Make haste, make haste," says guzzling Jimmy,
While Jack pulled out his snickersnee.

So Billy went up to the main-top gallant mast,
And down he fell on his bended knee.
He scarce had come to the twelfth commandment
When up he jumps. "There's land I see:

"Jerusalem and Madagascar,
And North and South Amerikee:
There's the British flag a-riding at anchor,
With Admiral Napier, K.C.B."

So when they got aboard of the Admiral's,
He hanged fat Jack and flogged Jimmee:
But as for little Bill he made him
The Captain of a Seventy-three.

William Makepeace Thackeray

THE BALLAD OF THE OYSTERMAN

It was a tall young oysterman lived by the river-side,
His shop was just upon the bank, his boat was on the tide;
The daughter of a fisherman, that was so straight and slim,
Lived over on the other bank, right opposite to him.

It was the pensive oysterman that saw a lovely maid,
Upon a moonlight evening, a-sitting in the shade;
He saw her wave her handkerchief, as much as if to say,
"I'm wide awake, young oysterman, and all the folks away."

Then up arose the oysterman, and to himself said he,
"I guess I'll leave the skiff at home, for fear that folks
    should see;
I read it in the story-book, that, for to kiss his dear,
Leander swam the Hellespont,—and I will swim this here."

And he has leaped into the waves, and crossed the shining
    stream,
And he has clambered up the bank, all in the moonlight
    gleam;
Oh there were kisses sweet as dew, and words as soft as
    rain,—
But they have heard her father's step, and in he leaps again!

Out spoke the ancient fisherman,—"Oh what was that, my
    daughter?"
"'Twas nothing but a pebble, sir, I threw into the water."
"And what is that, pray tell me, love, that paddles off so
    fast?"
"It's nothing but a porpoise, sir, that's been a-swimming
    past."

Out spoke the ancient fisherman,—"Now bring me my
    harpoon!
I'll get into my fishing-boat, and fix the fellow soon."
Down fell that pretty innocent, as falls a snow-white lamb,
Her hair drooped round her pallid cheeks, like seaweed on
    a clam.

Alas for those two loving ones! she waked not from her
    swound,
And he was taken with the cramp, and in the waves was
    drowned;
But Fate has metamorphosed them, in pity of their woe,
And now they keep an oyster-shop for mermaids down
    below.
                          Oliver Wendell Holmes

THE TWINS

In form and feature, face and limb,
   I grew so like my brother,
That folks got taking me for him,
   And each for one another.
It puzzled all our kith and kin,
   It reached a fearful pitch;
For one of us was born a twin,
   Yet not a soul knew which.

One day, to make the matter worse,
   Before our names were fixed,
As we were being washed by nurse,
   We got completely mixed;
And thus, you see, by fate's decree,
   Or rather nurse's whim,
My brother John got christened me,
   And I got christened him.

This fatal likeness even dogged
   My footsteps when at school,
And I was always getting flogged,
   For John turned out a fool.
I put this question, fruitlessly,
   To every one I knew,
"What *would* you do, if you were me,
   To prove that you were *you*?"

Our close resemblance turned the tide
   Of my domestic life,
For somehow, my intended bride
   Became my brother's wife.
In fact, year after year the same
   Absurd mistakes went on,

And when I died, the neighbors came
  And buried brother John.

Henry Sambrooke Leigh

CONTRARY MARY

You ask why Mary was called contrary?
Well, this is why, my dear:
She planted the most outlandish things
In her garden every year:
She was always sowing the queerest seed,
And when advised to stop,
Her answer was merely, "No, indeed—
Just wait till you see the crop!"

And here are some of the crops, my child
(Although not nearly all):
Bananarcissus and cucumberries,
And violettuce small;
Potatomatoes, melonions rare,
And rhubarberries round,
With porcupineapples prickly-rough
On a little bush close to the ground.

She gathered the stuff in mid-July
And sent it away to sell—
And now you'll see how she earned her name,
And how she earned it well.
Were the crops hauled off in a farmer's cart?
No, not by any means,
But in little June-buggies and automobeetles
And dragonflying machines!

Nancy Byrd Turner

ROBINSON CRUSOE

From "Davy and the Goblin"

The night was thick and hazy,
When the Piccadilly Daisy
Carried down the crew and captain in the sea;
And I think the water drowned 'em,
For they never, never found 'em,
And I know they didn't come ashore with me.

Oh! 'twas very sad and lonely
When I found myself the only
Population on this cultivated shore;
But I've made a little tavern
In a rocky little cavern,
And I sit and watch for people at the door.

I spent no time in looking
For a girl to do my cooking,
As I'm quite a clever hand at making stews;
But I had that fellow Friday
Just to keep the tavern tidy,
And to put a Sunday polish on my shoes.

I have a little garden
That I'm cultivating lard in,
As the things I eat are rather tough and dry;
For I live on toasted lizards,
Prickly pears, and parrot gizzards,
And I'm really very fond of beetle-pie.

The clothes I had were furry,
And it made me fret and worry
When I found the moths were eating off the hair;

And I had to scrape and sand 'em,
And I boiled 'em and I tanned 'em,
Till I got the fine morocco suit I wear.

I sometimes seek diversion
In a family excursion
With the few domestic animals you see;
And we take along a carrot
As refreshments for the parrot,
And a little can of jungleberry tea.

Then we gather as we travel
Bits of moss and dirty gravel,
And we chip off little specimens of stone;
And we carry home as prizes
Funny bugs of handy sizes,
Just to give the day a scientific tone.

If the roads are wet and muddy,
We remain at home and study,—
For the Goat is very clever at a sum,—
And the Dog, instead of fighting,
Studies ornamental writing,
While the Cat is taking lessons on the drum.

We retire at eleven,
And we rise again at seven;
And I wish to call attention, as I close,
To the fact that all the scholars
Are correct about their collars,
And particular in turning out their toes.

Charles Edward Carryl

CLEAN CLARA

What! not know our Clean Clara?
Why, the hot folks in Sahara,

And the cold Esquimaux,
Our little Clara know!
Clean Clara, the Poet sings,
Cleaned a hundred thousand things!

She cleaned the keys of the harpsichord,
She cleaned the hilt of the family sword,
She cleaned my lady, she cleaned my lord;
All the pictures in their frames,
Knights with daggers, and stomachered dames—
Cecils, Godfreys, Montforts, Graemes,
Winifreds—all those nice old names!

She cleaned the works of the eight-day clock,
She cleaned the spring of a secret lock,
She cleaned the mirror, she cleaned the cupboard;
All the books she India-rubbered!

She cleaned the Dutch tiles in the place,
She cleaned some very old-fashioned lace;
The Countess of Miniver came to her,
"Pray, my dear, will you clean my fur?"
All her cleanings are admirable;

To count your teeth you will be able,
If you look in the walnut table!

She cleaned the tent-stitch and the sampler;
She cleaned the tapestry, which was ampler;
Joseph going down into the pit,
And the Shunammite woman with the boy in a fit;
You saw the reapers, *not* in the distance,
And Elisha coming to the child's assistance,
With the house on the wall that was built for the prophet,
The chair, the bed, and the bolster of it;

The eyebrows all had a twirl reflective,
Just like an eel; to spare invective,
There was plenty of color, but no perspective.
However, Clara cleaned it all,
With a curious lamp, that hangs in the hall!
She cleaned the drops of the chandeliers,—
Madame, in mittens, was moved to tears!

She cleaned the cage of the cockatoo,
The oldest bird that ever grew;
I should say a thousand years old would do—
I'm sure she looked it; but nobody knew;
She cleaned the china, she cleaned the delf,
She cleaned the baby, she cleaned herself!

To-morrow morning she means to try
To clean the cobwebs from the sky;
Some people say the girl will rue it,
But my belief is she will do it.

So I've made up my mind to be there to see:
There's a beautiful place in the walnut-tree;
The bough is as firm as the solid rock;
She brings out her broom at six o'clock.

William Brighty Rands

THE DUEL

The gingham dog and the calico cat
Side by side on the table sat;
'Twas half past twelve, and (what do you think!)
Nor one nor t'other had slept a wink!
    The old Dutch clock and the Chinese plate
    Appeared to know as sure as fate
There was going to be a terrible spat.
        (*I wasn't there; I simply state*
        What was told to me by the Chinese plate!)

The gingham dog went "Bow-wow-wow!"
And the calico cat replied "Mee-ow!"
The air was littered, an hour or so,
With bits of gingham and calico,
    While the old Dutch clock in the chimney place
    Up with its hands before its face,
For it always dreaded a family row!
        (*Now mind: I'm only telling you*
        What the old Dutch clock declares is true!)

The Chinese plate looked very blue,
And wailed, "Oh, dear! what shall we do!"
But the gingham dog and the calico cat
Wallowed this way and tumbled that,
    Employing every tooth and claw
    In the awfullest way you ever saw—
And, oh! how the gingham and calico flew!
        (*Don't fancy I exaggerate—*
        I got my news from the Chinese plate!)

Next morning, where the two had sat
They found no trace of dog or cat:
And some folks think unto this day
That burglars stole that pair away!
    But the truth about the cat and pup
    Is this: they ate each other up!
Now what do you really think of that!
        (*The old Dutch clock it told me so,*
        And that is how I came to know.)

                    Eugene Field

THE DINKEY-BIRD

In an ocean, 'way out yonder
    (As all sapient people know),
Is the land of Wonder-Wander,
    Whither children love to go;

It's their playing, romping, swinging,
   That give great joy to me
While the Dinkey-Bird goes singing
   In the amfalula tree!

There the gum-drops grow like cherries
   And taffy's thick as peas—
Caramels you pick like berries
   When, and where, and how you please;
Big red sugar-plums are clinging
   To the cliffs beside that sea
Where the Dinkey-Bird is singing
   In the amfalula tree.

So when children shout and scamper
   And make merry all the day,
When there's naught to put a damper
   To the ardor of their play;
When I hear their laughter ringing,
   Then I'm sure as sure can be
That the Dinkey-Bird is singing
   In the amfalula tree.

For the Dinkey-Bird's bravuras
   And staccatos are so sweet—
His roulades, appoggiaturas,
   And robustos so complete,
That the youth of every nation—
   Be they near or far away—
Have especial delectation
   In that gladsome roundelay.

Their eyes grow bright and brighter
   Their lungs begin to crow,
Their hearts get light and lighter,
   And their cheeks are all aglow;

For an echo cometh bringing
  The news to all and me,
That the Dinkey-Bird is singing
  In the amfalula tree.

I'm sure you like to go there
  To see your feathered friend—
And so many goodies grow there
  You would like to comprehend!
Speed, little dreams, your winging
  To that land across the sea
Where the Dinkey-Bird is singing
  In the amfalula tree!

Eugene Field

IN FOREIGN PARTS

When I lived in Singapore,
It was something of a bore
To receive the bulky Begums who came trundling to my
    door;
They kept getting into tangles
With their bingle-bongle-bangles,
And the tiger used to bite them as he sat upon the floor.

When I lived in Timbuctoo,
Almost everyone I knew
Used to play upon the sackbut, singing "toodle-doodle-
    doo,"
And they made ecstatic ballads,
And consumed seductive salads,
Made of chicory and hickory and other things that grew.

When I lived at Rotterdam,
I possessed a spotted ram,
Who would never feed on anything but hollyhocks and ham;

But one day he butted down
All the magnates of the town,
So they slew him, though I knew him to be gentle as a
    lamb.

But!
When I got to Kandahar,
It was very, very far,
And the people came and said to me, "How *very* plain you
    are!"
So I sailed across the foam,
And I toddle-waddled home,
And no more I'll go a-rovering beyond the harbor bar.

Laura E. Richards

THE OWL AND THE EEL AND THE WARMING-PAN

The owl and the eel and the warming-pan,
They went to call on the soap-fat man.
The soap-fat man he was not within:
He'd gone for a ride on his rolling-pin.
So they all came back by way of the town,
And turned the meeting-house upside down.

Laura E. Richards

NONSENSE RHYMES

I

On DIGITAL EXTREMITIES:
A Poem, and a Gem It Is!

I'd Rather have Fingers than Toes;
I'd Rather have Ears than a Nose;
    And As for my Hair,
    I'm Glad it's All There;
I'll be Awfully Sad, when it Goes!

II

THE SUNSET: Picturing the Glow
It Casts upon a Dish of Dough.

The Sun is Low, to Say the Least,
    Although it is Well-Red;
Yet, Since it Rises in the Yeast,
    It Should be Better Bred!

III

THE WINDOW PANE: a Theme Symbolic,
Pertaining to the Melon Colic.

The Window has Four Little Pains;
    But One have I—
The Window Pains are in its Sash;
    I Wonder Why!

IV

THE PURPLE COW'S PROJECTED FEAST:
Reflections on a Mythic Beast,
Who's quite Remarkable, at Least.

I never saw a Purple Cow,
    I never hope to see one;
But I can tell you, anyhow,
    I'd rather see than be one!

                         Gelett Burgess

SEVEN FAMOUS LIMERICKS

There was a young lady of Niger
Who smiled as she rode on a tiger;
    They returned from the ride
    With the lady inside,
And the smile on the face of the tiger.

                         Cosmo Monkhouse

There was a small boy of Quebec
Who was buried in snow to the neck;
  When they said, "Are you friz?"
  He replied, "Yes, I is—
But we don't call this cold in Quebec."
Rudyard Kipling

The Reverend Henry Ward Beecher
Called a hen a most elegant creature.
  The hen, pleased with that,
  Laid an egg in his hat,—
And thus did the hen reward Beecher.
Oliver Wendell Holmes

As a beauty I'm not a great star,
There are others more handsome by far;
  But my face I don't mind it
  Because I'm behind it—
'Tis the folks out in front that I jar.
Anthony Euwer

A tutor who tooted the flute
Tried to tutor two tutors to toot.
  Said the two to the tutor,
  "Is it harder to toot or
To tutor two tutors to toot?"
Carolyn Wells

A canner, exceedingly canny,
One morning remarked to his granny,
  "A canner can can
  Anything that he can,
But a canner can't can a can, can he?"
Carolyn Wells

There was a young fellow named Tait,
Who dined with his girl at 8.08;

But I'd hate to relate
What that fellow named Tait
And his tête-à-tête ate at 8.08.

Carolyn Wells

MY SENSE OF SIGHT

My sense of sight is very keen,
My sense of hearing weak.
One time I saw a mountain pass,
But could not hear its peak.

Oliver Herford

I'M GLAD

I'm glad the sky is painted blue,
  And the earth is painted green,
With such a lot of nice fresh air
  All sandwiched in between.

IF

If all the world were apple-pie,
  And all the sea were ink,
And all the trees were bread and cheese,
  What should we have to drink?

HOW TO TELL THE WILD ANIMALS

If ever you should go by chance
  To jungles in the East,
And if there should to you advance
  A large and tawny beast,
If he roars at you as you're dyin'
You'll know it is the Asian Lion.

Or if some time when roaming round,
  A noble wild beast greets you,
With black stripes on a yellow ground,
  Just notice if he eats you.
This simple rule may help you learn
The Bengal Tiger to discern.

If strolling forth, a beast you view,
  Whose hide with spots is peppered,
As soon as he has leapt on you,
  You'll know it is the Leopard.
'Twill do no good to roar with pain,
He'll only lep and lep again.

If when you're walking round your yard,
  You meet a creature there,
Who hugs you very, very hard,
  Be sure it is the Bear.
If you have any doubt, I guess
He'll give you just one more caress.

Though to distinguish beasts of prey
  A novice might nonplus,
The Crocodiles you always may
  Tell from Hyenas thus:
Hyenas come with merry smiles;
But if they weep, they're Crocodiles.

The true Chameleon is small,
  A lizard sort of thing;
He hasn't any ears at all,
  And not a single wing.
If there is nothing on the tree,
'Tis the Chameleon you see.

                                    Carolyn Wells

CHILD'S NATURAL HISTORY

A SEAL

See, Chil-dren, the Fur-bear-ing Seal;
Ob-serve his mis-di-rect-ed zeal;
He dines with most ab-ste-mi-ous care
On Fish, Ice Water and Fresh Air,
A-void-ing cond-i-ments or spice
For fear his fur should not be nice
And fine and soft and smooth and meet
For Broad-way or for Re-gent Street.
And yet some-how I often feel
(Though for the kind Fur-bear-ing Seal
I harbor a Re-spect Pro-found)
He runs Fur-bear-ance in the ground.

THE YAK

This is the Yak, so neg-li-gee;
His coif-fure's like a stack of hay;
He lives so far from Any-where,
I fear the Yak neg-lects his hair,
And thinks, since there is none to see,
What mat-ter how un-kempt he be:
How would he feel if he but knew
That in this Pic-ture-book I drew
His Phys-i-og-no-my un-shorn,
For chil-dren to de-ride and scorn?

Oliver Herford

THE YAK

As a friend to the children, commend me the Yak;
    You will find it exactly the thing;
It will carry and fetch, you can ride on its back,
    Or lead it about with a string.

The Tartar who dwells on the plains of Thibet
(A desolate region of snow),
Has for centuries made it a nursery pet,
And surely the Tartar should know!

Then tell your papa where the Yak can be got,
And if he is awfully rich,
He will buy you the creature—or else he will not,
(I cannot be positive which).

Hilaire Belloc

THE PYTHON

A Python I should not advise,—
It needs a doctor for its eyes,
And has the measles yearly.
However, if you feel inclined
To get one (to improve your mind,
And not from fashion merely),
Allow no music near its cage;
And when it flies into a rage,
Chastise it most severely.

I had an Aunt in Yucatan
Who bought a Python from a man
And kept it for a pet.
She died because she never knew
These simple little rules and few;—
The snake is living yet.

Hilaire Belloc

SAGE COUNSEL

The Lion is the beast to fight:
He leaps along the plain,
And if you run with all your might,
He runs with all his mane.

I'm glad I'm not a Hottentot,
But if I were, with outward cal-lum
I'd either faint upon the spot
Or hie me up a leafy pal-lum.

The Chamois is the beast to hunt:
 He's fleeter than the wind,
And when the Chamois is in front
 The hunter is behind.
  The Tyrolese make famous cheese
  And hunt the Chamois o'er the chaz-zums;
  I'd choose the former, if you please,
  For precipices give me spaz-zums.

The Polar Bear will make a rug
 Almost as white as snow:
But if he gets you in his hug,
 He rarely lets you go.
  And polar ice looks very nice,
  With all the colors of a prissum:
  But, if you'll follow my advice,
  Stay home and learn your catechissum.
                    Arthur Quiller-Couch

THE FASTIDIOUS SERPENT

There was a snake that dwelt in Skye,
 Over the misty sea, oh;
He lived upon nothing but gooseberry-pie
 For breakfast, dinner, and tea, oh.

Now gooseberry-pie—as is very well known—
 Over the misty sea, oh,
Is not to be found under every stone,
 Nor yet upon every tree, oh.

And being so ill to please with his meat,
   Over the misty sea, oh,
The snake had sometimes nothing to eat,
   And an angry snake was he, oh.

Then he'd flick his tongue and his head he'd shake,
   Over the misty sea, oh,
Crying, "Gooseberry-pie! For goodness' sake,
   Some gooseberry-pie for me, oh!"

And if gooseberry-pie was not to be had,
   Over the misty sea, oh,
He'd twine and twist like an eel gone mad,
   Or a worm just stung by a bee, oh.

But though he might shout and wriggle about,
   Over the misty sea, oh,
The snake had often to go without
   His breakfast, dinner, and tea, oh.

Henry Johnstone

THE GNU WOOING

There was a lovely lady Gnu
Who browsed beneath a spreading yew.
   Its stately height was her delight;
A truly cooling shade it threw.
Upon it little tendrils grew
Which gave her gentle joy to chew.
   Yet oft she sighed, a-gazing wide,
And wished she knew another Gnu
(Some newer Gnu beneath the yew
To tell her tiny troubles to.)

She lived the idle moments through,
And days in dull succession flew,
   Till one fine eve she ceased to grieve—

A manly stranger met her view.
He gave a courtly bow or two;
She coolly looked him through and through:
    "I fear you make some slight mistake—
Perhaps it is the yew you knew!"
(Its branches blew and seemed to coo,
"Your cue, new Gnu; It's up to you!")

Said he: "If guests you would eschew,
I'll say adieu without ado;
    But let me add I knew your dad;
I'm on page two, the Gnu's 'Who's Who.'"
"Forgive," she cried, "the snub I threw!
I feared you were some parvegnu!
    'Tis my regret we've never met—
I knew a Gnu who knew of you."
(This wasn't true—what's that to you?
The new Gnu knew; she knew he knew.)

"Though there are other trees, 'tis true,"
Said she, "if you're attracted to
    The yews I use, and choose to chew
Their yewy dewy tendrils, do!"

.   .   .   .

The end is easily in view:
He wed her in a week or two.
    The "Daily Gnus" did quite enthuse,
And now, if all I hear is true,
Beneath the yew the glad day through
There romps a little gnuey new.

Burges Johnson

THE PLAINT OF THE CAMEL
From "The Admiral's Caravan"

Canary-birds feed on sugar and seed,
    Parrots have crackers to crunch;

And as for poodles, they tell me the noodles
    Have chickens and cream for their lunch.
        But there's never a question
        About MY digestion—
    ANYTHING does for me!

Cats, you're aware, can repose in a chair,
    Chickens can roost upon rails;
Puppies are able to sleep in a stable,
    And oysters can slumber in pails.
        But no one supposes
        A poor Camel doses—
    ANY PLACE does for me!

Lambs are enclosed where it's never exposed,
    Coops are constructed for hens;
Kittens are treated to houses well heated,
    And pigs are protected by pens.
        But a Camel comes handy
        Wherever it's sandy—
    ANYWHERE does for me!

People would laugh if you rode a giraffe,
    Or mounted the back of an ox;
It's nobody's habit to ride on a rabbit,
    Or try to bestraddle a fox.
        But as for a Camel, he's
        Ridden by families—
    ANY LOAD does for me!

A snake is as round as a hole in the ground,
    And weasels are wavy and sleek;
And no alligator could ever be straighter
    Than lizards that live in a creek,
        But a Camel's all lumpy
        And bumpy and humpy—
    ANY SHAPE does for me!

Charles Edward Carryl

v. Fairyland

THE FAIRY BOOK

When Mother takes the Fairy Book
   And we curl up to hear,
'Tis "All aboard for Fairyland!"
   Which seems to be so near.

For soon we reach the pleasant place
   Of Once Upon a Time,
Where birdies sing the hour of day,
   And flowers talk in rhyme;

Where Bobby is a velvet Prince,
   And where I am a Queen;
Where one can talk with animals,
   And walk about unseen;

Where Little People live in nuts,
   And ride on butterflies,
And wonders kindly come to pass
   Before your very eyes;

Where candy grows on every bush,
   And playthings on the trees,
And visitors pick basketfuls
   As often as they please.

It is the nicest time of day—
   Though Bedtime is so near,—
When Mother takes the Fairy Book
   And we curl up to hear.

Abbie Farwell Brown

FAIRYLAND

THE FAIRIES

Up the airy mountain,
  Down the rushy glen,
We daren't go a-hunting
  For fear of little men;
Wee folk, good folk,
  Trooping all together;
Green jacket, red cap,
  And white owl's feather!

Down along the rocky shore
  Some make their home,
They live on crispy pancakes
  Of yellow tide-foam;
Some in the reeds
  Of the black mountain lake,
With frogs for their watch-dogs,
  All night awake.

High on the hill-top
  The old King sits;
He is now so old and gray
  He's nigh lost his wits.
With a bridge of white mist
  Columbkill he crosses,
On his stately journeys
  From Slieveleague to Rosses;
Or going up with music
  On cold starry nights
To sup with the Queen
  Of the gay Northern Lights.

They stole little Bridget
    For seven years long;
When she came down again
    Her friends were all gone.
They took her lightly back,
    Between the night and morrow,
They thought that she was fast asleep,
    But she was dead with sorrow.
They have kept her ever since
    Deep within the lake,
On a bed of flag-leaves,
    Watching till she wake.

By the craggy hill-side,
    Through the mosses bare,
They have planted thorn-trees
    For pleasure here and there.
If any man so daring
    As dig them up in spite,
He shall find their sharpest thorns
    In his bed at night.

Up the airy mountain,
    Down the rushy glen,
We daren't go a-hunting
    For fear of little men;
Wee folk, good folk,
    Trooping all together;
Green jacket, red cap,
    And white owl's feather!

William Allingham

FAIRY SONGS

I

From "A Midsummer-Night's Dream"

Over hill, over dale,
   Through bush, through brier,
Over park, over pale,
   Through flood, through fire,
I do wander everywhere,
Swifter than the moonè's sphere;
And I serve the fairy queen,
To dew her orbs upon the green:
The cowslips tall her pensioners be;
In their gold coats spots you see;
Those be rubies, fairy favors,
In those freckles live their savors:
I must go seek some dew-drops here,
And hang a pearl in every cowslip's ear.

II

From "The Tempest"

Where the bee sucks, there suck I;
   In a cowslip's bell I lie;
There I couch when owls do cry.
On the bat's back I do fly
After summer merrily:
   Merrily, merrily, shall I live now,
   Under the blossom that hangs on the bough.

William Shakespeare

QUEEN MAB

A little fairy comes at night,
   Her eyes are blue, her hair is brown,
With silver spots upon her wings,
   And from the moon she flutters down.

She has a little silver wand,
   And when a good child goes to bed
She waves her hand from right to left,
   And makes a circle round its head.

And then it dreams of pleasant things,
   Of fountains filled with fairy fish,
And trees that bear delicious fruit,
   And bow their branches at a wish:

Of arbors filled with dainty scents
   From lovely flowers that never fade;
Bright flies that glitter in the sun,
   And glow-worms shining in the shade:

And talking birds with gifted tongues,
   For singing songs and telling tales,
And pretty dwarfs to show the way
   Through fairy hills and fairy dales.

But when a bad child goes to bed,
   From left to right she weaves her rings,
And then it dreams all through the night
   Of only ugly horrid things!

Then lions come with glaring eyes,
   And tigers growl, a dreadful noise,
And ogres draw their cruel knives,
   To shed the blood of girls and boys.

Then stormy waves rush on to drown,
   Or raging flames come scorching round,
Fierce dragons hover in the air,
   And serpents crawl along the ground.

Then wicked children wake and weep,
   And wish the long black gloom away;
But good ones love the dark, and find
   The night as pleasant as the day.

Thomas Hood

THE FAIRY THRALL

On gossamer nights when the moon is low,
   And stars in the mist are hiding,
Over the hill where the foxgloves grow
   You may see the fairies riding.
     Kling! Klang! Kling!
     Their stirrups and their bridles ring,
And their horns are loud and their bugles blow,
When the moon is low.

They sweep through the night like a whistling wind,
   They pass and have left no traces;
But one of them lingers far behind
   The flight of the fairy faces.
     She makes no moan,
     She sorrows in the dark alone,
She wails for the love of human kind,
Like a whistling wind.

"Ah! why did I roam where the elfins ride,
   Their glimmering steps to follow?
They bore me far from my loved one's side,
   To wander o'er hill and hollow.
     Kling! Klang! Kling!
     Their stirrups and their bridles ring,
But my heart is cold in the cold night-tide,
Where the elfins ride."

Mary C. G. Byron

FAIRIES

There are fairies at the bottom of our garden!
   It's not so very, very far away;
You pass the gardener's shed and you just keep straight
     ahead—
   I do so hope they've really come to stay.
There's a little wood, with moss in it and beetles,
   And a little stream that quietly runs through;
You wouldn't think they'd dare to come merry-making
     there—
       Well, they do.

There are fairies at the bottom of our garden!
   They often have a dance on summer nights;
The butterflies and bees make a lovely little breeze,
   And the rabbits stand about and hold the lights.
Did you know that they could sit upon the moonbeams
   And pick a little star to make a fan,
And dance away up there in the middle of the air?
       Well, they can.

There are fairies at the bottom of our garden!
   You cannot think how beautiful they are;
They all stand up and sing when the Fairy Queen and King
   Come gently floating down upon their car.
The King is very proud and *very* handsome;
   The Queen—now can you guess who that could be
(She's a little girl all day, but at night she steals away)?
      Well—it's *Me!*

                       Rose Fyleman

RILLOBY-RILL

   Grasshoppers four a-fiddling went
     Heigh-ho! never be still!

They earned but little towards their rent,
But all day long with their elbows bent
　　They fiddled a tune called Rilloby-rilloby,
　　Fiddled a tune called Rilloby-rill.

Grasshoppers soon on Fairies came,
　　Heigh-ho! never be still!
Fairies asked with a manner of blame,
"Where do you come from, what is your name?
　　What do you want with your Rilloby-rilloby,
　　What do you want with your Rilloby-rill?"

"Madam, you see before you stand,
　　Heigh-ho! never be still!
The Old Original Favorite Grand
Grasshoppers' Green Herbarian Band,
　　And the tune we play is Rilloby-rilloby,
　　Madam, the tune is Rilloby-rill."

Fairies hadn't a word to say,
　　Heigh-ho! never be still!
Fairies seldom are sweet by day:
But the Grasshoppers merrily fiddled away;
　　Oh, but they played with a willoby-willoby,
　　Oh, but they played with a willoby-will!

Fairies slumber and sulk at noon,
　　Heigh-ho! never be still!
But at last the kind old motherly moon
Brought them dew in a silver spoon,
　　And they turned to ask for Rilloby-rilloby,
　　One more round of Rilloby-rill.

Ah, but nobody now replied,
　　Heigh-ho! never be still!
When day went down the music died,

Grasshoppers four lay side by side,
   And there was an end of their Rilloby-rilloby,
There was an end of their Rilloby-rill.

Henry Newbolt

PUK-WUDJIES

They live 'neath the curtain
   Of fir woods and heather,
And never take hurt in
   The wildest of weather,
But best they love Autumn—she's brown as themselves—
And they are the brownest of all the brown elves;
   When loud sings the West Wind,
   The bravest and best wind,
And puddles are shining in all the cart ruts,
   They turn up the dead leaves,
   The russet and red leaves,
Where squirrels have taught them to look out for nuts!

The hedge-cutters hear them
   Where berries are glowing,
The scythe circles near them
   At time of the mowing;
But most they love woodlands when Autumn's winds pipe,
And all through the cover the beechnuts are ripe,
   And great spikey chestnuts,
   The biggest and best nuts,
Blown down in the ditches, fair windfalls lie cast,
   And no tree begrudges
   The little Puk-Wudjies
A pocket of acorns, a handful of mast!

So should you be roaming
   Where branches are sighing,
When up in the gloaming
   The moon-wrack is flying,

And hear through the darkness, again and again,
What's neither the wind nor the spatter of rain—
    A flutter, a flurry,
    A scuffle, a scurry,
A bump like the rabbits that bump on the ground,
    A patter, a bustle
    Of small things that rustle,
You'll know the Puk-Wudjies are somewhere around!
                      Patrick R. Chalmers

WHEN I WAS SIX

When I was only six years old,
    Heigh-ho! for Folly O!
I wandered in a fairy fold,
    Heigh holly! to and fro.

I rode upon a blossom's back
    Up hill and over sea;
And all the little Pixie pack
    For fun would follow me.

O, golden was the gown I wore
    Of buttercups and air,
And twenty diamond stars or more
    Were pinned upon my hair.

All day I chased the laughing sky
    Above the busy town,
But when the moon unwinked her eye,
    Ho, ho! I hurried down.

And then within the baby's shoe
    I hid my lady's pearls;
From maid to merry maid I flew
    And knotted all their curls.

I pulled the preacher's saintly gown
   And lost his open page;
I tickled out the withered frown
   Of every sallow sage.

And when the children were abed,
   I tapped the window-pane,
And laughed as someone softly said:
   "Whist! goblins there again!"

Ho, ho! I flitted here and there
   Amid my elfin band,
While on the green, in frolic fair,
   We tripped it hand in hand.

As air and moonlight I was free
   Within that fairy fold,
For all the world belonged to me
   When I was six years old.

Zora Cross

THE VISITOR

The white goat Amaryllis,
   She wandered at her will
At time of daffodillies
   Afar and up the hill:
We hunted and we holloa'd
   And back she came at dawn,
But what d'you think had followed?—
   A little, pagan Faun!

His face was like a berry,
   His ears were high and pricked:
Tip-tap—his hoofs came merry
   As up the path he clicked;

A junket for his winning
  We set in dairy delf;
He eat it—peart and grinning
  As Christian as yourself!

He stayed about the steading
  A fortnight, say, or more;
A blanket for his bedding
  We spread beside the door;
And when the cocks crowed clearly
  Before the dawn was ripe,
He'd call the milkmaids cheerly
  Upon a reedy pipe!

That fortnight of his staying
  The work went smooth as silk:
The hens were all in laying,
  The cows were all in milk;
And then—and then one morning
  The maids woke up at day
Without his oaten warning,—
  And found he'd gone away.

He left no trace behind him;
  But still the milkmaids deem
That they, perhaps, may find him
  With butter and with cream:
Beside the door they set them
  In bowl and golden pat,
But no one comes to get them—
  Unless, maybe, the cat.

The white goat Amaryllis,
  She wanders at her will
At time of daffodillies,
  Away up Woolcombe hill;

She stays until the morrow,
    Then back she comes at dawn;
But never—to our sorrow—
    The little, pagan Faun.
                                    Patrick R. Chalmers

I'D LOVE TO BE A FAIRY'S CHILD

Children born of fairy stock
Never need for shirt or frock,
Never want for food or fire,
Always get their heart's desire:
Jingle pockets full of gold,
Marry when they're seven years old.
Every fairy child may keep
Two strong ponies and ten sheep;
All have houses, each his own,
Built of brick or granite stone;
They live on cherries, they run wild—
I'd love to be a Fairy's child.
                                    Robert Graves

THE ELF AND THE DORMOUSE

Under a toadstool crept a wee Elf,
Out of the rain, to shelter himself.

Under the toadstool sound asleep,
Sat a big Dormouse all in a heap.

Trembled the wee Elf, frightened, and yet
Fearing to fly away lest he get wet.

To the next shelter—maybe a mile!
Sudden the wee Elf smiled a wee smile,

Tugged till the toadstool toppled in two.
Holding it over him, gayly he flew.

Soon he was safe home, dry as could be.
Soon woke the Dormouse—"Good gracious me!

"Where is my toadstool?" loud he lamented.
—And that's how umbrellas first were invented.

Oliver Herford

THE LITTLE ELF

I met a little Elf-man, once,
    Down where the lilies blow.
I asked him why he was so small,
    And why he didn't grow.

He slightly frowned, and with his eye
    He looked me through and through.
"I'm quite as big for me," said he,
    "As you are big for you."

John Kendrick Bangs

THE FAIRIES' SHOPPING

Where do you think the Fairies go
To buy their blankets ere the snow?

When Autumn comes, with frosty days,
The sorry, shivering little Fays
Begin to think it's time to creep
Down to their caves for Winter sleep.
But first they come from far and near
To buy, where shops are not too dear.

(The wind and frost bring prices down,
So Fall's their time to come to town!)

Where on the hill-side rough and steep
Browse all day long the cows and sheep,
The mullein's yellow candles burn
Over the heads of dry sweet fern:
All summer long the mullein weaves
His soft and thick and woolly leaves.
Warmer blankets were never seen
Than these broad leaves of fuzzy green.

(The cost of each is but a shekel
Made from the gold of honeysuckle!)

To buy their sheets and fine white lace
(With which to trim a pillow-case),
They only have to go next door,
Where stands a sleek brown spider's store,
And there they find the misty threads
Ready to cut into sheets and spreads;
Then, for a pillow, pluck with care
Some soft-winged seeds as light as air;
Just what they want the thistle brings,
But thistles are such surly things—
And so, though it is somewhat high,
The clematis the Fairies buy.

The only bedsteads that they need
Are silky pods of ripe milk-weed,
With hangings of the dearest things—
Autumn leaves, or butterflies' wings!
And dandelions' fuzzy heads
They use to stuff their feather beds;
And yellow snapdragons supply
The nightcaps that the Fairies buy,

To which some blades of grass they pin,
And tie them 'neath each little chin.

Then, shopping done, the Fairies cry,
"Our Summer's gone! oh sweet, good-bye!"
And sadly to their caves they go,
And hide away from Winter's snow—
And then, though winds and storms may beat,
The Fairies' sleep is warm and sweet!

Margaret Deland

ALICE BRAND

From "The Lady of the Lake"

I

Merry it is in the good greenwood,
  When the mavis and merle are singing,
When the deer sweeps by, and the hounds are in cry,
  And the hunter's horn is ringing.

"O Alice Brand, my native land
  Is lost for love of you;
And we must hold by wood and wold,
  As outlaws wont to do.

"O Alice, 'twas all for thy locks so bright,
  And 'twas all for thine eyes so blue,
That on the night of our luckless flight,
  Thy brother bold I slew.

"Now must I teach to hew the beech
  The hand that held the glaive,
For leaves to spread our lowly bed,
  And stakes to fence our cave.

"And for vest of pall, thy fingers small,
　　That wont on harp to stray,
A cloak must shear from the slaughtered deer,
　　To keep the cold away."

"O Richard! if my brother died,
　　'Twas but a fatal chance;
For darkling was the battle tried,
　　And fortune sped the lance.

"If pall and vair no more I wear,
　　Nor thou the crimson sheen,
As warm, we'll say, is the russet gray,
　　As gay the forest-green.

"And, Richard, if our lot be hard,
　　And lost thy native land,
Still Alice has her own Richard,
　　And he his Alice Brand."

II

'Tis merry, 'tis merry, in good greenwood,
　　So blithe Lady Alice is singing;
On the beech's pride, and oak's brown side,
　　Lord Richard's ax is ringing.

Up spoke the moody Elfin King,
　　Who woned within the hill,—
Like wind in the porch of a ruined church,
　　His voice was ghostly shrill.

"Why sounds yon stroke on beech and oak,
　　Our moonlight circle's screen?
Or who comes here to chase the deer,
　　Beloved of our Elfin Queen?
Or who may dare on wold to wear
　　The fairies' fatal green?

"Up, Urgan, up! to yon mortal hie,
  For thou wert christened man;
For cross or sign thou wilt not fly,
  For muttered word or ban.

"Lay on him the curse of the withered heart,
  The curse of the sleepless eye;
Till he wish and pray that his life would part,
  Nor yet find leave to die."

III

'Tis merry, 'tis merry, in good greenwood,
  Though the birds have stilled their singing,
The evening blaze doth Alice raise,
  And Richard is fagots bringing.

Up Urgan starts, that hideous dwarf,
  Before Lord Richard stands,
And, as he crossed and blessed himself,
"I fear not sign," quoth the grisly elf,
  "That is made with bloody hands."

But out then spoke she, Alice Brand,
  That woman void of fear,—
"And if there's blood upon his hand,
  'Tis but the blood of deer."

"Now loud thou liest, thou bold of mood!
  It cleaves into his hand,
The stain of thine own kindly blood,
  The blood of Ethert Brand."

Then forward stepped she, Alice Brand,
  And made the holy sign,—
"And if there's blood on Richard's hand,
  A spotless hand is mine.

"And I conjure thee, demon elf,
  By Him whom demons fear,
To show us whence thou art thyself,
  And what thine errand here?"

IV

" 'Tis merry, 'tis merry, in Fairy-land,
  When fairy birds are singing,
When the court doth ride by their monarch's side,
  With bit and bridle ringing.

"And gaily shines the Fairy-land—
  But all is glistening show,
Like the idle gleam that December's beam
  Can dart on ice and snow.

"And fading, like that varied gleam,
  Is our inconstant shape,
Who now like knight and lady seem,
  And now like dwarf and ape.

"It was between the night and day,
  When the Fairy King has power,
That I sunk down in a sinful fray,
And, 'twixt life and death, was snatched away
  To the joyless Elfin bower.

"But wist I of a woman bold,
  Who thrice my brow durst sign,
I might regain my mortal mold,
  As fair a form as thine."

She crossed him once—she crossed him twice—
  That lady was so brave;
The fouler grew his goblin hue,
  The darker grew the cave.

She crossed him thrice, that lady bold;
   He rose beneath her hand
The fairest knight on Scottish mold,
   Her brother, Ethert Brand!

Merry it is in good greenwood,
   When the mavis and merle are singing,
But merrier were they in Dunfermline gray,
   When all the bells were ringing.

                        Walter Scott

THE FAIRIES OF THE CALDON-LOW

A MIDSUMMER LEGEND

"And where have you been, my Mary,
   And where have you been from me?"
"I've been to the top of the Caldon-Low,
   The midsummer night to see!"

"And what did you see, my Mary,
   All up on the Caldon-Low?"
"I saw the glad sunshine come down,
   And I saw the merry winds blow."

"And what did you hear, my Mary,
   All up on the Caldon-Hill?"
"I heard the drops of the water made,
   And the ears of the green corn fill."

"Oh tell me all, my Mary—
   All—all that ever you know;
For you must have seen the fairies
   Last night on the Caldon-Low!"

"Then take me on your knee, mother,
   And listen, mother of mine:

A hundred fairies danced last night,
    And the harpers they were nine.

"And their harp-strings rang so merrily
    To their dancing feet so small;
But, oh! the words of their talking
    Were merrier far than all!"

"And what were the words, my Mary,
    That you did hear them say?"
"I'll tell you all, my mother,
    But let me have my way.

"Some of them played with the water,
    And rolled it down the hill;
'And this,' they said, 'shall speedily turn
    The poor old miller's mill.

" 'For there has been no water
    Ever since the first of May;
And a busy man will the miller be
    At the dawning of the day!

" 'Oh! the miller, how he will laugh,
    When he sees the mill-dam rise!
The jolly old miller, how he will laugh,
    Till the tears fill both his eyes!'

"And some they seized the little winds,
    That sounded over the hill,
And each put a horn into his mouth,
    And blew both loud and shrill:

" 'And there,' said they, 'the merry winds go
    Away from every horn;
And they shall clear the mildew dank
    From the blind old widow's corn:

" 'Oh, the poor blind widow—
 Though she has been blind so long,
She'll be merry enough when the mildew's gone,
 And the corn stands tall and strong!'

"And some they brought the brown linseed
 And flung it down the Low:
'And this,' said they, 'by the sunrise
 In the weaver's croft shall grow!

" 'Oh, the poor lame weaver!
 How will he laugh outright
When he sees his dwindling flax-field
 All full of flowers by night!'

"And then outspoke a brownie,
 With a long beard on his chin:
'I have spun up all the tow,' said he,
 'And I want some more to spin.

" 'I've spun a piece of hempen cloth
 And I want to spin another—
A little sheet for Mary's bed,
 And an apron for her mother!'

"With that I could not help but laugh,
 And I laughed out loud and free;
And then on the top of the Caldon-Low
 There was no one left but me.

"And all on the top of the Caldon-Low
 The mists were cold and gray,
And nothing I saw but the mossy stones
 That round about me lay.

"But, coming down from the hill-top,
 I heard, afar below,

How busy the jolly miller was,
   And how merry the wheel did go!

"And I peeped into the widow's field,
   And, sure enough, was seen
The yellow ears of the mildewed corn
   All standing stout and green.

"And down the weaver's croft I stole,
   To see if the flax were sprung;
And I met the weaver at his gate
   With the good news on his tongue!

"Now, this is all I heard, mother,
   And all that I did see;
So, prithee, make my bed, mother,
   For I'm tired as I can be!"

Mary Howitt

A SONG OF SHERWOOD

Sherwood in the twilight, is Robin Hood awake?
Gray and ghostly shadows are gliding through the brake;
Shadows of the dappled deer, dreaming of the morn,
Dreaming of a shadowy man that winds a shadowy horn.

Robin Hood is here again: all his merry thieves
Hear a ghostly bugle-note shivering through the leaves,
Calling as he used to call, faint and far away,
In Sherwood, in Sherwood, about the break of day.

Merry, merry England has kissed the lips of June:
All the wings of fairyland were here beneath the moon,
Like a flight of rose-leaves fluttering in a mist
Of opal and ruby and pearl and amethyst.

Merry, merry England is waking as of old,
With eyes of blither hazel and hair of brighter gold:
For Robin Hood is here again beneath the bursting spray
In Sherwood, in Sherwood, about the break of day.

Love is in the greenwood building him a house
Of wild rose and hawthorn and honeysuckle boughs:
Love is in the greenwood, dawn is in the skies,
And Marian is waiting with a glory in her eyes.

Hark! The dazzled laverock climbs the golden steep!
Marian is waiting: is Robin Hood asleep?
Round the fairy grass-rings frolic elf and fay,
In Sherwood, in Sherwood, about the break of day.

Oberon, Oberon, rake away the gold,
Rake away the red leaves, roll away the mould,
Rake away the gold leaves, roll away the red,
And wake Will Scarlett from his leafy forest bed.

Friar Tuck and Little John are riding down together
With quarter-staff and drinking-can and gray goose-
feather;
The dead are coming back again, the years are rolled away
In Sherwood, in Sherwood, about the break of day.

Softly over Sherwood the south wind blows;
All the heart of England hid in every rose
Hears across the greenwood the sunny whisper leap,
Sherwood in the red dawn, is Robin Hood asleep?

Hark, the voice of England wakes him as of old
And, shattering the silence with a cry of brighter gold,
Bugles in the greenwood echo from the steep,
Sherwood in the red dawn, is Robin Hood asleep?

Where the deer are gliding down the shadowy glen
All across the glades of fern he calls his merry men—
Doublets of the Lincoln green glancing through the May
In Sherwood, in Sherwood, about the break of day—

Calls them and they answer: from aisles of oak and ash
Rings the *Follow! Follow!* and the boughs begin to crash;
The ferns begin to flutter and the flowers begin to fly;
And through the crimson dawning the robber band goes by.

Robin! Robin! Robin! All his merry thieves
Answer as the bugle-note shivers through the leaves:
Calling as he used to call, faint and far away,
In Sherwood, in Sherwood, about the break of day.

Alfred Noyes

THE FAIRY BOOK

In summer, when the grass is thick, if mother has the time,
She shows me with her pencil how a poet makes a rhyme,
And often she is sweet enough to choose a leafy nook,
Where I cuddle up so closely when she reads the Fairy
    book.

In winter, when the corn's asleep, and birds are not in song,
And crocuses and violets have been away too long,
Dear mother puts her thimble by in answer to my look,
And I cuddle up so closely when she reads the Fairy book.

And mother tells the servants that of course they must
    contrive
To manage all the household things from four till half-
    past five,
For we really cannot suffer interruption from the cook,
When we cuddle close together with the happy Fairy book.

Norman Gale

THE FAIRY FOLK

Come cuddle close in daddy's coat
　　Beside the fire so bright,
And hear about the fairy folk
　　That wander in the night.
For when the stars are shining clear
　　And all the world is still,
They float across the silver moon
　　From hill to cloudy hill.

Their caps of red, their cloaks of green,
　　Are hung with silver bells,
And when they're shaken with the wind
　　Their merry ringing swells.
And riding on the crimson moth,
　　With black spots on her wings,
They guide them down the purple sky
　　With golden bridle rings.

They love to visit girls and boys
　　To see how sweet they sleep,
To stand beside their cosy cots
　　And at their faces peep.
For in the whole of fairy land
　　They have no finer sight
Than little children sleeping sound
　　With faces rosy bright.

On tip-toe crowding round their heads,
　　When bright the moonlight beams,
They whisper little tender words
　　That fill their minds with dreams;
And when they see a sunny smile,
　　With lightest finger tips

They lay a hundred kisses sweet
  Upon the ruddy lips.

And then the little spotted moths
  Spread out their crimson wings,
And bear away the fairy crowd
  With shaking bridle rings.
Come, bairnies, hide in daddy's coat,
  Beside the fire so bright—
Perhaps the little fairy folk
  Will visit you to-night.

Robert Bird

OH! WHERE DO FAIRIES HIDE THEIR HEADS

Oh! where do fairies hide their heads,
  When snow lies on the hills,
When frost has spoiled their mossy beds,
  And crystallized their rills?
Beneath the moon they cannot trip
  In circles o'er the plain;
And draughts of dew they cannot sip,
  Till green leaves come again.

Perhaps, in small, blue diving-bells
  They plunge beneath the waves,
Inhabiting the wreathèd shells
  That lie in coral caves.
Perhaps, in red Vesuvius
  Carousals they maintain;
And cheer their little spirits thus,
  Till green leaves come again.

When they return, there will be mirth
  And music in the air.
And fairy wings upon the earth,
  And mischief everywhere.

The maids, to keep the elves aloof,
  Will bar the doors in vain;
No key-hole will be fairy-proof,
  When green leaves come again.

Thomas Haynes Bayly

THE LAST VOYAGE OF THE FAIRIES

Down the bright stream the fairies float,—
A water-lily is their boat.
Long rushes they for paddles take,
Their mainsail of a bat's wing make;
The tackle is of cobwebs neat,—
With glow-worm lantern all's complete.

So down the broadening stream they float,
With Puck as pilot of the boat,
The Queen on speckled moth-wings lies,
And lifts at times her languid eyes
To mark the green and mossy spots
Where bloom the blue forget-me-nots:
Oberon, on his rose-bud throne,
Claims the fair valley as his own:
And elves and fairies, with a shout
Which may be heard a yard about,
Hail him as Elfland's mighty King,
And hazel-nuts in homage bring,
And bend the unreluctant knee,
And wave their wands in loyalty.

Down the broad stream the fairies float,
An unseen power impels their boat;
The banks fly past—each wooded scene—
The elder copse—the poplars green—
And soon they feel the briny breeze
With salt and savor of the seas.

Still down the stream the fairies float,
An unseen power impels their boat,
Until they mark the rushing tide
Within the estuary wide.

And now they're tossing on the sea,
Where waves roll high and winds blow free,—
Ah, mortal vision nevermore
Shall see the fairies on the shore,
Or watch upon a summer night
Their mazy dances of delight!
Far, far away upon the sea,
The waves roll high, the breeze blows free;
The Queen on speckled moth-wings lies,
Slow gazing with a strange surprise
Where swim the sea-nymphs on the tide,
Or on the backs of dolphins ride;
The King, upon his rose-bud throne,
Pales as he hears the waters moan;
The elves have ceased their sportive play,
Hushed by the slowly sinking day;
And still afar, afar they float,
The fairies in their fragile boat,
Farther and farther from the shore,
And lost to mortals evermore!

W. H. Davenport Adams

FAIRY SONG

Have ye left the greenwood lone?
Are your steps forever gone?
Fairy King and Elfin Queen,
Come ye to the sylvan scene,
From your dim and distant shore,
Never more?

Shall the pilgrim never hear
With a thrill of joy and fear,
In the hush of moonlight hours,
Voices from the folded flowers,
Faint sweet flutter-notes as of yore,
                    Never more?

"Mortal! ne'er shall bowers of earth
Hear again our midnight mirth:
By our brooks and dingles green
Since unhallowed steps have been,
Ours shall thread the forests hoar
                    Never more.

"Ne'er on earth-born lily's stem
Will we hang the dewdrop's gem;
Ne'er shall reed or cowslip's head
Quiver to our dancing tread,
By sweet fount or murmuring shore,
                    Never more!"
                    Felicia Dorothea Hemans

FAREWELL TO THE FAIRIES

Farewell, rewards and fairies!
  Good housewives now may say,
For slatterns now in dairies
  Do fare as well as they.
And though they sweep their hearths no less
  Than maids were wont to do,
Yet who of late, for cleanliness,
  Finds sixpence in her shoe?

At morning and at evening both
  You merry were and glad;

So little care of sleep or sloth
   These pretty ladies had;
When Tom came home from labor,
   Or Ciss to milking rose,
Then merrily went their tabor
   And nimbly went their toes.

Witness those rings and roundelays
   Of theirs, which yet remain,
Were footed in Queen Mary's days
   On many a grassy plain;
But since of late, Elizabeth,
   And later, James came in,
They never danced on any heath
   As when the time hath been.

Richard Corbet

vi. The Glad Evangel

A CHRISTMAS CAROL

The Christ-child lay on Mary's lap,
  His hair was like a light.
(O weary, weary were the world,
  But here is all aright.)

The Christ-child lay on Mary's breast,
  His hair was like a star.
(O stern and cunning are the kings,
  But here the true hearts are.)

The Christ-child lay on Mary's heart,
  His hair was like a fire.
(O weary, weary is the world,
  But here the world's desire.)

The Christ-child stood at Mary's knee,
  His hair was like a crown,
And all the flowers looked up at Him,
  And all the stars looked down.

Gilbert Keith Chesterton

THE GLAD EVANGEL

CAROL

When the herds were watching
    In the midnight chill,
Came a spotless lambkin
    From the heavenly hill.

Snow was on the mountains,
    And the wind was cold,
When from God's own garden
    Dropped a rose of gold.

When 'twas bitter winter,
    Houseless and forlorn
In a star-lit stable
    Christ the Babe was born.

Welcome, heavenly lambkin;
    Welcome, golden rose;
Alleluia, Baby,
    In the swaddling clothes!

William Canton

CHRISTMAS CAROL

As Joseph was a-waukin',
    He heard an angel sing,
"This night shall be the birthnight
    Of Christ our heavenly King.

"His birth-bed shall be neither
    In housen nor in hall,

239

Nor in the place of paradise,
　　But in the oxen's stall.

"He neither shall be rockèd
　　In silver nor in gold,
But in the wooden manger
　　That lieth in the mould.

"He neither shall be washen
　　With white wine nor with red,
But with the fair spring water
　　That on you shall be shed.

"He neither shall be clothèd
　　In purple nor in pall,
But in the fair, white linen
　　That usen babies all."

As Joseph was a-waukin',
　　Thus did the angel sing,
And Mary's son at midnight
　　Was born to be our King.

Then be you glad, good people,
　　At this time of the year;
And light you up your candles,
　　For His star it shineth clear.

A CAROL

He came all so still
　　Where His mother was,
As dew in April
　　That falleth on the grass.

He came all so still
  Where His mother lay,
As dew in April
  That falleth on the spray.

He came all so still
  To his mother's bower,
As dew in April
  That falleth on the flower.

Mother and maiden
  Was never none but she!
Well might such a lady
  God's mother be.

GOD REST YOU MERRY, GENTLEMEN

God rest you merry, gentlemen,
  Let nothing you dismay,
For Jesus Christ, our Saviour,
  Was born upon this day,
To save us all from Satan's power
  When we were gone astray.
    O tidings of comfort and joy!
    For Jesus Christ, our Saviour,
    Was born on Christmas Day.

In Bethlehem, in Jewry,
  This blessèd babe was born,
And laid within a manger,
  Upon this blessèd morn;
The which His mother, Mary,
  Nothing did take in scorn.

From God our Heavenly Father,
  A blessèd angel came;

And unto certain shepherds
   Brought tidings of the same:
How that in Bethlehem was born
   The Son of God by name.

"Fear not," then said the angel,
   "Let nothing you affright,
This day is born a Saviour
   Of virtue, power, and might,
So frequently to vanquish all
   The friends of Satan quite."

The shepherds at these tidings
   Rejoicèd much in mind,
And left their flocks a-feeding
   In tempest, storm, and wind,
And went to Bethlehem straightway,
   This blessèd babe to find.

But when to Bethlehem they came,
   Whereat this infant lay,
They found Him in a manger,
   Where oxen feed on hay,
His mother Mary kneeling,
   Unto the Lord did pray.

Now to the Lord sing praises,
   All you within this place,
And with true love and brotherhood
   Each other now embrace;
This holy tide of Christmas
   All others doth deface.
      O tidings of comfort and joy!
      For Jesus Christ, our Saviour,
      Was born on Christmas Day.

A CHRISTMAS CAROL

There's a song in the air!
There's a star in the sky
There's a mother's deep prayer
And a baby's low cry!
And the star rains its fire while the Beautiful sing,
For the manger of Bethlehem cradles a king.

There's a tumult of joy
O'er the wonderful birth,
For the virgin's sweet boy
Is the Lord of the earth,
Ay! the star rains its fire and the Beautiful sing,
For the manger of Bethlehem cradles a king.

In the light of that star
Lie the ages impearled;
And that song from afar
Has swept over the world.
Every home is aflame, and the Beautiful sing
In the homes of the nations that Jesus is King.

We rejoice in the light
And we echo the song
That comes down through the night
From the heavenly throng.
Ay! we shout to the lovely evangel they bring,
And we greet in his cradle our Saviour and King!

Josiah Gilbert Holland

CHRISTMAS CAROLS

It came upon the midnight clear,
That glorious song of old,

From angels bending near the earth
  To touch their harps of gold:
"Peace on the earth, good will to men
  From heaven's all-gracious King"—
The world in solemn stillness lay
  To hear the angels sing.

Still through the cloven skies they come
  With peaceful wings unfurled,
And still their heavenly music floats
  O'er all the weary world;
Above its sad and lowly plains
  They bend on hovering wing,
And ever o'er its Babel-sounds
  The blessèd angels sing.

But with the woes of sin and strife
  The world has suffered long;
Beneath the angel-strain have rolled
  Two thousand years of wrong;
And man, at war with man, hears not
  The love-song which they bring;—
Oh, hush the noise, ye men of strife,
  And hear the angels sing!

And ye, beneath life's crushing load,
  Whose forms are bending low,
Who toil along the climbing way
  With painful steps and slow,
Look now! for glad and golden hours
  Come swiftly on the wing;—
Oh, rest beside the weary road
  And hear the angels sing!

For lo! the days are hastening on
  By prophet bards foretold,

When with the ever circling years
  Comes round the age of gold;
When Peace shall over all the earth
  Its ancient splendors fling,
And the whole world give back the song
  Which now the angels sing.

Edmund Hamilton Sears

WHILE SHEPHERDS WATCHED THEIR FLOCKS BY NIGHT

While shepherds watched their flocks by night,
  All seated on the ground,
The angel of the Lord came down,
  And glory shone around.

"Fear not," said he, for mighty dread
  Had seized their troubled mind;
"Glad tidings of great joy I bring
  To you and all mankind.

"To you, in David's town, this day
  Is born, of David's line,
The Saviour, who is Christ the Lord,
  And this shall be the sign:

"The heavenly babe you there shall find
  To human view displayed,
All meanly wrapped in swaddling bands,
  And in a manger laid."

Thus spake the seraph; and forthwith
  Appeared a shining throng
Of angels, praising God, who thus
  Addressed their joyful song:

"All glory be to God on high,
    And to the earth be peace;
Good-will henceforth from Heaven to men
    Begin and never cease."

Nahum Tate

WHILE SHEPHERDS WATCHED

Like small curled feathers, white and soft,
    The little clouds went by,
Across the moon, and past the stars,
    And down the western sky:
In upland pastures, where the grass
    With frosted dew was white,
Like snowy clouds the young sheep lay,
    That first, best Christmas night.

The shepherds slept; and, glimmering faint,
    With twist of thin, blue smoke,
Only their fire's crackling flames
    The tender silence broke—
Save when a young lamb raised his head,
    Or, when the night wind blew,
A nesting bird would softly stir,
    Where dusky olives grew—

With finger on her solemn lip,
    Night hushed the shadowy earth,
And only stars and angels saw
    The little Saviour's birth;
Then came such flash of silver light
    Across the bending skies,
The wondering shepherds woke, and hid
    Their frightened, dazzled eyes!

And all their gentle sleepy flock
    Looked up, then slept again,

Nor knew the light that dimmed the stars
    Brought endless Peace to men—
Nor even heard the gracious words
    That down the ages ring—
"The Christ is born! the Lord has come,
    Good-will on earth to bring!"

Then o'er the moonlit, misty fields,
    Dumb with the world's great joy,
The shepherds sought the white-walled town,
    Where lay the baby boy—
And oh, the gladness of the world,
    The glory of the skies,
Because the longed-for Christ looked up
    In Mary's happy eyes!

                              Margaret Deland

BEFORE THE PALING OF THE STARS

Before the paling of the stars,
    Before the winter morn,
Before the earliest cockcrow,
    Jesus Christ was born:
Born in a stable,
    Cradled in a manger,
In the world His hands had made
    Born a stranger.

Priest and king lay fast asleep
    In Jerusalem,
Young and old lay fast asleep
    In crowded Bethlehem;
Saint and Angel, ox and ass,
    Kept a watch together
Before the Christmas daybreak
    In the winter weather.

Jesus on His Mother's breast
   In the stable cold,
Spotless Lamb of God was He,
   Shepherd of the fold:
Let us kneel with Mary maid,
   With Joseph bent and hoary,
With Saint and Angel, ox and ass,
   To hail the King of Glory.

Christina Georgina Rossetti

THE THREE KINGS

Three Kings came riding from far away,
   Melchior and Gaspar and Balthasar;
Three Wise Men out of the East were they,
And they travelled by night and they slept by day,
   For their guide was a beautiful, wonderful star.

The star was so beautiful, large and clear,
   That all the other stars of the sky
Became a white mist in the atmosphere;
And by this they knew that the coming was near
   Of the Prince foretold in the prophecy.

Three caskets they bore on their saddle-bows,
   Three caskets of gold with golden keys;
Their robes were of crimson silk, with rows
Of bells and pomegranates and furbelows,
   Their turbans like blossoming almond-trees.

And so the Three Kings rode into the West,
   Through the dusk of night, over hill and dell,
And sometimes they nodded with beard on breast,
And sometimes talked, as they paused to rest,
   With the people they met at some wayside well.

"Of the child that is born," said Baltasar,
  "Good people, I pray you, tell us the news,
For we in the East have seen his star,
And have ridden fast, and have ridden far,
  To find and worship the King of the Jews."

And the people answered, "You ask in vain;
  We know of no king but Herod the Great!"
They thought the Wise Men were men insane,
As they spurred their horses across the plain
  Like riders in haste, and who cannot wait.

And when they came to Jerusalem,
  Herod the Great, who had heard this thing,
Sent for the Wise Men and questioned them;
And said, "Go down unto Bethlehem,
  And bring me tidings of this new king."

So they rode away, and the star stood still,
  The only one in the gray of morn;
Yes, it stopped,—it stood still of its own free will,
Right over Bethlehem on the hill,
  The city of David, where Christ was born.

And the Three Kings rode through the gate and the guard,
  Through the silent street, till their horses turned
And neighed as they entered the great inn-yard;
But the windows were closed, and the doors were barred,
  And only a light in the stable burned.

And cradled there in the scented hay,
  In the air made sweet by the breath of kine,
The little child in the manger lay,
The Child that would be King one day
  Of a kingdom not human, but divine.

His mother, Mary of Nazareth,
  Sat watching beside his place of rest,
Watching the even flow of his breath,
For the joy of life and the terror of death
  Were mingled together in her breast.

They laid their offerings at his feet:
  The gold was their tribute to a King;
The frankincense, with its odor sweet,
Was for the Priest, the Paraclete;
  The myrrh for the body's burying.

And the mother wondered and bowed her head,
  And sat as still as a statue of stone;
Her heart was troubled yet comforted,
Remembering what the Angel had said
  Of an endless reign and of David's throne.

Then the Kings rode out of the city gate,
  With a clatter of hoofs in proud array;
But they went not back to Herod the Great,
For they knew his malice and feared his hate,
  And returned to their homes by another way.

Henry Wadsworth Longfel ow

THE ADORATION OF THE WISE MEN

Saw you never in the twilight,
  When the sun had left the skies,
Up in heaven the clear stars shining,
  Through the gloom with silver eyes?
So of old the wise men watching,
  Saw a little stranger star,
And they knew the King was given,
  And they followed it from far.

Heard you never of the story,
　　How they crossed the desert wild,
Journeyed on by plain and mountain,
　　Till they found the Holy Child?
How they opened all their treasure,
　　Kneeling to that Infant King,
Gave the gold and fragrant incense,
　　Gave the myrrh in offering?

Know ye not that lowly Baby
　　Was the bright and morning star,
He who came to light the Gentiles,
　　And the darkened isles afar?
And we too may seek his cradle,
　　There our heart's best treasures bring,
Love, and Faith, and true devotion,
　　For our Saviour, God, and King.

Cecil Frances Alexander

THE BALLAD OF THE CROSS

Melchior, Gaspar, Balthazar,
　　Great gifts they bore and meet;
White linen for His body fair
　　And purple for His feet;
And golden things—the joy of kings—
　　And myrrh to breathe Him sweet.

It was the shepherd Terish spake,
　　"Oh, poor the gift I bring—
A little cross of broken twigs,
　　A hind's gift to a king—
Yet, haply, He may smile to see
　　And know my offering."

And it was Mary held her son
  Full softly to her breast,
"Great gifts and sweet are at Thy feet
  And wonders king-possessed,
O little Son, take Thou the one
  That pleasures Thee the best."

It was the Christ-Child in her arms
  Who turned from gaud and gold,
Who turned from wondrous gifts and great,
  From purple woof and fold,
And to His breast the cross He pressed
  That scarce His hands could hold.

'Twas king and shepherd went their way—
  Great wonder tore their bliss;
'Twas Mary clasped her little Son
  Close, close to feel her kiss,
And in His hold the cross lay cold
  Between her heart and His!

                              Theodosia Garrison

CAROL

We saw him sleeping in his manger bed,
And falter'd feet and heart in holy dread
Until we heard the maiden mother call:
Come hither, sirs, he is so sweet and small.

She was more fair than ye have look'd upon,
She was the moon, and he her little sun;
O Lord, we cry'd, have mercy on us all!
But ah, quod she, he is so sweet and small.

Whereat the blessed beasts with one accord
Gave tongue to praise their little blessed Lord,
Oxen and asses singing in their stall,
The King of Kings he is so sweet and small.

                              Gerald Bullett

LULLABY IN BETHLEHEM

There hath come an host to see Thee,
Baby dear,
Bearded men with eyes of flame
And lips of fear,
For the heavens, they say, have broken
Into blinding gulfs of glory,
And the Lord, they say, hath spoken
In a little, wondrous story,
Baby dear.

There have come three kings to greet Thee,
Baby dear,
Crowned with gold and clad in purple,
They draw near,
They have brought rare silks to bind Thee,
At Thy feet behold they spread them,
From their thrones they sprang to find Thee,
And a blazing star hath led them,
Baby dear.

I have neither jade nor jasper,
Baby dear,
Thou art all my hope and glory,
And my fear,
Yet for all the gems that strew Thee,
And the kingly gowns that fold Thee,
Yea, though all the world should woo Thee,
Thou art mine—and fast I hold Thee,
Baby dear.

H. H. Bashford

MARY'S BABY

Joseph, mild and noble, bent above the straw:
A pale girl, a frail girl, suffering he saw.

"O my Love, my Mary, my Bride, I pity thee!"
"Nay, Dear," said Mary, "all is well with me."
    "Baby, my Baby, O my Babe," she sang.
    Suddenly the golden night all with music rang.

Angels leading shepherds, shepherds leading sheep:
The silence of worship broke the mother's sleep.
All the meek and lowly of all the world were there;
Smiling, she showed them that her child was fair.
    "Baby, my Baby," kissing Him she said.
    Suddenly a flaming star through the heavens sped.

Three old men and weary knelt them side by side,
The world's wealth foreswearing, majesty and pride:
Worldly might and wisdom before a Child bent low:
Weeping, Maid Mary said, "I love Him so!"
    "Baby, my Baby," and the Baby slept.
    Suddenly on Calvary all the olives wept.

                      Shaemas O'Sheel

HOW FAR IS IT TO BETHLEHEM

How far is it to Bethlehem?
    Not very far.
Shall we find the stable-room
    Lit by a star?

Can we see the little Child,
    Is He within?
If we lift the wooden latch
    May we go in?

May we stroke the creatures there,
    Ox, ass, or sheep?
May we peep like them and see
    Jesus asleep?

If we touch His tiny hand
   Will He awake?
Will He know we've come so far
   Just for His sake?

Great Kings have precious gifts,
   And we have naught;
Little smiles and little tears
   Are all we brought.

For all weary children
   Mary must weep.
Here, on His bed of straw,
   Sleep, children, sleep.

God, in His Mother's arms,
   Babes in the byre,
Sleep, as they sleep who find
   Their heart's desire.

                  Frances Chesterton

A CHRISTMAS FOLK-SONG

The little Jesus came to town;
The wind blew up, the wind blew down;
Out in the street the wind was bold;
Now who would house Him from the cold?

Then opened wide a stable door,
Fair were the rushes on the floor;
The Ox put forth a hornèd head:
"Come, little Lord, here make Thy bed."

Uprose the Sheep were folded near:
"Thou Lamb of God, come, enter here."
He entered there to rush and reed,
Who was the Lamb of God indeed.

The little Jesus came to town;
With ox and sheep He laid Him down;
Peace to the byre, peace to the fold,
For that they housed Him from the cold!

Lizette Woodworth Reese

GATES AND DOORS

A BALLAD OF CHRISTMAS EVE

There was a gentle hostler
  (And blessed be his name!)
He opened up the stable
  The night Our Lady came.
Our Lady and St. Joseph,
  He gave them food and bed,
And Jesus Christ has given him
  A glory round his head.

*So let the gate swing open
  However poor the yard,
Lest weary people visit you
  And find their passage barred.
Unlatch the door at midnight
  And let your lantern's glow
Shine out to guide the traveler's feet
  To you across the snow.*

There was a courteous hostler
  (He is in Heaven to-night)
He held Our Lady's bridle
  And helped her to alight.
He spread clean straw before her
  Whereon she might lie down,
And Jesus Christ has given him
  An everlasting crown.

Unlock the door this evening
  And let your gate swing wide,
Let all who ask for shelter
  Come speedily inside.
What if your yard be narrow?
  What if your house be small?
There is a Guest is coming
  Will glorify it all.

There was a joyous hostler
  Who knelt on Christmas morn
Beside the radiant manger
  Wherein his Lord was born.
His heart was full of laughter,
  His soul was full of bliss
When Jesus, on His Mother's lap,
  Gave him His hand to kiss.

Unbar your heart this evening
  And keep no stranger out,
Take from your soul's great portal
  The barrier of doubt.
To humble folk and weary
  Give hearty welcoming,
Your breast shall be to-morrow
  The cradle of a King.

Joyce Kilmer

THE HOUSE OF CHRISTMAS

There fared a mother driven forth
  Out of an inn to roam;
In the place where she was homeless
  All men are at home.

The crazy stable close at hand,
With shaking timber and shifting sand,
Grew a stronger thing to abide and stand
    Than the square stones of Rome.

For men are homesick in their homes,
    And strangers under the sun,
And they lay their heads in a foreign land
    Whenever the day is done.
Here we have battle and blazing eyes,
And chance and honor and high surprise;
But our homes are under miraculous skies
    Where the Yule tale was begun.

A Child in a foul stable,
    Where the beasts feed and foam,
Only where He was homeless
    Are you and I at home;
We have hands that fashion and heads that know,
But our hearts we lost—how long ago!—
In a place no chart nor ship can show
    Under the sky's dome.

This world is wild as an old wives' tale,
    And strange the plain things are,
The earth is enough and the air is enough
    For our wonder and our war;
But our rest is as far as the fire-drake swings
And our peace is put in impossible things
Where clashed and thundered unthinkable wings
    Round an incredible star.

To an open house in the evening
    Home shall men come,
To an older place than Eden
    And a taller town than Rome.

To the end of the way of the wandering star,
To the things that cannot be and that are,
To the place where God was homeless
   And all men are at home.
                                Gilbert Keith Chesterton

A CHILD'S PRAYER

(EX ORE INFANTIUM)

Little Jesus, wast Thou shy
Once, and just so small as I?
And what did it feel like to be
Out of Heaven, and just like me?
Didst Thou sometimes think of *there*,
And ask where all the angels were?
I should think that I would cry
For my house all made of sky;
I would look about the air,
And wonder where my angels were;
And at waking 'twould distress me—
Not an angel there to dress me!

Hadst Thou ever any toys,
Like us little girls and boys?
And didst Thou play in Heaven with all
The angels, that were not too tall,
With stars for marbles?   Did the things
Play *Can you see me?* through their wings?

Didst Thou kneel at night to pray,
And didst Thou join Thy hands, this way?
And did they tire sometimes, being young,
And make the prayer seem very long?
And dost Thou like it best, that we
Should join our hands and pray to Thee?

I used to think, before I knew,
The prayer not said unless we do.
And did Thy Mother at the night
Kiss Thee and fold the clothes in right?
And didst Thou feel quite good in bed,
Kissed, and sweet, and Thy prayers said?

Thou canst not have forgotten all
That it feels like to be small:
And Thou know'st I cannot pray
To Thee in my father's way—
When Thou wast so little, say,
Could'st Thou talk Thy Father's way?—
So, a little child, come down
And hear a child's tongue like Thy own;
Take me by the hand and walk,
And listen to my baby-talk.
To Thy Father show my prayer
(He will look, Thou art so fair),
And say: "O Father, I Thy son,
Bring the prayer of a little one."

And He will smile, that children's tongue
Has not changed since Thou wast young!

Francis Thompson

A CHILD'S SONG OF CHRISTMAS

My counterpane is soft as silk,
My blankets white as creamy milk.
    The hay was soft to Him, I know,
    Our little Lord of long ago.

    Above the roofs the pigeons fly
    In silver wheels across the sky.

The stable-doves they cooed to them,
Mary and Christ in Bethlehem.

Bright shines the sun across the drifts,
And bright upon my Christmas gifts.
    They brought Him incense, myrrh, and gold,
    Our little Lord who lived of old.

Oh, soft and clear our mother sings
Of Christmas joys and Christmas things.
    God's holy angels sang to them,
    Mary and Christ in Bethlehem.

Our hearts they hold all Christmas dear,
And earth seems sweet and heaven seems near,
    Oh, heaven was in His sight, I know,
    That little Child of long ago.

                    Marjorie L. C. Pickthall

CHRISTMAS BELLS

I heard the bells on Christmas Day
Their old, familiar carols play,
        And wild and sweet
        The words repeat
Of peace on earth, good-will to men!

And thought how, as the day had come,
The belfries of all Christendom
        Had rolled along
        The unbroken song
Of peace on earth, good-will to men!

Till, ringing, singing on its way,
The world revolved from night to day,

A voice, a chime,
A chant sublime
Of peace on earth, good-will to men!

Then from each black, accursed mouth
The cannon thundered in the South,
    And with the sound
    The carols drowned
Of peace on earth, good-will to men!

It was as if an earthquake rent
The hearth-stones of a continent,
    And made forlorn
    The households born
Of peace on earth, good-will to men!

And in despair I bowed my head;
"There is no peace on earth," I said,
    "For hate is strong,
    And mocks the song
Of peace on earth, good-will to men!"

Then pealed the bells more loud and deep:
"God is not dead, nor doth He sleep!
    The Wrong shall fail,
    The Right prevail,
With peace on earth, good-will to men!"

Henry Wadsworth Longfellow

THE CHRISTMAS TREE IN THE NURSERY

With wild surprise
Four great eyes
In two small heads
From neighboring beds
Looked out—and winked—
And glittered and blinked

At a very queer sight
In the dim dawn-light.
As plain as can be
A fairy tree
Flashes and glimmers
And shakes and shimmers.
Red, green, and blue
Meet their view;
Silver and gold
Sharp eyes behold;
Small moons, big stars;
And jams in jars,
And cakes, and honey,
And thimbles, and money,
Pink dogs, blue cats,
Little squeaking rats,
And candles, and dolls,
And crackers, and polls,
A real bird that sings,
And tokens and favors,
And all sorts of things
For the little shavers.

Four black eyes
Grow big with surprise;
And then grow bigger
When a tiny figure,
Jaunty and airy,
A fairy! a fairy!
From the tree-top cries,
"Open wide! Black Eyes!
Come, children, wake now!
Your joys you may take now!"

Quick as you can think
  Twenty small toes
  In four pretty rows,

Like little piggies pink,
 All kick in the air—
And before you can wink
 The tree stands bare!

Richard Watson Gilder

CHRISTMAS ISLAND

Fringed with coral, floored with lava,
Three-score leagues to south of Java,
So is Christmas Island charted
By geographers blind-hearted,
—Just a dot, by their dull notion,
On the burning Indian Ocean;
Merely a refreshment station
For the birds in long migration;
Its pomegranates, custard-apples
That the dancing sunshine dapples,
Cocoanuts with milky hollows
Only feast wing-weary swallows
Or the tropic fowl there dwelling.
Don't believe a word they're telling!
Christmas Island, though it seem land,
Is a floating bit of dreamland
Gone adrift from childhood, planted
By the winds with seeds enchanted,
Seeds of candied plum and cherry:
Here the Christmas Saints make merry.

Even saints must have vacation;
So they chose from all creation
As a change from iceberg castles
Hung with snow in loops and tassels,
Christmas Island for a summer
Residence. The earliest comer

Is our own saint, none diviner,
Santa Claus. His ocean-liner
Is a sleigh that's scudding fast.
Mistletoe climbs up the mast,
And the sail, so full of caper,
Is of tissue wrapping-paper.
As he steers, he hums a carol;
But instead of fur apparel
Smudged with soot, he's spick and spandy
In white linen, dear old dandy.
With a Borealis sash on,
And a palm-leaf hat in fashion
Wreathed about with holly berry.
Welcome, Santa! Rest you merry!

Next, his chubby legs bestriding
Such a Yule-log, who comes riding
Overseas, the feast to dish up,
But—aha!—the boys' own bishop,
Good St. Nicholas! And listen!
Out of Denmark, old Jule-nissen,
Kindly goblin, bent, rheumatic,
In the milk-bowl set up attic
For his Christmas cheer, comes bobbing
Through the waves. He'll be hob-nobbing
With Knecht Clobes, Dutchman true,
Sailing in a wooden shoe.
When the sunset gold enamels
All the sea, three cloudy camels
Bear the Kings with stately paces,
Taking islands for oases,
While a star-boat brings Kriss Kringle.
Singing *Noël* as they mingle,
Drinking toasts in sunshine sherry,
How the Christmas Saints make merry!

While a gray contralto pigeon
Coos that loving is religion,
How they laugh and how they rollick,
How they fill the isle with frolic.
Up the Christmas Trees they clamber,
Lighting candles rose and amber,
Till the sudden moonbeams glisten.
Then all kneel but old Jule-nissen,
Who, a heathen elf stiff-jointed,
Doffs his night-cap, red and pointed;
For within the moon's pale luster
They behold bright figures cluster;
Their adoring eyes look on a
Silver-throned serene Madonna,
With the Christ-Child, rosy sweeting,
Smiling to their loyal greeting.
Would that on this Holy Night
We might share such blissful sight,
—We might find a fairy ferry
To that isle where saints make merry!

Katharine Lee Bates

SANTA CLAUS

He comes in the night! He comes in the night!
    He softly, silently comes;
While the little brown heads on the pillows so white
    Are dreaming of bugles and drums.
He cuts through the snow like a ship through the foam,
    While the white flakes around him whirl;
Who tells him I know not, but he soon finds the home
    Of each good little boy and girl.

His sleigh it is long, and deep, and wide;
    It will carry a host of things,

While dozens of drums hang over the side,
  With the sticks sticking under the strings.
And yet not the sound of a drum is heard,
  Not a bugle blast is blown,
As he mounts to the chimney-top like a bird,
  And drops to the hearth like a stone.

The little red stockings he silently fills,
  Till the stockings will hold no more;
The bright little sleds for the great snow hills
  Are quickly set down on the floor.
Then Santa Claus mounts to the roof like a bird,
  And springs to his seat in the sleigh;
Not the sound of a bugle or drum is heard
  As he noiselessly gallops away.

He rides to the East, and he rides to the West,
  Of his goodies he touches not one;
He waits for the crumbs of the Christmas feast
  When the dear little folks are done.
Old Santa Claus does all the good that he can;
  This beautiful mission is his;
Then, children, be kind to the little old man,
  When you find who the little man is.

JEST 'FORE CHRISTMAS

Father calls me William, sister calls me Will,
Mother calls me Willie, but the fellers call me Bill!
Mighty glad I ain't a girl—ruther be a boy,
Without them sashes, curls, an' things that's worn by
    Fauntleroy!
Love to chawnk green apples an' go swimmin' in the lake—
Hate to take the castor-ile they give for belly-ache!
'Most all the time, the whole year round, there ain't no
    flies on me,
But jest 'fore Christmas I'm as good as I kin be!

Got a yeller dog named Sport, sick him on the cat;
First thing she knows she doesn't know where she is at!
Got a clipper sled, an' when us kids goes out to slide,
'Long comes the grocery cart, an' we all hook a ride!
But sometimes when the grocery man is worrited an' cross,
He reaches at us with his whip, an' larrups up his hoss,
An' then I laff an' holler, "Oh, ye never teched *me!*"
But jest 'fore Christmas I'm as good as I kin be!

Gran'ma says she hopes that when I git to be a man,
I'll be a missionarer like her oldest brother, Dan,
As was et up by the cannibuls that lives in Ceylon's Isle
Where every prospeck pleases, an' only man is vile!
But gran'ma she has never been to see a Wild West show,
Nor read the life of Daniel Boone, or else I guess she'd
     know
That Buff'lo Bill an' cow-boys is good enough for me!
Excep' jest 'fore Christmas, when I'm good as I kin be!

And then old Sport he hangs around, so solemn-like an' still
His eyes they keep a-sayin': "What's the matter, little
     Bill?"
The old cat sneaks down off her perch an' wonders what's
     become
Of them two enemies of hern that used to make things
     hum!
But I am so perlite an' 'tend so earnestly to biz,
That mother says to father: "How improved our Willie is!"
But father, havin' been a boy hisself, suspicions me
When, jest 'fore Christmas, I'm as good as I kin be!

For Christmas, with its lots an' lots of candies, cakes, an'
     toys,
Was made, they say, for proper kids an' not for naughty
     boys;

So wash yer face an' bresh yer hair, an' mind yer p's an' q's,
An' don't bust out yer pantaloons, an' don't wear out yer
shoes;
Say "Yessum" to the ladies, an' "Yessur" to the men,
An' when they's company, don't pass yer plate for pie
again;
But, thinkin' of the things yer'd like to see upon that tree,
Jest 'fore Christmas be as good as yer kin be!

Eugene Field

KRISS KRINGLE

Just as the moon was fading amid her misty rings,
And every stocking was stuffed with childhood's precious
things,
Old Kriss Kringle looked round, and saw on the elm-tree
bough,
High-hung, an oriole's nest, silent and empty now.

"Quite like a stocking," he laughed, "pinned up there on
the tree!
Little I thought the birds expected a present from me!"

Then old Kriss Kringle, who loves a joke as well as the
best,
Dropped a handful of flakes in the oriole's empty nest.

Thomas Bailey Aldrich

A VISIT FROM ST. NICHOLAS

'Twas the night before Christmas, when all through the
house
Not a creature was stirring, not even a mouse;
The stockings were hung by the chimney with care,
In hopes that ST. NICHOLAS soon would be there;

The children were nestled all snug in their beds,
While visions of sugar-plums danced in their heads;
And mamma in her 'kerchief, and I in my cap,
Had just settled our brains for a long winter's nap,
When out on the lawn there arose such a clatter,
I sprang from the bed to see what was the matter.
Away to the window I flew like a flash,
Tore open the shutters and threw up the sash.
The moon on the breast of the new-fallen snow
Gave the lustre of mid-day to objects below,
When, what to my wondering eyes should appear,
But a miniature sleigh, and eight tiny reindeer,
With a little old driver, so lively and quick,
I knew in a moment it must be St. Nick.
More rapid than eagles his coursers they came,
And he whistled, and shouted, and called them by name;
"Now, *Dasher!* now, *Dancer!* now, *Prancer* and *Vixen!*
On, *Comet!* on, *Cupid!* on, *Donder* and *Blitzen!*
To the top of the porch! to the top of the wall!
Now dash away! dash away! dash away all!"
As dry leaves that before the wild hurricane fly,
When they meet with an obstacle, mount to the sky,
So up to the house-top the coursers they flew,
With the sleigh full of toys, and St. Nicholas too.
And then, in a twinkling, I heard on the roof
The prancing and pawing of each little hoof.
As I drew in my head, and was turning around,
Down the chimney St. Nicholas came with a bound.
He was dressed all in fur, from his head to his foot,
And his clothes were all tarnished with ashes and soot;
A bundle of toys he had flung on his back,
And he looked like a peddler just opening his pack.
His eyes—how they twinkled! his dimples how merry!
His cheeks were like roses, his nose like a cherry!
His droll little mouth was drawn up like a bow,
And the beard of his chin was as white as the snow;

The stump of a pipe he held tight in his teeth,
And the smoke it encircled his head like a wreath;
He had a broad face and a little round belly,
That shook, when he laughed, like a bowlful of jelly.
He was chubby and plump, a right jolly old elf,
And I laughed when I saw him, in spite of myself;
A wink of his eye and a twist of his head,
Soon gave me to know I had nothing to dread;
He spoke not a word, but went straight to his work,
And filled all the stockings; then turned with a jerk,
And laying his finger aside of his nose
And giving a nod, up the chimney he rose;
He sprang to his sleigh, to his team gave a whistle,
And away they all flew like the down of a thistle,
But I heard him exclaim, ere he drove out of sight,
"Happy Christmas to all, and to all a good-night."

Clement Clarke Moore

VII. This Wonderful World

THE WONDERFUL WORLD

Great, wide, beautiful, wonderful World,
With the wonderful water round you curled,
And the wonderful grass upon your breast,
World, you are beautifully dressed.

The wonderful air is over me,
And the wonderful wind is shaking the tree—
It walks on the water, and whirls the mills,
And talks to itself on the top of the hills.

You friendly Earth, how far do you go,
With the wheat-fields that nod and the rivers that flow,
With cities and gardens and cliffs and isles,
And the people upon you for thousands of miles?

Ah! you are so great, and I am so small,
I hardly can think of you, World, at all;
And yet, when I said my prayers to-day,
My mother kissed me, and said, quite gay,

"If the wonderful World is great to you,
And great to father and mother too,
You are more than the Earth, though you are such a dot!
You can love and think, and the Earth cannot!"

William Brighty Rands

THIS WONDERFUL WORLD

THE WORLD'S MUSIC

The world's a very happy place,
   Where every child should dance and sing,
And always have a smiling face,
   And never sulk for anything.

I waken when the morning's come,
   And feel the air and light alive
With strange sweet music like the hum
   Of bees about their busy hive.

The linnets play among the leaves
   At hide-and-seek, and chirp and sing;
While, flashing to and from the eaves,
   The swallows twitter on the wing.

The twigs that shake, and boughs that sway,
   And tall old trees you could not climb,
And winds that come, but cannot stay,
   Are gaily singing all the time.

From dawn to dark the old mill-wheel
   Makes music, going round and round;
And dusty-white with flour and meal,
   The miller whistles to its sound.

And if you listen to the rain
   When leaves and birds and bees are dumb,
You hear it pattering on the pane
   Like Andrew beating on his drum.

The coals beneath the kettle croon,
   And clap their hands and dance in glee;
And even the kettle hums a tune
   To tell you when it's time for tea.

The world is such a happy place,
   That children, whether big or small,
Should always have a smiling face,
   And never, never sulk at all.

Gabriel Setoun

THE GLADNESS OF NATURE

Is this a time to be cloudy and sad,
   When our mother Nature laughs around;
When even the deep blue heavens look glad,
   And gladness breathes from the blossoming ground?

There are notes of joy from the hang-bird and wren
   And the gossip of swallows through all the sky;
The ground-squirrel gaily chirps by his den,
   And the wilding bee hums merrily by.

The clouds are at play in the azure space
   And their shadows at play on the bright-green vale,
And here they stretch to the frolic chase,
   And there they roll on the easy gale.

There's a dance of leaves in that aspen bower,
   There's a titter of winds in that beechen tree,
There's a smile on the fruit, and a smile on the flower,
   And a laugh from the brook that runs to the sea.

And look at the broad-faced sun, how he smiles
   On the dewy earth that smiles in his ray,

On the leaping waters and gay young isles;
 Ay, look, and he'll smile thy gloom away.

William Cullen Bryant

OUT IN THE FIELDS

The little cares that fretted me,
  I lost them yesterday
Among the fields above the sea,
  Among the winds that play,
Among the lowing of the herds,
  The rustling of the trees,
Among the singing of the birds,
  The humming of the bees.

The foolish fears of what might pass
  I cast them all away
Among the clover-scented grass,
  Among the new-mown hay,
Among the hushing of the corn,
  Where drowsy poppies nod,
Where ill thoughts die and good are born—
  Out in the fields of God.

Unknown
(Has been erroneously attributed to Elizabeth
Barrett Browning and to Louise Imogen Guiney.)

A PRAYER

Teach me, Father, how to go
Softly as the grasses grow;
Hush my soul to meet the shock
Of the wild world as a rock;
But my spirit, propt with power,
Make as simple as a flower.
Let the dry heart fill its cup,
Like a poppy looking up;

Let life lightly wear her crown,
Like a poppy looking down,
When its heart is filled with dew,
And its life begins anew.

Teach me, Father, how to be
Kind and patient as a tree.
Joyfully the crickets croon
Under shady oak at noon;
Beetle, on his mission bent,
Tarries in that cooling tent.
Let me, also, cheer a spot,
Hidden field or garden grot—
Place where passing souls can rest
On the way and be their best.

Edwin Markham

MIRACLES

Why, who makes much of a miracle?
As to me I know of nothing else but miracles,
Whether I walk the streets of Manhattan,
Or dart my sight over the roofs of houses toward the sky,
Or wade with naked feet along the beach just in the edge
    of the water,
Or stand under trees in the woods,
Or talk by day with any one I love,
Or sit at table at dinner with the rest,
Or look at strangers opposite me riding in the car,
Or watch honey-bees busy around the hive of a summer
    forenoon,
Or animals feeding in the fields,
Or birds, or the wonderfulness of insects in the air,
Or the wonderfulness of the sundown, or of stars shining so
    quiet and bright,

Or the exquisite delicate thin curve of the new moon in
    spring;
These with the rest, one and all, are to me miracles,
The whole referring, yet each distinct and in its place.

To me every hour of the light and dark is a miracle,
Every cubic inch of space is a miracle,
Every square yard of the surface of the earth is spread
    with the same,
Every foot of the interior swarms with the same.

To me the sea is a continual miracle,
The fishes that swim—the rocks—the motion of the waves
    —the ships with men in them,
What stranger miracles are there?

Walt Whitman

FRIENDS

How good to lie a little while
    And look up through the tree—
The sky is like a kind big smile
    Bent sweetly over me.

The Sunshine flickers through the lace
    Of leaves above my head,
And kisses me upon the face
    Like Mother, before bed.

The Wind comes stealing o'er the grass
    To whisper pretty things;
And though I cannot see him pass,
    I feel his careful wings.

So many gentle Friends are near
    Whom one can scarcely see,

A child should never feel a fear,
  Wherever he may be.

Abbie Farwell Brown

A B C'S IN GREEN

The trees are God's great alphabet:
With them He writes in shining green
Across the world His thoughts serene.
He scribbles poems against the sky
With a gay, leafy lettering,
For us and for our bettering.

The wind pulls softly at His page,
And every star and bird
Repeats in dutiful delight His word,
And every blade of grass
Flutters to class.

Like a slow child that does not heed,
I stand at summer's knees,
And from the primer of the wood
I spell that life and love are good,
I learn to read.

Leonora Speyer

TO MAKE A PRAIRIE

To make a prairie it takes a clover and one bee,—
One clover, and a bee,
And revery.
The revery alone will do
If bees are few.

Emily Dickinson

HILLS

I never loved your plains;—
　Your gentle valleys,
Your drowsy country lanes
　And pleached alleys.

I want my hills!—the trail
　That scorns the hollow.
Up, up the ragged shale
　Where few will follow.

Up, over wooded crest
　And mossy boulder
With strong thigh, heaving chest,
　And swinging shoulder.

So let me hold my way,
　By nothing halted,
Until at close of day,
　I stand, exalted,

High on my hills of dream—
　Dear hills that know me!
And then, how fair will seem
　The lands below me.

How pure, at vesper-time,
　The far bells chiming!
God, give me hills to climb,
　And strength for climbing!

Arthur Guiterman

THE BROOK'S SONG

From "The Brook"

I come from haunts of coot and hern,
   I make a sudden sally,
And sparkle out among the fern,
   To bicker down a valley.

By thirty hills I hurry down,
   Or slip between the ridges,
By twenty thorps, a little town,
   And half a hundred bridges.

Till last by Philip's farm I flow
   To join the brimming river,
For men may come and men may go,
   But I go on for ever.

I chatter over stony ways,
   In little sharps and trebles,
I bubble into eddying bays,
   I babble on the pebbles.

With many a curve my banks I fret
   By many a field and fallow,
And many a fairy foreland set
   With willow-weed and mallow.

I chatter, chatter, as I flow
   To join the brimming river,
For men may come and men may go,
   But I go on for ever.

I wind about, and in and out,
   With here a blossom sailing,
And here and there a lusty trout,
   And here and there a grayling,

And here and there a foamy flake
  Upon me, as I travel
With many a silvery water-break
  Above the golden gravel,

And draw them all along, and flow
  To join the brimming river,
For men may come and men may go,
  But I go on for ever.

I steal by lawns and grassy plots,
  I slide by hazel covers;
I move the sweet forget-me-nots
  That grow for happy lovers.

I slip, I slide, I gloom, I glance,
  Among my skimming swallows;
I make the netted sunbeam dance
  Against my sandy shallows.

I murmur under moon and stars
  In brambly wildernesses;
I linger by my shingly bars,
  I loiter round my cresses;

And out again I curve and flow
  To join the brimming river,
For men may come and men may go,
  But I go on for ever.

Alfred Tennyson

THE WHOLE DUTY OF BERKSHIRE BROOKS

To build the trout a crystal stair;
To comb the hillside's thick green hair;
To water jewel-weed and rushes;
To teach first notes to baby thrushes;

To flavor raspberry and apple
And make a whirling pool to dapple
With scattered gold of late October;
To urge wise laughter on the sober
And lend a dream to those who laugh;
To chant the beetle's epitaph;
To mirror the blue dragonfly,
Frail air-plane of a slender sky;
Over the stones to lull and leap
Herding the bubbles like white sheep;
The claims of worry to deny,
And whisper sorrow into sleep!

Grace Hazard Conkling

A BOY'S SONG

Where the pools are bright and deep,
Where the gray trout lies asleep,
Up the river and over the lea,
That's the way for Billy and me.

Where the blackbird sings the latest,
Where the hawthorn blooms the sweetest,
Where the nestlings chirp and flee,
That's the way for Billy and me.

Where the mowers mow the cleanest,
Where the hay lies thick and greenest,
There to track the homeward bee,
That's the way for Billy and me.

Where the hazel bank is steepest,
Where the shadow falls the deepest,
Where the clustering nuts fall free,
That's the way for Billy and me.

Why the boys should drive away
Little sweet maidens from the play,
Or love to banter and fight so well,
That's the thing I never could tell.

But this I know, I love to play
Through the meadow, among the hay;
Up the water and over the lea,
That's the way for Billy and me.

James Hogg

GOING DOWN HILL ON A BICYCLE

With lifted feet, hands still,
I am poised, and down the hill
Dart, with heedful mind;
The air goes by in a wind.

Swifter and yet more swift,
Till the heart with a mighty lift
Makes the lungs laugh, the throat cry:—
"O bird, see; see, bird, I fly.

"Is this, is this your joy?
O bird, then I, though a boy,
For a golden moment share
Your feathery life in air!"

Say, heart, is there aught like this
In a world that is full of bliss?
'Tis more than skating, bound
Steel-shod to the level ground.

Speed slackens now, I float
Awhile in my airy boat;

Till, when the wheels scarce crawl,
My feet to the treadles fall.

Alas, that the longest hill
Must end in a vale; but still,
Who climbs with toil, wheresoe'er,
Shall find wings waiting there.

Henry Charles Beeching

SONG

The year's at the spring,
And day's at the morn;
Morning's at seven;
The hill-side's dew-pearled;
The lark's on the wing;
The snail's on the thorn;
God's in His Heaven—
All's right with the world!

Robert Browning

THE COMING OF SPRING

There's something in the air
That's new and sweet and rare—
A scent of summer things—
A whir as if of wings.

There's something, too, that's new
In the color of the blue
That's in the morning sky,
Before the sun is high.

And though on plain and hill
'Tis winter, winter still,

There's something seems to say
That winter's had its day.

And all this changing tint,
This whispering stir and hint
Of bud and bloom and wing,
Is the coming of the spring.

And to-morrow or to-day
The brooks will break away
From their icy, frozen sleep,
And run, and laugh, and leap.

And the next thing, in the woods,
The catkins in their hoods
Of fur and silk will stand,
A sturdy little band.

And the tassels soft and fine
Of the hazel will entwine,
And the elder branches show
Their buds against the snow.

So, silently but swift,
Above the wintry drift,
The long days gain and gain,
Until on hill and plain,

Once more, and yet once more,
Returning as before,
We see the bloom of birth
Make young again the earth.

Nora Perry

EARLY SPRING

Once more the Heavenly Power
Makes all things new,

And domes the red-plowed hills
  With loving blue;
The blackbirds have their wills,
  The throstles too.

Opens a door in Heaven;
  From skies of glass
A Jacob's ladder falls
  On greening grass,
And o'er the mountain-walls
  Young angels pass.

Before them fleets the shower,
  And burst the buds,
And shine the level lands,
  And flash the floods;
The stars are from their hands
  Flung through the woods,

The woods with living airs
  How softly fanned,
Light airs from where the deep,
  All down the sand,
Is breathing in his sleep,
  Heard by the land.

O, follow, leaping blood,
  The season's lure!
O heart, look down and up,
  Serene, secure,
Warm as the crocus cup,
  Like snow-drops, pure!

Past, Future glimpse and fade
  Through some slight spell,

A gleam from yonder vale,
  Some far blue fell,
And sympathies, how frail,
  In sound and smell!

Till at thy chuckled note,
  Thou twinkling bird,
The fairy fancies range,
  And, lightly stirred,
Ring little bells of change
  From word to word.

For now the Heavenly Power
  Makes all things new,
And thaws the cold, and fills
  The flower with dew;
The blackbirds have their wills,
  The poets too.

Alfred Tennyson

A MEMORY

Four ducks on a pond,
A grass-bank beyond,
A blue sky of spring,
White clouds on the wing;
What a little thing
To remember for years—
To remember with tears!

William Allingham

ROBIN'S COME!

From the elm-tree's topmost bough,
  Hark! the Robin's early song!

Telling one and all that now
   Merry spring-time hastes along;
Welcome tidings dost thou bring,
Little harbinger of spring:
           Robin's come!

Of the winter we are weary,
   Weary of the frost and snow;
Longing for the sunshine cheery,
   And the brooklet's gurgling flow;
Gladly then we hear thee sing
The reveille of spring:
           Robin's come!

Ring it out o'er hill and plain,
   Through the garden's lonely bowers,
Till the green leaves dance again,
   Till the air is sweet with flowers!
Wake the cowslips by the rill,
Wake the yellow daffodil;
           Robin's come!

Then, as thou wert wont of yore,
   Build thy nest and rear thy young,
Close beside our cottage door,
   In the woodbine leaves among;
Hurt or harm thou need'st not fear,
Nothing rude shall venture near:
           Robin's come!

Swinging still o'er yonder lane
   Robin answers merrily;
Ravished by the sweet refrain,
   Alice claps her hands in glee,
Calling from the open door,
With her soft voice, o'er and o'er,
           Robin's come!

                   William Warner Caldwell

FEBRUARY

The robin on my lawn,
He was the first to tell
How, in the frozen dawn,
This miracle befell,
Waking the meadows white
With hoar, the iron road
A-gleam with splintered light,
And ice where water flowed:
Till, when the low sun drank
Those milky mists that cloak
Hanger and hollied bank,
The winter world awoke
To hear the feeble bleat
Of lambs on downland farms:
A blackbird whistled sweet;
Old beeches moved their arms
Into a mellow haze
Aërial, newly-born:
And I, alone, agaze,
Stood waiting for the thorn
To break in blossom white
Or burst in a green flame. . . .
So, in a single night,
Fair February came,
Bidding my lips to sing
Or whisper their surprise,
With all the joy of spring
And morning in her eyes.

Francis Brett Young

WRITTEN IN MARCH

The cock is crowing,
The stream is flowing,

The small birds twitter,
The lake doth glitter,
The green field sleeps in the sun;
The oldest and youngest
Are at work with the strongest;
The cattle are grazing,
Their heads never raising;
There are forty feeding like one!

Like an army defeated
The snow hath retreated,
And now doth fare ill
On the top of the bare hill;
The ploughboy is whooping—anon—anon
There's joy in the mountains;
There's life in the fountains;
Small clouds are sailing,
Blue sky prevailing;
The rain is over and gone!

William Wordsworth

SONG

April, April,
Laugh thy girlish laughter;
Then, the moment after,
Weep thy girlish tears!
April, that mine ears
Like a lover greetest,
If I tell thee, sweetest,
All my hopes and fears,
April, April,
Laugh thy golden laughter,
But, the moment after,
Weep thy golden tears!

William Watson

HOME-THOUGHTS FROM ABROAD

Oh, to be in England
Now that April's there,
And whoever wakes in England
Sees, some morning, unaware,
That the lowest boughs and the brushwood sheaf
Round the elm-tree bole are in tiny leaf,
While the chaffinch sings on the orchard bough
In England—now!

And after April, when May follows,
And the white-throat builds, and all the swallows!
Hark, where my blossomed pear-tree in the hedge
Leans to the field and scatters on the clover
Blossoms and dewdrops—at the bent spray's edge—
That's the wise thrush: he sings each song twice over
Lest you should think he never could recapture
The first fine careless rapture!
And though the fields look rough with hoary dew,
All will be gay when noontide wakes anew
The buttercups, the little children's dower
—Far brighter than this gaudy melon-flower!

Robert Browning

SWEET WILD APRIL

O sweet wild April came over the hills,
He skipped with the winds and he tripped with the rills;
His raiment was all of the daffodils.
   Sing hi, sing hey, sing ho!

O sweet wild April came down the lea,
Dancing along with his sisters three:
Carnation, and Rose, and tall Lily.
   Sing hi, sing hey, sing ho!

O sweet wild April on pastoral quill
Came piping in moonlight by hollow and hill,
In starlight at midnight, by dingle and rill.
  Sing hi, sing hey, sing ho!

Where sweet wild April his melody played,
Trooped cowslip, and primrose, and iris, the maid,
And silver narcissus, a star in the shade.
  Sing hi, sing hey, sing ho!

When sweet wild April dipped down the dale,
Pale cuckoopint brightened, and windflower frail,
And white-thorn, the wood-bride, in virginal veil.
  Sing hi, sing hey, sing ho!

When sweet wild April through deep woods pressed,
Sang cuckoo above him, and lark on his crest,
And Philomel fluttered close under his breast.
  Sing hi, sing hey, sing ho!

O sweet wild April, wherever you went
The bondage of winter was broken and rent,
Sank elfin ice-city and frost-goblin's tent.
  Sing hi, sing hey, sing ho!

Yet sweet wild April, the blithe, the brave,
Fell asleep in the fields by a windless wave
And Jack-in-the-Pulpit preached over his grave.
  Sing hi, sing hey, sing ho!

O sweet wild April, farewell to thee!
And a deep sweet sleep to thy sisters three,—
Carnation, and Rose, and tall Lily.
  Sing hi, sing hey, sing ho!
                              William Force Stead

APRIL RAIN

It is not raining rain for me,
　　It's raining daffodils;
In every dimpled drop I see
　　Wild flowers on the hills.

The clouds of gray engulf the day
　　And overwhelm the town;
It is not raining rain to me,
　　It's raining roses down.

It is not raining rain to me,
　　But fields of clover bloom,
Where any buccaneering bee
　　Can find a bed and room.

A health unto the happy,
　　A fig for him who frets!
It is not raining rain to me,
　　It's raining violets.

Robert Loveman

APRIL

All night the small feet of the rain
　　Within my garden ran,
And gentle fingers tapped the pane
　　Until the dawn began.

The rill-like voices called and sang
　　The slanting roof beside;
"The children of the clouds have come;
　　Awake! Awake!" they cried.

"Weep no more the drooping rose,
 Nor mourn the thirsting tree;
The little children of the storm
 Have gained their liberty."

All night the small feet of the rain
 About my garden ran;
Their rill-like voices called and cried
 Until the dawn began.

Dora Sigerson Shorter

AN APRIL MORNING

Once more in misted April
 The world is growing green,
Along the winding river
 The plumey willows lean.

Beyond the sweeping meadows
 The looming mountains rise,
Like battlements of dreamland
 Against the brooding skies.

In every wooded valley
 The buds are breaking through,
As though the heart of all things
 No languor ever knew.

The golden wings and bluebirds
 Call to their heavenly choirs,
The pines are blued and drifted
 With smoke of brushwood fires.

And in my sister's garden
 Where little breezes run,

The golden daffodillies
Are blowing in the sun.

Bliss Carman

MAKE ME OVER, MOTHER APRIL

From "Spring Song"

Make me over, Mother April,
When the sap begins to stir!
When thy flowery hand delivers
All the mountain-prisoned rivers,
And thy great heart beats and quivers
To revive the days that were,
Make me over, Mother April,
When the sap begins to stir!

Take my dust and all my dreaming,
Count my heart-beats one by one,
Send them where the winters perish;
Then some golden noon recherish
And restore them in the sun,
Flower and scent and dust and dreaming
With their heart-beats every one!

Set me in the urge and tide-drift
Of the streaming hosts a-wing!
Breast of scarlet, throat of yellow,
Raucous challenge, wooings mellow—
Every migrant is my fellow,
Making northward with the Spring.
Loose me in the urge and tide-drift
Of the streaming hosts a-wing!

Give me the old clue to follow,
Through the labyrinth of night!

Clod of clay with heart of fire,
Things that burrow and aspire,
With the vanishing desire,
For the perishing delight,—
Only the old clue to follow,
Through the labyrinth of night!

Make me over in the morning
From the rag-bag of the world!
Scraps of dream and duds of daring,
Home-brought stuff from far sea-faring
Faded colors once so flaring,
Shreds of banners long since furled!
Hues of ash and glints of glory,
In the rag-bag of the world!

Only make me over, April,
When the sap begins to stir!
Make me man or make me woman,
Make me oaf or ape or human,
Cup of flower or cone of fir;
Make me anything but neuter
When the sap begins to stir!

Bliss Carman

SPRING MARKET

It's foolish to bring money
    To any spring wood,
Jewels won't help you,
    Gold's no good.

Silver won't buy you
    One small leaf.
You may bring joy here,
    You may bring grief.

You should look for
  Tufted moss,
Marked where a light foot
  Ran across.

Where the old rose hips
  Shrivel brown
And dried clematis
  Bloom hangs down.

There you'll find what
  Everyman needs,
Wild religion
  Without any creeds,

Green that lifts its
  Blossoming head,
New life springing
  Among the dead.

You needn't bring money
  To this market place,
Or think you can bargain for
  Wild flower grace.

Louise Driscoll

A STARLING'S SPRING RONDEL

I clink my castanet
  And beat my little drum;
    For spring at last has come,
And on my parapet
Of chestnut, gummy-wet,
  Where bees begin to hum,
I clink my castanet,
  And beat my little drum.

"Spring goes," you say, "suns set."
  So be it! Why be glum?
  Enough, the spring has come;
And without fear or fret
I clink my castanet,
  And beat my little drum.

James Cousins

BABY SEED SONG

Little brown brother, oh! little brown brother,
  Are you awake in the dark?
Here we lie cosily, close to each other:
  Hark to the song of the lark—
"Waken!" the lark says, "waken and dress you;
  Put on your green coats and gay,
Blue sky will shine on you, sunshine caress you—
  Waken! 'tis morning—'tis May!"

Little brown brother, oh! little brown brother,
  What kind of flower will you be?
I'll be a poppy—all white, like my mother;
  Do be a poppy like me.
What! you're a sun-flower? How I shall miss you
  When you're grown golden and high!
But I shall send all the bees up to kiss you;
  Little brown brother, good-bye.

Edith Nesbit

SONG: ON MAY MORNING

Now the bright morning-star, day's harbinger,
Comes dancing from the east, and leads with her
The flowery May, who from her green lap throws
The yellow cowslip and the pale primrose.
Hail, bounteous May, that dost inspire
Mirth and youth and warm desire!

Woods and groves are of thy dressing,
Hill and dale doth boast thy blessing.
Thus we salute thee with our early song,
And welcome thee, and wish thee long.

John Milton

MAY IS BUILDING HER HOUSE

May is building her house. With apple blooms
   She is roofing over the glimmering rooms;
Of the oak and the beech hath she builded its beams,
   And, spinning all day at her secret looms,
With arras of leaves each wind-sprayed wall
She pictureth over, and peopleth it all
   With echoes and dreams,
   And singing of streams.

May is building her house. Of petal and blade,
Of the roots of the oak, is the flooring made,
   With a carpet of mosses and lichen and clover,
   Each small miracle over and over,
And tender, traveling green things strayed.

Her windows, the morning and evening star,
And her rustling doorways, ever ajar
   With the coming and going
   Of fair things blowing,
The thresholds of the four winds are.

May is building her house. From the dust of things
She is making the songs and the flowers and the wings;
   From October's tossed and trodden gold
   She is making the young year out of the old;
     Yea: out of winter's flying sleet
     She is making all the summer sweet,

And the brown leaves spurned of November's feet
She is changing back again to spring's.

Richard Le Gallienne

JUNE

From the Prelude to "The Vision of Sir Launfal"

Over his keys the musing organist,
   Beginning doubtfully and far away,
First lets his fingers wander as they list,
   And builds a bridge from Dreamland for his lay:
Then, as the touch of his loved instrument
   Gives hope and fervor, nearer draws his theme,
First guessed by faint auroral flushes sent
   Along the wavering vista of his dream.

   Not only around our infancy
   Doth heaven with all its splendors lie;
   Daily, with souls that cringe and plot,
   We Sinais climb and know it not.

Over our manhood bend the skies;
   Against our fallen and traitor lives
The great winds utter prophecies;
   With our faint hearts the mountain strives;
Its arms outstretched, the druid wood
   Waits with its benedicite;
And to our age's drowsy blood
   Still shouts the inspiring sea.

Earth gets its price for what Earth gives us;
   The beggar is taxed for a corner to die in,
The priest hath his fee who comes and shrives us,
   We bargain for the graves we lie in;
At the devil's booth are all things sold,
Each ounce of dross costs its ounce of gold;

For a cap and bells our lives we pay,
Bubbles we buy with a whole soul's tasking:
'Tis heaven alone that is given away,
'Tis only God may be had for the asking;
No price is set on the lavish summer;
June may be had by the poorest comer.

And what is so rare as a day in June?
Then, if ever, come perfect days;
Then Heaven tries earth if it be in tune,
And over it softly her warm ear lays;
Whether we look, or whether we listen,
We hear life murmur, or see it glisten;
Every clod feels a stir of might,
An instinct within it that reaches and towers,
And, groping blindly above it for light,
Climbs to a soul in grass and flowers;
The flush of life may well be seen
Thrilling back over hills and valleys;
The cowslip startles in meadows green,
The buttercup catches the sun in its chalice,
And there's never a leaf nor a blade too mean
To be some happy creature's palace;
The little bird sits at his door in the sun,
Atilt like a blossom among the leaves,
And lets his illumined being o'errun
With the deluge of summer it receives;
His mate feels the eggs beneath her wings,
And the heart in her dumb breast flutters and sings;
He sings to the wide world and she to her nest,—
In the nice ear of Nature which song is the best?

Now is the high-tide of the year,
And whatever of life hath ebbed away
Comes flooding back with a ripply cheer,
Into every bare inlet and creek and bay;

Now the heart is so full that a drop overfills it,
We are happy now because God wills it;
No matter how barren the past may have been,
'Tis enough for us now that the leaves are green;
We sit in the warm shade and feel right well
How the sap creeps up and the blossoms swell;
We may shut our eyes, but we cannot help knowing
That skies are clear and grass is growing;
The breeze comes whispering in our ear,
That dandelions are blossoming near,
That maize has sprouted, that streams are flowing,
That the river is bluer than the sky,
That the robin is plastering his house hard by;
And if the breeze kept the good news back,
For other couriers we should not lack;
  We could guess it all by yon heifer's lowing,
And hark! how clear bold chanticleer,
Warmed with the new wine of the year,
    Tells all in his lusty crowing!

James Russell Lowell

CANTICLE

Devoutly worshipping the oak,
  Wherein the barred owl stares,
The little feathered forest folk
  Are praying sleepy prayers.

Praying the summer to be long
  And drowsy to the end,
And daily full of sun and song
  That broken hopes may mend.

Praying the golden age to stay
  Until the whip-poor-will

Appoints a windy moving day,
And hurries from the hill.

William Griffith

MIDSUMMER

Around this lovely valley rise
The purple hills of Paradise.

O, softly on yon banks of haze,
Her rosy face the Summer lays!

Becalmed along the azure sky,
The argosies of cloudland lie,
Whose shores, with many a shining rift,
Far off their pearl-white peaks uplift.

Through all the long midsummer-day
The meadow-sides are sweet with hay.
I seek the coolest sheltered seat,
Just where the field and forest meet,—
Where grow the pine-trees tall and bland,
The ancient oaks austere and grand,
And fringy roots and pebbles fret
The ripples of the rivulet.

I watch the mowers, as they go
Through the tall grass, a white-sleeved row.
With even stroke their scythes they swing,
In tune their merry whetstones ring.
Behind the nimble youngsters run,
And toss the thick swaths in the sun.
The cattle graze, while, warm and still,
Slopes the broad pasture, basks the hill,
And bright, where summer breezes break,
The green wheat crinkles like a lake.

The butterfly and humblebee
Come to the pleasant woods with me;
Quickly before me runs the quail,
Her chickens skulk behind the rail;
High up the lone wood-pigeon sits,
And the woodpecker pecks and flits.
Sweet woodland music sinks and swells,
The brooklet rings its tinkling bells,
The swarming insects drone and hum,
The partridge beats its throbbing drum.
The squirrel leaps among the boughs,
And chatters in his leafy house.
The oriole flashes by; and, look!
Into the mirror of the brook,
Where the vain bluebird trims his coat,
Two tiny feathers fall and float.

As silently, as tenderly,
The down of peace descends on me.
O, this is peace! I have no need
Of friend to talk, of book to read:
A dear Companion here abides;
Close to my thrilling heart He hides;
The holy silence is His Voice:
I lie and listen, and rejoice.

John Townsend Trowbridge

TO AUTUMN

Season of mists and mellow fruitfulness!
Close bosom-friend of the maturing sun;
Conspiring with him how to load and bless
With fruit the vines that round the thatch-eaves run;
To bend with apples the mossed cottage-trees,
And fill all fruit with ripeness to the core;
To swell the gourd, and plump the hazel shells

With a sweet kernel; to set budding more,
And still more, later flowers for the bees,
Until they think warm days will never cease,
For Summer has o'erbrimmed their clammy cells.

Who hath not seen thee oft amid thy store?
Sometimes whoever seeks abroad may find
Thee sitting careless on a granary floor,
Thy hair soft-lifted by the winnowing wind;
Or on a half-reaped furrow sound asleep,
Drowsed with the fume of poppies, while thy hook
Spares the next swath and all its twinèd flowers;
And sometimes like a gleaner thou dost keep
Steady thy laden head across a brook;
Or by a cider-press, with patient look,
Thou watchest the last oozings, hours by hours.

Where are the songs of Spring? Ay, where are they?
Think not of them, thou hast thy music too,
While barrèd clouds bloom the soft-dying day
And touch the stubble-plains with rosy hue:
Then in a wailful choir the small gnats mourn
Among the river shallows, borne aloft
Or sinking as the light wind lives or dies;
And full-grown lambs loud bleat from hilly bourn;
Hedge-crickets sing, and now with treble soft
The redbreast whistles from a garden-croft,
And gathering swallows twitter in the skies.

                                        John Keats

SEPTEMBER

Crickets are making
    The merriest din,
All the fields waking
    With shrill violin.

Now all the swallows
　　Debate when to go;
In the valleys and hollows
　　The mists are like snow.

Dahlias are glowing
　　In purple and red
Where once were growing
　　Pale roses instead.

Piled up leaves smoulder,
　　All hazy the noon,
Nights have grown colder,
　　The frost will come soon.

Early lamps burning,
　　So soon the night falls,
Leaves, crimson turning,
　　Make bright the stone walls.

Summer recalling
　　At turn of the year,
Fruit will be falling,
　　September is here.

Edward Bliss Reed

A VAGABOND SONG

There is something in the autumn that is native to my
　　blood—
Touch of manner, hint of mood;
And my heart is like a rhyme,
With the yellow and the purple and the crimson keeping
　　time.

The scarlet of the maples can shake me like a cry
Of bugles going by.

And my lonely spirit thrills
To see the frosty asters like a smoke upon the hills.

There is something in October sets the gypsy blood astir;
We must rise and follow her,
When from every hill of flame
She calls and calls each vagabond by name.

Bliss Carman

OCTOBER'S BRIGHT BLUE WEATHER

O suns and skies and clouds of June,
    And flowers of June together,
Ye cannot rival for one hour
    October's bright blue weather;

When loud the bumblebee makes haste,
    Belated, thriftless vagrant,
And goldenrod is dying fast,
    And lanes with grapes are fragrant;

When gentians roll their fingers tight
    To save them for the morning,
And chestnuts fall from satin burrs
    Without a sound of warning;

When on the ground red apples lie
    In piles like jewels shining,
And redder still on old stone walls
    Are leaves of woodbine twining;

When all the lovely wayside things
    Their white-winged seeds are sowing,
And in the fields, still green and fair,
    Late aftermaths are growing;

When springs run low, and on the brooks,
    In idle golden freighting,
Bright leaves sink noiseless in the hush
    Of woods, for winter waiting;

When comrades seek sweet country haunts,
    By twos and twos together,
And count like misers, hour by hour,
    October's bright blue weather.

O sun and skies and flowers of June,
    Count all your boasts together,
Love loveth best of all the year
    October's bright blue weather.

                                    Helen Hunt Jackson

OCTOBER'S PARTY

October gave a party;
    The leaves by hundreds came—
The Chestnuts, Oaks, and Maples,
    And leaves of every name.
The Sunshine spread a carpet,
    And everything was grand,
Miss Weather led the dancing,
    Professor Wind the band.

The Chestnuts came in yellow,
    The Oaks in crimson dressed;
The lovely Misses Maple
    In scarlet looked their best;
All balanced to their partners,
    And gaily fluttered by;
The sight was like a rainbow
    New fallen from the sky.

Then, in the rustic hollow,
　　At hide-and-seek they played,
The party closed at sundown,
　　And everybody stayed.
Professor Wind played louder;
　　They flew along the ground;
And then the party ended
　　In jolly "hands around."

George Cooper

HOW THE LEAVES CAME DOWN

I'll tell you how the leaves came down.
　　The great Tree to his children said:
"You're getting sleepy, Yellow and Brown,
　　Yes, very sleepy, little Red.
　　It is quite time to go to bed."

"Ah!" begged each silly, pouting leaf,
　　"Let us a little longer stay;
Dear Father Tree, behold our grief!
　　'Tis such a very pleasant day,
　　We do not want to go away."

So, just for one more merry day
　　To the great Tree the leaflets clung,
Frolicked and danced, and had their way,
　　Upon the autumn breezes swung,
　　Whispering all their sports among—

"Perhaps the great Tree will forget,
　　And let us stay until the spring,
If we all beg, and coax, and fret."
　　But the great Tree did no such thing;
　　He smiled to hear them whispering.

"Come, children, all to bed," he cried;
    And ere the leaves could urge their prayer,
He shook his head, and far and wide,
    Fluttering and rustling everywhere,
    Down sped the leaflets through the air.

I saw them; on the ground they lay,
    Golden and red, a huddled swarm,
Waiting till one from far away,
    White bedclothes heaped upon her arm,
    Should come to wrap them safe and warm.

The great bare Tree looked down and smiled.
    "Goodnight, dear little leaves," he said.
And from below each sleepy child
    Replied, "Goodnight," and murmurèd,
    "It is *so* nice to go to bed!"

Susan Coolidge

THE KITTEN AND THE FALLING LEAVES

That way look, my Infant, lo!
What a pretty baby-show!
See the Kitten on the wall,
Sporting with the leaves that fall,
Withered leaves—one—two—and three—
From the lofty elder-tree!
Through the calm and frosty air
Of this morning bright and fair,
Eddying round and round they sink
Softly, slowly: one might think,
From the motions that are made,
Every little leaf conveyed
Sylph or Fairy hither tending—
To this lower world descending,
Each invisible and mute,
In his wavering parachute.

But the Kitten, how she starts,
Crouches, stretches, paws, and darts!
First at one, and then its fellow
Just as light and just as yellow;
There are many now—now one—
Now they stop and there are none.
What intenseness of desire
In her upward eye of fire!
With a tiger-leap half-way
Now she meets the coming prey,
Lets it go as fast, and then
Has it in her power again:
Now she works with three or four,
Like an Indian conjuror;
Quick as he in feats of art,
Far beyond in joy of heart.
Were her antics played in the eye
Of a thousand standers-by,
Clapping hands with shout and stare,
What would little Tabby care
For the plaudits of the crowd?
Over happy to be proud,
Over wealthy in the treasure
Of her own exceeding pleasure!

William Wordsworth

ROBIN REDBREAST

Good-by, good-by to Summer!
  For Summer's nearly done;
The garden smiling faintly,
  Cool breezes in the sun;
Our thrushes now are silent,
  Our swallows flown away,—
But Robin's here in coat of brown,
  And scarlet breast-knot gay.

Robin, Robin Redbreast,
   O Robin dear!
Robin sings so sweetly
   In the falling of the year.

Bright yellow, red, and orange,
   The leaves come down in hosts;
The trees are Indian princes,
   But soon they'll turn to ghosts;
The scanty pears and apples
   Hang russet on the bough;
It's Autumn, Autumn, Autumn late,
   'Twill soon be Winter now.
     Robin, Robin Redbreast,
       O Robin dear!
     And what will this poor Robin do?
       For pinching days are near.

The fireside for the cricket,
   The wheat-stack for the mouse,
When trembling night-winds whistle
   And moan all round the house.
The frosty ways like iron,
   The branches plumed with snow,—
Alas! in Winter dead and dark,
   Where can poor Robin go?
     Robin, Robin Redbreast,
       O Robin dear!
     And a crumb of bread for Robin,
       His little heart to cheer.

William Allingham

THE FROST

The Frost looked forth, one still, clear night,
And he said, "Now I shall be out of sight;

So through the valley and over the height
    In silence I'll take my way.
I will not go like that blustering train,
The wind and the snow, the hail and the rain,
Who make so much bustle and noise in vain,
    But I'll be as busy as they!"

Then he went to the mountain, and powdered his crest
He climbed up the trees, and their boughs he dressed
With diamonds and pearls, and over the breast
    Of the quivering lake he spread
A coat of mail, that it need not fear
The downward point of many a spear
That he hung on its margin, far and near,
    Where a rock could rear its head.

He went to the windows of those who slept,
And over each pane like a fairy crept;
Wherever he breathed, wherever he stepped,
    By the light of the moon were seen
Most beautiful things. There were flowers and trees,
There were bevies of birds and swarms of bees,
There were cities, thrones, temples, and towers, and these
    All pictured in silver sheen!

But he did one thing that was hardly fair,—
He peeped in the cupboard, and, finding there
That all had forgotten for him to prepare,—
    "Now, just to set them a-thinking,
I'll bite this basket of fruit," said he;
"This costly pitcher I'll burst in three,
And the glass of water they've left for me
    Shall '*tchick!*' to tell them I'm drinking."
                 Hannah Flagg Gould

JACK FROST

The door was shut, as doors should be,
  Before you went to bed last night;
Yet Jack Frost has got in, you see,
  And left your window silver white.

He must have waited till you slept;
  And not a single word he spoke,
But pencilled o'er the panes and crept
  Away again before you woke.

And now you cannot see the hills
  Nor fields that stretch beyond the lane;
But there are fairer things than these
  His fingers traced on every pane.

Rocks and castles towering high;
  Hills and dales, and streams and fields;
And knights in armor riding by,
  With nodding plumes and shining shields.

And here are little boats, and there
  Big ships with sails spread to the breeze;
And yonder, palm trees waving fair
  On islands set in silver seas,

And butterflies with gauzy wings;
  And herds of cows and flocks of sheep;
And fruit and flowers and all the things
  You see when you are sound asleep.

For, creeping softly underneath
  The door when all the lights are out,
Jack Frost takes every breath you breathe,
  And knows the things you think about.

He paints them on the window pane
   In fairy lines with frozen steam;
And when you wake you see again
   The lovely things you saw in dream.

Gabriel Setoun

WHEN THE FROST IS ON THE PUNKIN *

When the frost is on the punkin and the fodder's in the
   shock,
And you hear the kyouck and gobble of the struttin'
   turkey-cock,
And the clackin' of the guineys, and the cluckin' of the
   hens,
And the rooster's hallylooer as he tiptoes on the fence;
O, it's then's the times a feller is a-feelin' at his best,
With the risin' sun to greet him from a night of peaceful
   rest,
As he leaves the house, bareheaded, and goes out to feed
   the stock,
When the frost is on the punkin and the fodder's in the
   shock.

They's something kind o' harty-like about the atmusfere
When the heat of summer's over and the coolin' fall is
   here—
Of course we miss the flowers, and the blossoms on the
   trees,
And the mumble of the hummin'-birds and buzzin' of the
   bees;
But the air's so appetizin'; and the landscape through the
   haze
Of a crisp and sunny morning of the airly autumn days

---

* From the Biographical Edition of the Complete Works of James
Whitcomb Riley, Copyright, 1913, by special permission of the publishers,
The Bobbs-Merrill Company.

Is a pictur' that no painter has the colorin' to mock—
When the frost is on the punkin and the fodder's in the
    shock.

The husky, rusty russel of the tossels of the corn,
And the raspin' of the tangled leaves, as golden as the
    morn;
The stubble in the furries—kind o' lonesome-like, but still
A-preachin' sermuns to us of the barns they growed to fill;
The strawstack in the medder, and the reaper in the shed;
The hosses in theyr stalls below—the clover overhead!—
O, it sets my hart a-clickin' like the tickin' of a clock,
When the frost is on the punkin and the fodder's in the
    shock.

Then your apples all is getherd, and the ones a feller keeps
Is poured around the celler-floor in red and yeller heaps;
And your cider-makin' 's over, and your wimmern-folks is
    through
With their mince and apple-butter, and theyr souse and
    saussage, too!
I don't know how to tell it—but ef sich a thing could be
As the Angels wantin' boardin', and they'd call around on
    me—
I'd want to 'commodate 'em—all the whole-indurin' flock
When the frost is on the punkin and the fodder's in the
    shock!

James Whitcomb Riley

SNOW-FLAKES

Whenever a snow-flake leaves the sky,
It turns and turns to say "Good-bye!
Good-bye, dear cloud, so cool and gray!"
Then lightly travels on its way.

And when a snow-flake finds a tree,
"Good-day!" it says—"Good-day to thee!
Thou art so bare and lonely, dear,
I'll rest and call my comrades here."

But when a snow-flake, brave and meek,
Lights on a rosy maiden's cheek,
It starts—"How warm and soft the day!
'Tis summer!"—and it melts away.

Mary Mapes Dodge

DIRGE FOR THE YEAR

Orphan hours, the year is dead,
  Come and sigh, come and weep!
Merry hours, smile instead,
  For the year is but asleep.
See, it smiles as it is sleeping,
Mocking your untimely weeping.

As an earthquake rocks a corse
  In its coffin in the clay,
So white Winter, that rough nurse,
  Rocks the dead-cold year to-day;
Solemn hours! wail aloud
For your mother in her shroud.

As the wild air stirs and sways
  The tree-swung cradle of a child,
So the breath of these rude days
  Rocks the year:—be calm and mild,
Trembling hours; she will arise
With new love within her eyes.

January gray is here,
  Like a sexton by her grave;

February bears the bier;
　March with grief doth howl and rave,
And April weeps—but, O, ye hours,
Follow with May's fairest flowers.

Percy Bysshe Shelley

FOR A DEWDROP

Small shining drop, no lady's ring
Holds so beautiful a thing.
At sun-up in the early air
The sweetness of the world you snare.
Within your little mirror lie
The green grass and the wingèd fly,
The lowest flower, the tallest tree
In your crystal I can see,
Why, in your tiny globe you hold
The sun himself, a midge of gold.
It makes me wonder if the world
In which so many things are curled,
The world which all men real call,
Is not the real world at all,
But just a drop of dew instead
Swinging on a spider's thread.

Eleanor Farjeon

IT IS A BEAUTEOUS EVENING

It is a beauteous evening, calm and free;
The holy time is quiet as a Nun
Breathless with adoration; the broad sun
Is sinking down in his tranquillity;
The gentleness of heaven broods o'er the Sea;
Listen! the mighty Being is awake,
And doth with his eternal motion make

A sound like thunder—everlastingly.
Dear Child! dear Girl! that walkest with me here,
If thou appear untouched by solemn thought,
Thy nature is not therefore less divine:
Thou liest in Abraham's bosom all the year,
And worship'st at the Temple's inner shrine,
God being with thee when we know it not.

William Wordsworth

HYMN TO THE NIGHT

I heard the trailing garments of the Night
    Sweep through her marble halls!
I saw her sable skirts all fringed with light
    From the celestial walls!

I felt her presence, by its spell of might,
    Stoop o'er me from above;
The calm, majestic presence of the Night,
    As of the one I love.

I heard the sounds of sorrow and delight,
    The manifold, soft chimes,
That fill the haunted chambers of the Night,
    Like some old poet's rhymes.

From the cool cisterns of the midnight air
    My spirit drank repose;
The fountain of perpetual peace flows there,—
    From those deep cisterns flows.

O holy Night! from thee I learn to bear
    What man has borne before!
Thou layest thy finger on the lips of Care,
    And they complain no more.

Peace! Peace! Orestes-like I breathe this prayer!
  Descend with broad-winged flight,
The welcome, the thrice-prayed for, the most fair,
  The best-belovèd Night!

Henry Wadsworth Longfellow

TO NIGHT

Swiftly walk o'er the western wave,
    Spirit of Night!
Out of the misty eastern cave
Where, all the long and lone daylight,
Thou wovest dreams of joy and fear,
Which make thee terrible and dear,
    Swift be thy flight—

Wrap thy form in a mantle gray,
    Star-inwrought!
Blind with thine hair the eyes of Day;
Kiss her until she be wearied out,
Then wander o'er city, and sea, and land,
Touching all with thine opiate wand—
    Come, long-sought!

When I arose and saw the dawn,
    I sighed for thee;
When light rode high, and the dew was gone,
And noon lay heavy on flower and tree,
And the weary Day turned to his rest,
Lingering like an unloved guest,
    I sighed for thee.

Thy brother Death came, and cried,
    "Would'st thou me?"
Thy sweet child Sleep, the filmy-eyed,
Murmured like a noontide bee,

"Shall I nestle near thy side?
Would'st thou me?"—And I replied,
        "No, not thee."

Death will come when thou art dead,
        Soon, too soon—
Sleep will come when thou art fled;
Of neither would I ask the boon
I ask of thee, belovèd Night—
Swift be thine approaching flight,
        Come soon, soon!

Percy Bysshe Shelley

THE WIND AND THE MOON

Said the Wind to the Moon, "I will blow you out;
        You stare
        In the air
        Like a ghost in a chair,
Always looking what I am about—
I hate to be watched; I'll blow you out."

The Wind blew hard, and out went the Moon.
        So, deep
        On a heap
        Of clouds to sleep,
Down lay the Wind, and slumbered soon,
Muttering low, "I've done for that Moon."

He turned in his bed; she was there again!
        On high
        In the sky,
        With her one ghost eye,
The Moon shone white and alive and plain.
Said the Wind, "I will blow you out again."

The Wind blew hard, and the Moon grew dim.
  "With my sledge,
  And my wedge,
   I have knocked off her edge!
If only I blow right fierce and grim,
The creature will soon be dimmer than dim."

He blew and he blew, and she thinned to a thread.
  "One puff
  More's enough
   To blow her to snuff!
One good puff more where the last was bred,
And glimmer, glimmer, glum will go the thread."

He blew a great blast, and the thread was gone.
  In the air
  Nowhere
   Was a moonbeam bare;
Far off and harmless the shy stars shone—
Sure and certain the Moon was gone!

The Wind he took to his revels once more;
  On down,
  In town,
   Like a merry-mad clown,
He leaped and halloed with whistle and roar—
"What's that?" The glimmering thread once
  more!

He flew in a rage—he danced and blew;
  But in vain
  Was the pain
   Of his bursting brain;
For still the broader the Moon-scrap grew,
The broader he swelled his big cheeks and blew.

Slowly she grew—till she filled the night,
          And shone
          On her throne
          In the sky alone,
A matchless, wonderful silvery light,
Radiant and lovely, the queen of the night.

Said the Wind: "What a marvel of power am I!
          With my breath,
          Good faith!
          I blew her to death—
First blew her away right out of the sky—
Then blew her in; what strength have I!"

But the Moon she knew nothing about the affair;
          For high
          In the sky,
          With her one white eye,
Motionless, miles above the air,
She had never heard the great Wind blare.

George Macdonald

THE PIPER ON THE HILL

There sits a piper on the hill
    Who pipes the livelong day,
And when he pipes both loud and shrill,
    The frightened people say:
"The wind, the wind is blowing up,
    'Tis rising to a gale."
The women hurry to the shore
    To watch some distant sail.
The wind, the wind, the wind, the wind,
    Is blowing to a gale.

But when he pipes all sweet and low,
    The piper on the hill,

I hear the merry women go
  With laughter, loud and shrill:
"The wind, the wind is coming south,
  'Twill blow a gentle day."
They gather on the meadow-land
  To toss the yellow hay.
The wind, the wind, the wind, the wind,
  Is blowing south to-day.

And in the morn, when winter comes,
  To keep the piper warm,
The little Angels shake their wings
  To make a feather storm:
"The snow, the snow has come at last!"
  The happy children call,
And "ring around" they dance in glee,
  And watch the snowflakes fall.
The wind, the wind, the wind, the wind,
  Has spread a snowy pall.

But when at night the piper plays,
  I have not any fear,
Because God's windows open wide
  The pretty tune to hear;
And when each crowding spirit looks,
  From its star window-pane,
A watching mother may behold
  Her little child again.
The wind, the wind, the wind, the wind,
  May blow her home again.

                        Dora Sigerson Shorter

THE WIND'S SONG

O winds that blow across the sea,
  What is the story that you bring?

Leaves clap their hands on every tree
   And birds about their branches sing.

You sing to flowers and trees and birds
   Your sea-songs over all the land.
Could you not stay and whisper words
   A little child might understand?

The roses nod to hear you sing;
   But though I listen all the day,
You never tell me anything
   Of father's ship so far away.

Its masts are taller than the trees;
   Its sails are silver in the sun;
There's not a ship upon the seas
   So beautiful as father's one.

With wings spread out it flies so fast
   It leaves the waves all white with foam.
Just whisper to me, blowing past,
   If you have seen it sailing home.

I feel your breath upon my cheek,
   And in my hair, and on my brow.
Dear winds, if you could only speak,
   I know that you would tell me now.

My father's coming home, you'd say,
   With precious presents, one, two, three,
A shawl for mother, beads for May,
   And eggs and shells for Rob and me.

The winds sing songs where'er they roam;
   The leaves all clap their little hands;
For father's ship is coming home
   With wondrous things from foreign lands.

Gabriel Setoun

WHO HAS SEEN THE WIND

Who has seen the wind?
　　Neither I nor you:
But when the leaves hang trembling,
　　The wind is passing through.

Who has seen the wind?
　　Neither you nor I:
But when the trees bow down their heads,
　　The wind is passing by.

Christina Georgina Rossetti

THE WIND

I saw you toss the kites on high
And blow the birds about the sky;
And all around I heard you pass,
Like ladies' skirts across the grass—
　　O wind, a-blowing all day long,
　　O wind, that sings so loud a song!

I saw the different things you did,
But always you yourself you hid.
I felt you push, I heard you call,
I could not see yourself at all—
　　O wind, a-blowing all day long,
　　O wind, that sings so loud a song!

O you that are so strong and cold,
O blower, are you young or old?
Are you a beast of field and tree
Or just a stronger child than me?
　　O wind, a-blowing all day long,
　　O wind, that sings so loud a song.

Robert Louis Stevenson

THE WIND

Why does the wind so want to be
Here in my little room with me?
He's all the world to blow about,
But just because I keep him out
He cannot be a moment still,
But frets upon my window sill,
And sometimes brings a noisy rain
To help him batter at the pane.

Upon my door he comes to knock.
He rattles, rattles at the lock
And lifts the latch and stirs the key—
Then waits a moment breathlessly,
And soon, more fiercely than before,
He shakes my little trembling door,
And though "Come in, come in!" I say,
He neither comes nor goes away.

Barefoot across the chilly floor
I run and open wide the door;
He rushes in and back again
He goes to batter door and pane,
Pleased to have blown my candle out.
He's all the world to blow about,
Why does he want so much to be
Here in my little room with me?

Elizabeth Rendall

CLOUDS

One day I could not read or play,
   I was too tired to sleep;
I watched the sky from where I lay,
   And saw the clouds like sheep.

I saw the clouds like sheep pass by
  Across the fields of Heaven,
So many that they filled the sky,
  From morning-tide till even.

The wind their shepherd was, and he
  Drove with such loving skill,
They could not tell they were not free
  To wander at their will.

And so from morn to eve they passed,
  New-washed and fleecy white;
And came into their folds at last
  Behind the hills of night.

And when the flock was passed and gone,
  Then, slowly as could be,
There came one little lamb alone,
  For he was tired, like me.

Norman Ault

GREEN THINGS GROWING

O the green things growing, the green things growing,
The faint sweet smell of the green things growing!
I should like to live, whether I smile or grieve,
Just to watch the happy life of my green things growing.

O the fluttering and the pattering of those green things
    growing!
How they talk each to each, when none of us are knowing;
In the wonderful white of the weird moonlight
Or the dim dreamy dawn when the cocks are crowing.

I love, I love them so—my green things growing!
And I think that they love me, without false showing;

For by many a tender touch, they comfort me so much,
With the soft mute comfort of green things growing.

And in the rich store of their blossoms glowing
Ten for one I take they're on me bestowing:
Oh, I should like to see, if God's will it may be,
Many, many a summer of my green things growing!

But if I must be gathered for the angel's sowing,
Sleep out of sight awhile, like the green things growing,
Though dust to dust return, I think I'll scarcely mourn,
If I may change into green things growing.

Dinah Maria Mulock Craik

MY GARDEN

A garden is a lovesome thing, God wot!
Rose plot,
Fringed pool,
Ferned grot—
The veriest school
Of peace; and yet the fool
Contends that God is not—
Not God! in gardens! when the eve is cool?
Nay, but I have a sign:
'Tis very sure God walks in mine.

Thomas Edward Brown

A CHANTED CALENDAR

First came the primrose,
On the bank high,
Like a maiden looking forth
From the window of her tower
When the battle rolls below,
So looked she,
And saw the storms go by.

Then came the wind-flower
In the valley left behind,
As a wounded maiden, pale
With purple streaks of woe,
When the battle has rolled by
Wanders to and fro,
So tottered she,
Dishevelled in the wind.

Then came the daisies,
On the first of May,
Like a bannered show's advance
While the crowd runs by the way,
With ten thousand flowers about them,
They came trooping through the fields.
As a happy people come,
So came they,
As a happy people come
When the war has rolled away,
With dance and tabor, pipe and drum,
And all make holiday.

Then came the cowslip,
Like a dancer in the fair,
She spread her little mat of green,
And on it danced she.
With a fillet bound about her brow,
A fillet round her happy brow,
A golden fillet round her brow,
And rubies in her hair.

Sydney Dobell

BUTTERCUPS

There must be fairy miners
    Just underneath the mould,

Such wondrous quaint designers
  Who live in caves of gold.

They take the shining metals,
  And beat them into shreds;
And mould them into petals,
  To make the flowers' heads.

Sometimes they melt the flowers
  To tiny seeds like pearls,
And store them up in bowers
  For little boys and girls.

And still a tiny fan turns
  Above a forge of gold,
To keep, with fairy lanterns,
  The world from growing old.

Wilfrid Thorley

BUTTERCUPS

Buttercups, buttercups,
  What do you hold?
Buttercups, buttercups,
  Minting your gold.

How do your rootlets
  Filch from the mire
The sunken sunbeams
  To fountains of fire?

What bosoms have crumbled
  To lift you there,—
Golden *Amens*
  To Beauty's prayer.

You tip-toe and listen
   To birds that rejoice,—
Those bits of a rainbow,
   Blessed with a voice.

I also am hearing
   Your golden words,
O buttercups, buttercups,—
   Rooted birds!

Louis Ginsberg

TO DAFFODILS

Fair Daffodils, we weep to see
   You haste away so soon;
As yet the early-rising sun
   Has not attained his noon.
               Stay, stay,
   Until the hasting day
               Has run
   But to the even-song;
And, having prayed together, we
   Will go with you along.

We have short time to stay as you,
   We have as short a spring;
As quick a growth to meet decay,
   As you, or anything.
               We die
   As your hours do, and dry
               Away,
   Like to the summer's rain;
Or as the pearls of morning's dew,
   Ne'er to be found again.

Robert Herrick

TO THE DAISY

With little here to do or see
Of things that in the great world be,
Daisy! again I talk to thee,
    For thou art worthy,
Thou unassuming common-place
Of Nature, with that homely face,
And yet with something of a grace,
    Which love makes for thee!

Oft on the dappled turf at ease
I sit, and play with similes,
Loose types of things through all degrees,
    Thoughts of thy raising:
And many a fond and idle name
I give to thee, for praise or blame,
As is the humor of the game,
    While I am gazing.

A nun demure of lowly port;
Or sprightly maiden, of Love's court,
In thy simplicity the sport
    Of all temptations;
A queen in crown of rubies dressed;
A starveling in a scanty vest;
Are all, as seems to suit thee best,
    Thy appellations.

A little cyclops, with one eye
Staring to threaten and defy,
That thought comes next—and instantly
    The freak is over,
The shape will vanish—and behold
A silver shield with boss of gold,

That spreads itself, some fairy bold
  In fight to cover!

I see thee glittering from afar—
And then thou art a pretty star;
Not quite so fair as many are
  In heaven above thee!
Yet like a star, with glittering crest,
Self-poised in air thou seem'st to rest;—
May peace come never to his nest,
  Who shall reprove thee!

Bright flower, for by that name at last,
When all my reveries are past,
I call thee, and to that cleave fast,
  Sweet silent creature!
That breath'st with me in sun and air,
Do thou, as thou art wont, repair
My heart with gladness, and a share
  Of thy meek nature!

                              William Wordsworth

LITTLE DANDELION

Gay little Dandelion
  Lights up the meads,
Swings on her slender foot,
  Telleth her beads,
Lists to the robin's note
  Poured from above;
Wise little Dandelion
  Asks not for love.

Cold lie the daisy banks
  Clothed but in green,
Where, in the days agone,
  Bright hues were seen.

Wild pinks are slumbering,
  Violets delay;
True little Dandelion
  Greeteth the May.

Brave little Dandelion!
  Fast falls the snow,
Bending the daffodil's
  Haughty head low.
Under that fleecy tent,
  Careless of cold,
Blithe little Dandelion
  Counteth her gold.

Meek little Dandelion
  Groweth more fair,
Till dies the amber dew
  Out from her hair.
High rides the thirsty sun,
  Fiercely and high;
Faint little Dandelion
  Closeth her eye.

Pale little Dandelion,
  In her white shroud,
Heareth the angel-breeze
  Call from the cloud;
Tiny plumes fluttering
  Make no delay;
Little winged Dandelion
  Soareth away.

Helen Barron Bostwick

TO THE DANDELION

Dear common flower, that grow'st beside the way,
Fringing the dusty road with harmless gold,

First pledge of blithesome May,
Which children pluck, and, full of pride, uphold,
   High-hearted buccaneers, o'erjoyed that they
An Eldorado in the grass have found,
Which not the rich earth's ample round
      May match in wealth, thou art more dear to me
      Than all the prouder summer-blooms may be.

Gold such as thine ne'er drew the Spanish prow
Through the primeval hush of Indian seas,
   Nor wrinkled the lean brow
Of age, to rob the lover's heart of ease;
   'Tis the Spring's largess, which she scatters now
To rich and poor alike, with lavish hand,
Though most hearts never understand
      To take it at God's value, but pass by
      The offered wealth with unrewarded eye.

Thou art my tropics and mine Italy;
To look at thee unlocks a warmer clime;
   The eyes thou givest me
Are in the heart, and heed not space or time:
   Not in mid June the golden-cuirassed bee
Feels a more summer-like warm ravishment
In the white lily's breezy tent,
      His fragrant Sybaris, than I, when first
      From the dark green thy yellow circles burst.

Then think I of deep shadows on the grass,
Of meadows where in sun the cattle graze,
   Where, as the breezes pass,
The gleaming rushes lean a thousand ways,
   Of leaves that slumber in a cloudy mass,
Or whiten in the wind, of waters blue
That from the distance sparkle through
      Some woodland gap, and of a sky above,
      Where one white cloud like a stray lamb doth move.

My childhood's earliest thoughts are linked with thee;
The sight of thee calls back the robin's song,
    Who, from the dark old tree
Beside the door, sang clearly all day long,
    And I, secure in childish piety,
Listened as if I heard an angel sing
With news from heaven, which he could bring
    Fresh every day to my untainted ears
    When birds and flowers and I were happy peers.

How like a prodigal doth nature seem,
When thou, for all thy gold, so common art!
    Thou teachest me to deem
More sacredly of every human heart,
    Since each reflects in joy its scanty gleam
Of heaven, and could some wondrous secret show,
Did we but pay the love we owe,
    And with a child's undoubting wisdom look
    On all these living pages of God's book.

                              James Russell Lowell

THE IVY GREEN

Oh, a dainty plant is the Ivy green,
    That creepeth o'er ruins old!
Of right choice food are his meals I ween,
    In his cell so lone and cold.
The wall must be crumbled, the stone decayed,
    To pleasure his dainty whim;
And the mouldering dust that years have made
    Is a merry meal for him.
        Creeping where no life is seen,
        A rare old plant is the Ivy green.

Fast he stealeth on, though he wears no wings,
    And a staunch old heart has he.

How closely he twineth, how tight he clings
  To his friend, the huge Oak Tree!
And slily he traileth along the ground,
  And his leaves he gently waves,
As he joyously hugs and crawleth round
  The rich mould of dead men's graves.
    Creeping where grim death has been,
    A rare old plant is the Ivy green.

Whole ages have fled and their works decayed,
  And nations have scattered been;
But the stout old Ivy shall never fade,
  From its hale and hearty green.
The brave old plant, in its lonely days,
  Shall fatten upon the past:
For the stateliest building man can raise
  Is the Ivy's food at last.
    Creeping on, where time has been,
    A rare old plant is the Ivy green.

Charles Dickens

THE LILAC

Who thought of the lilac?
"I," dew said.
"I made up the lilac
out of my head."

"She made up the lilac!
Pooh!" thrilled a linnet,
and each dew-note had a
lilac in it.

Humbert Wolfe

LITTLE WHITE LILY

Little White Lily sat by a stone,
Drooping and waiting till the sun shone.

Little White Lily sunshine has fed;
Little White Lily is lifting her head.

Little White Lily said: "It is good,
Little White Lily's clothing and food."
Little White Lily dressed like a bride!
Shining with whiteness, and crownèd beside!

Little White Lily drooping with pain,
Waiting and waiting for the wet rain,
Little White Lily holdeth her cup;
Rain is fast falling and filling it up.

Little White Lily said: "Good again,
When I am thirsty to have the nice rain.
Now I am stronger, now I am cool;
Heat cannot burn me, my veins are so full."

Little White Lily smells very sweet;
On her head sunshine, rain at her feet.
Thanks to the sunshine, thanks to the rain,
Little White Lily is happy again.

George Macdonald

THE VOICE OF THE GRASS

Here I come creeping, creeping everywhere;
    By the dusty roadside,
    On the sunny hillside,
    Close by the noisy brook,
    In every shady nook,
I come creeping, creeping everywhere.

Here I come creeping, smiling everywhere;
    All round the open door,
    Where sit the agèd poor;

Here where the children play,
In the bright and merry May,
I come creeping, creeping everywhere.

Here I come creeping, creeping everywhere;
In the noisy city street
My pleasant face you'll meet,
Cheering the sick at heart
Toiling his busy part,—
Silently creeping, creeping everywhere.

Here I come creeping, creeping everywhere;
You cannot see me coming,
Nor hear my low sweet humming;
For in the starry night,
And the glad morning light,
I come quietly creeping everywhere.

Here I come creeping, creeping everywhere;
More welcome than the flowers
In summer's pleasant hours;
The gentle cow is glad,
And the merry bird not sad,
To see me creeping, creeping everywhere.

Here I come creeping, creeping everywhere;
My humble song of praise
Most joyfully I raise
To Him at whose command
I beautify the land,
Creeping, silently creeping everywhere.

Sarah Roberts Boyle

THE GRASS

The grass so little has to do,—
A sphere of simple green,

With only butterflies to brood,
   And bees to entertain,

And stir all day to pretty tunes
   The breezes fetch along,
And hold the sunshine in its lap
   And bow to everything;

And thread the dews all night, like pearls,
   And make itself so fine,—
A duchess were too common
   For such a noticing.

And even when it dies, to pass
   In odors so divine,
As lowly spices gone to sleep,
   Or amulets of pine.

And then to dwell in sovereign barns,
   And dream the days away,—
The grass so little has to do,
   I wish I were the hay!

Emily Dickinson

WHEN IN THE WOODS I WANDER ALL ALONE

When in the woods I wander all alone,
The woods that are my solace and delight,
Which I more covet than a prince's throne,
My toil by day and canopy by night;
(Light heart, light foot, light food, and slumber light,
These lights shall light us to old age's gate,
While monarchs, whom rebellious dreams affright,
Heavy with fear, death's fearful summons wait;)
Whilst here I wander, pleased to be alone,
Weighing in thought the world's no-happiness,

I cannot choose but wonder at its moan,
Since so plain joys the woody life can bless:
Then live who may where honied words prevail,
I with the deer, and with the nightingale!

Edward Hovell-Thurlow

TREES

I think that I shall never see
A poem lovely as a tree.

A tree whose hungry mouth is pressed
Against the earth's sweet flowing breast;

A tree that looks at God all day
And lifts her leafy arms to pray;

A tree that may in summer wear
A nest of robins in her hair;

Upon whose bosom snow has lain;
Who intimately lives with rain.

Poems are made by fools like me,
But only God can make a tree.

Joyce Kilmer

BE DIFFERENT TO TREES

The talking oak
To the ancients spcke.

But any tree
Will talk to me.

What truths I know
I garnered so.

But those who want to talk and tell,
    And those who will not listeners be,
Will never hear a syllable
    From out the lips of any tree.

Mary Carolyn Davies

PLANT A TREE

He who plants a tree
    Plants a hope.
Rootlets up through fibers blindly grope;
Leaves unfold into horizons free.
    So man's life must climb
    From the clods of time
    Unto heavens sublime.
Canst thou prophesy, thou little tree,
What the glory of thy boughs shall be?

He who plants a tree
    Plants a joy;
Plants a comfort that will never cloy;
Every day a fresh reality,
    Beautiful and strong,
    To whose shelter throng
    Creatures blithe with song.
If thou couldst but know, thou happy tree,
Of the bliss that shall inhabit thee!

He who plants a tree,—
    He plants peace.
Under its green curtains jargons cease.
Leaf and zephyr murmur soothingly;
    Shadows soft with sleep
    Down tired eyelids creep,

Balm of slumber deep.
Never hast thou dreamed, thou blessed tree,
Of the benediction thou shalt be.

He who plants a tree,—
He plants youth;
Vigor won for centuries in sooth;
Life of time, that hints eternity!
Boughs their strength uprear;
New shoots, every year
On old growths appear;
Thou shalt teach the ages, sturdy tree,
Youth of soul is immortality.

He who plants a tree,—
He plants love;
Tents of coolness spreading out above
Wayfarers, he may not live to see.
Gifts that grow are best;
Hands that bless are blest;
Plant! life does the rest!
Heaven and earth help him who plants a tree,
And his work its own reward shall be.

Lucy Larcom

WHAT DO WE PLANT

What do we plant when we plant the tree?
We plant the ship, which will cross the sea.
We plant the mast to carry the sails;
We plant the planks to withstand the gales—
The keel, the keelson, the beam, the knee;
We plant the ship when we plant the tree.

What do we plant when we plant the tree?
We plant the houses for you and me.

We plant the rafters, the shingles, the floors,
We plant the studding, the lath, the doors,
The beams and siding, all parts that be;
We plant the house when we plant the tree.

What do we plant when we plant the tree?
A thousand things that we daily see;
We plant the spire that out-towers the crag,
We plant the staff for our country's flag,
We plant the shade, from the hot sun free;
We plant all these when we plant the tree.

Henry Abbey

THE PLANTING OF THE APPLE-TREE

Come, let us plant the apple-tree.
Cleave the tough greensward with the spade;
Wide let its hollow bed be made;
There gently lay the roots, and there
Sift the dark mould with kindly care,
  And press it o'er them tenderly,
As, round the sleeping infant's feet,
We softly fold the cradle-sheet;
  So plant we the apple-tree.

What plant we in this apple-tree?
Buds, which the breath of summer days
Shall lengthen into leafy sprays;
Boughs where the thrush, with crimson breast,
Shall haunt, and sing, and hide her nest;
  We plant, upon the sunny lea,
A shadow for the noontide hour,
A shelter from the summer shower,
  When we plant the apple-tree.

What plant we in this apple-tree?
Sweets for a hundred flowery springs

To load the May-wind's restless wings,
When, from the orchard-row, he pours
Its fragrance through our open doors;
　　A world of blossoms for the bee,
Flowers for the sick girl's silent room,
For the glad infant sprigs of bloom,
　　We plant with the apple-tree.

What plant we in this apple-tree?
Fruits that shall swell in sunny June,
And redden in the August noon,
And drop, when gentle airs come by,
That fan the blue September sky,
　　While children come, with cries of glee,
And seek them where the fragrant grass
Betrays their bed to those who pass,
　　At the foot of the apple-tree.

And when, above this apple-tree,
The winter stars are quivering bright,
And winds go howling through the night,
Girls, whose young eyes o'erflow with mirth,
Shall peel its fruit by cottage-hearth,
　　And guests in prouder homes shall see,
Heaped with the grape of Cintra's vine
And golden orange of the line,
　　The fruit of the apple-tree.

The fruitage of this apple-tree
Winds and our flag of stripe and star
Shall bear to coasts that lie afar,
Where men shall wonder at the view,
And ask in what fair groves they grew;
　　And sojourners beyond the sea
Shall think of childhood's careless day,
And long, long hours of summer play,
　　In the shade of the apple-tree.

Each year shall give this apple-tree
A broader flush of roseate bloom,
A deeper maze of verdurous gloom,
And loosen, when the frost-clouds lower,
The crisp brown leaves in thicker shower.
     The years shall come and pass, but we
Shall hear no longer, where we lie,
The summer's songs, the autumn's sigh,
     In the boughs of the apple-tree.

And time shall waste this apple-tree.
Oh, when its agèd branches throw
Thin shadows on the ground below,
Shall fraud and force and iron will
Oppress the weak and helpless still?
     What shall the tasks of mercy be,
Amid the toils, the strifes, the tears
Of those who live when length of years
     Is wasting this little apple-tree?

"Who planted this old apple-tree?"
The children of that distant day
Thus to some agèd man shall say;
And, gazing on its mossy stem,
The gray-haired man shall answer them:
     "A poet of the land was he,
Born in the rude but good old times;
'Tis said he made some quaint old rhymes,
     On planting the apple-tree."
                              William Cullen Bryant

BIRCH TREES

The night is white,
     The moon is high,

The birch trees lean
  Against the sky.

The cruel winds
  Have blown away
Each little leaf
  Of silver gray.

O lonely trees
  As white as wool . . .
That moonlight makes
  So beautiful.

John Richard Moreland

POPLARS

The poplar is a lonely tree,
It has no branches spreading wide
Where birds may sing or squirrels hide.
It throws no shadow on the grass
Tempting the wayfarers who pass
To stop and sit there quietly.

The poplar is a slender tree,
It has no boughs where children try
To climb far off into the sky,
To hold a swing, it's far too weak,
Too small it is for hide-and-seek,
Friendless, forsaken it must be.

The poplar is a restless tree,
At every breeze its branches bend
And signal to the child, "Come, friend."
Its leaves forever whispering
To thrush and robin, "Stay and sing,"
They pass. It quivers plaintively.

Poplars are lonely.   They must grow
Close to each other in a row.

Edward Bliss Reed

EPITAPH ON A HARE

Here lies, whom hound did ne'er pursue,
    Nor swifter greyhound follow,
Whose foot ne'er tainted morning dew,
    Nor ear heard huntsman's hallo;

Old Tiney, surliest of his kind,
    Who, nursed with tender care,
And to domestic bounds confined,
    Was still a wild Jack-hare.

Though duly from my hand he took
    His pittance every night,
He did it with a jealous look,
    And, when he could, would bite. . . .

A Turkey carpet was his lawn,
    Whereon he loved to bound,
To skip and gambol like a fawn,
    And swing his rump around.

His frisking was at evening hours,
    For then he lost his fear;
But most before approaching showers,
    Or when a storm drew near.

Eight years and five round-rolling moons
    He thus saw steal away,
Dozing out all his idle noons,
    And every night at play.

I kept him for his humor's sake,
    For he would oft beguile
My heart of thoughts that made it ache,
    And force me to a smile.

But now, beneath this walnut-shade
    He finds his long, last home,
And waits, in snug concealment laid,
    Till gentler Puss shall come.

He, still more agèd, feels the shocks
    From which no care can save,
And, partner once of Tiney's box,
    Must soon partake his grave.

William Cowper

THE DONKEY

When fishes flew and forests walked
    And figs grew upon thorn,
Some moment when the moon was blood
    Then surely I was born;

With monstrous head and sickening cry
    And ears like errant wings,
The devil's walking parody
    On all four-footed things.

The tattered outlaw of the earth,
    Of ancient crooked will;
Starve, scourge, deride me: I am dumb,
    I keep my secret still.

Fools! For I also had my hour;
    One far fierce hour and sweet:

There was a shout about my ears,
    And palms before my feet.

                            Gilbert Keith Chesterton

OBITUARY

Finding Francesca full of tears, I said,
"Tell me thy trouble!" "Oh, my dog is dead!
Murdered by poison!—no one knows for what!—
Was ever dog born capable of that?"
"Child,"—I began to say, but checked my thought,—
"A better dog can easily be bought."
For no—what animal could him replace?
Those loving eyes! That fond, confiding face!
Those dear, dumb touches! Therefore I was dumb.
From word of mine could any comfort come?
A bitter sorrow 'tis to lose a brute
Friend, dog or horse, for grief must then be mute,—
So many smile to see the rivers shed
Of tears for one poor, speechless creature dead.
When parents die there's many a word to say—
Kind words, consoling—one can always pray;
When children die 'tis natural to tell
Their mother, "Certainly, with them 'tis well!"
But for a dog, 'twas all the life he had,
Since death is end of dogs, or good or bad.
This was his world; he was contented here;
Imagined nothing better, naught more dear,
Than his young mistress; sought no brighter sphere;
Having no sin, asked not to be forgiven;
Ne'er guessed at God nor ever dreamed of heaven.
Now he has passed away, so much of love
Goes from our life, without one hope above!
When a dog dies there's nothing to be said
But—kiss me, darling! dear old Smiler's dead.

                            Thomas William Parsons

THE SNAIL

To grass, or leaf, or fruit, or wall,
The Snail sticks close, nor fears to fall,
As if he grew there, house and all
             Together.
Within that house secure he hides,
When danger imminent betides
Of storm, or other harm besides
             Of weather.

Give but his horns the slightest touch,
His self-collecting power is such,
He shrinks into his house with much
             Displeasure.
Where'er he dwells, he dwells alone,
Except himself, has chattels none,
Well satisfied to be his own
             Whole treasure.

Thus, hermit-like, his life he leads,
Nor partner of his banquet needs,
And if he meets one, only feeds
             The faster.
Who seeks him must be worse than blind
(He and his house are so combined),
If, finding it, he fails to find
             Its master.

From the Latin of Vincent Bourne,
by William Cowper

THE HUMBLE-BEE

Burly, dozing humble-bee,
Where thou art is clime for me.

Let them sail for Porto Rique,
Far-off heats through seas to seek;
I will follow thee alone,
Thou animated torrid-zone!
Zigzag steerer, desert cheerer,
Let me chase thy waving lines;
Keep me nearer, me thy hearer,
Singing over shrubs and vines.

Insect lover of the sun,
Joy of thy dominion!
Sailor of the atmosphere;
Swimmer through the waves of air;
Voyager of light and noon;
Epicurean of June;
Wait, I prithee, till I come
Within earshot of thy hum,—
All without is martyrdom.

When the south wind, in May days,
With a net of shining haze
Silvers the horizon wall,
And with softness touching all,
Tints the human countenance
With a color of romance,
And infusing subtle heats,
Turns the sod to violets,
Thou, in sunny solitudes,
Rover of the underwoods,
The green silence dost displace
With thy mellow, breezy bass.

Hot midsummer's petted crone,
Sweet to me thy drowsy tone
Tells of countless sunny hours,
Long days, and solid banks of flowers;

Of gulfs of sweetness without bound
In Indian wildernesses found;
Of Syrian peace, immortal leisure,
Firmest cheer, and birdlike pleasure.

Aught unsavory or unclean
Hath my insect never seen;
But violets and bilberry bells,
Maple-sap and daffodels,
Grass with green flag half-mast high,
Succory to match the sky,
Columbine with horn of honey,
Scented fern, and agrimony,
Clover, catchfly, adder's tongue
And brier-roses, dwelt among;
All beside was unknown waste,
All was picture as he passed.

Wiser far than human seer,
Yellow-breeched philosopher!
Seeing only what is fair,
Sipping only what is sweet,
Thou dost mock at fate and care,
Leave the chaff, and take the wheat.
When the fierce northwestern blast
Cools sea and land so far and fast,
Thou already slumberest deep;
Woe and want thou canst outsleep;
Want and woe, which torture us,
Thy sleep makes ridiculous.

Ralph Waldo Emerson

TO AN INSECT

I love to hear thine earnest voice,
   Wherever thou art hid,

Thou testy little dogmatist,
  Thou pretty Katydid!
Thou mindest me of gentlefolks,—
  Old gentlefolks are they,—
Thou say'st an undisputed thing
  In such a solemn way.

Thou art a female, Katydid!
  I know it by the trill
That quivers through thy piercing notes,
  So petulant and shrill;
I think there is a knot of you
  Beneath the hollow tree,—
A knot of spinster Katydids,—
  Do Katydids drink tea?

Oh, tell me where did Katy live,
  And what did Katy do?
And was she very fair and young,
  And yet so wicked, too?
Did Katy love a naughty man,
  Or kiss more cheeks than one?
I warrant Katy did no more
  Than many a Kate has done.

Dear me! I'll tell you all about
  My fuss with little Jane,
And Ann, with whom I used to walk
  So often down the lane,
And all that tore their locks of black,
  Or wet their eyes of blue,—
Pray tell me, sweetest Katydid,
  What did poor Katy do?

Ah no! the living oak shall crash,
  That stood for ages still,

The rock shall rend its mossy base
  And thunder down the hill,
Before the little Katydid
  Shall add one word, to tell
The mystic story of the maid
  Whose name she knows so well.

Peace to the ever-murmuring race!
  And when the latest one
Shall fold in death her feeble wings
  Beneath the autumn sun,
Then shall she raise her fainting voice,
  And lift her drooping lid,
And then the child of future years
  Shall hear what Katy did.

Oliver Wendell Holmes

THE CRICKET

Little inmate, full of mirth,
Chirping on my kitchen hearth,
Wheresoe'er be thine abode
Always harbinger of good,
Pay me for thy warm retreat
With a song more soft and sweet;
In return thou shalt receive
Such a strain as I can give.

Thus thy praise shall be expressed,
Inoffensive, welcome guest!
While the rat is on the scout,
And the mouse with curious snout,
With what vermin else infest
Every dish, and spoil the best;
Frisking thus before the fire,
Thou hast all thy heart's desire.

Though in voice and shape they be
Formed as if akin to thee,
Thou surpassest, happier far,
Happiest grasshoppers that are;
Theirs is but a summer's song,
Thine endures the winter long,
Unimpaired, and shrill, and clear
Melody throughout the year.

Neither night nor dawn of day
Puts a period to thy play:
Sing then—and extend thy span
Far beyond the date of man;
Wretched man, whose years are spent
In repining discontent,
Lives not, agèd though he be,
Half a span, compared with thee.

From the Latin of Vincent Bourne,
by William Cowper

GRASSHOPPER GREEN

Grasshopper Green is a comical chap;
    He lives on the best of fare.
Bright little trousers, jacket, and cap,
    These are his summer wear.
Out in the meadow he loves to go,
    Playing away in the sun;
It's hopperty, skipperty, high and low,
    Summer's the time for fun.

Grasshopper Green has a quaint little house;
    It's under the hedge so gay.
Grandmother Spider, as still as a mouse,
    Watches him over the way.
Gladly he's calling the children, I know,
    Out in the beautiful sun;

It's hopperty, skipperty, high and low,
Summer's the time for fun.

THE GRASSHOPPER

Happy insect, what can be
In happiness compared to thee?
Fed with nourishment divine,
The dewy morning's gentle wine!
Nature waits upon thee still,
And thy verdant cup does fill;
'Tis filled wherever thou dost tread,
Nature's self's thy Ganymede.
Thou dost drink, and dance, and sing,
Happier than the happiest king!
All the fields which thou dost see,
All the plants belong to thee;
All the summer hours produce,
Fertile made with early juice.
Man for thee does sow and plow,
Farmer he, and landlord thou!
Thou dost innocently enjoy;
Nor dost thy luxury destroy.
The shepherd gladly heareth thee,
More harmonious than he.
Thee country hinds with gladness hear,
Prophet of the ripened year!
Thee Phœbus loves, and does inspire;
Phœbus is himself thy sire.
To thee, of all things upon earth,
Life is no longer than thy mirth.
Happy insect! happy thou,
Dost neither age nor winter know;
But when thou'st drunk, and danced, and sung
Thy fill, the flowery leaves among,

(Voluptuous, and wise withal,
Epicurean animal!)
Sated with thy summer feast,
Thou retir'st to endless rest.

After Anacreon, by Abraham Cowley

THE TRAIL OF THE BIRD

We wish to declare how the birds of the air
   All high Institutions designed,
And holding in awe Art, Science, and Law,
   Delivered the same to mankind.
To begin with: of old, Man went naked and cold
   Whenever it pelted or froze,
Till we showed him how feathers were proof against
      weathers;
   With that he bethought him of hose.
And next it was plain that he in the rain
   Was forced to sit dripping and blind,
While the reed-warbler swung in a nest with her young,
   Deep-sheltered and warm from the wind.
So our homes in the boughs made him think of the house;
   And the swallow, to help him invent,
Revealed the best way to economise clay,
   And bricks to combine with cement.
The knowledge withal of the carpenter's awl
   Is drawn from the nuthatch's bill,
And the sand-marten's pains in the hazel-clad lanes
   Instructed the mason to drill.
Is there one of the arts more dear to men's hearts,
   To the bird's inspiration they owe it,
For the nightingale first sweet music rehearsed,
   Prima Donna, composer, and poet.
The owl's dark retreats showed sages the sweets
   Of brooding to spin or unravel
Fine webs in one's brain, philosophical, vain,—

The swallows the pleasures of travel,
Who chirped in such strain of Greece, Italy, Spain,
    And Egypt, that men, when they heard,
Were mad to fly forth from their nests in the north,
    And follow the trail of the bird.

W. J. Courthope

OVERTONES

I heard a bird at break of day
    Sing from the autumn trees
A song so mystical and calm,
    So full of certainties,
No man, I think, could listen long
    Except upon his knees.
Yet this was but a simple bird,
    Alone, among dead trees.

William Alexander Percy

ANSWER TO A CHILD'S QUESTION

Do you ask what the birds say? The Sparrow, the Dove,
The Linnet, and Thrush say, "I love and I love!"
In the winter they're silent—the wind is so strong;
What it says, I don't know, but it sings a loud song.
But green leaves, and blossoms, and sunny warm weather,
And singing, and loving—all come back together.
But the Lark is so brimful of gladness and love,
The green fields below him, the blue sky above,
That he sings, and he sings, and forever sings he—
"I love my Love, and my Love loves me!"

Samuel Taylor Coleridge

THE BUILDING OF THE NEST

They'll come again to the apple tree—
    Robin and all the rest—

When the orchard branches are fair to see,
  In the snow of the blossom dressed;
And the prettiest thing in the world will be
  The building of the nest.

Weaving it well, so round and trim,
  Hollowing it with care,—
Nothing too far away for him,
  Nothing for her too fair,—
Hanging it safe on the topmost limb,
  Their castle in the air.

Ah! mother bird, you'll have weary days
  When the eggs are under your breast,
And shadow may darken the dancing rays
  When the wee ones leave the nest;
But they'll find their wings in a glad amaze,
  And God will see to the rest.

So come to the trees with all your train
  When the apple blossoms blow;
Through the April shimmer of sun and rain,
  Go flying to and fro;
And sing to our hearts as we watch again
  Your fairy building grow.

Margaret Sangster

TO AN IRISH BLACKBIRD

Wet your feet, wet your feet,
  This is what he seems to say,
Calling from the dewy thicket
  At the breaking of the day.

Wet your feet, wet your feet,
  Silver toned he sounds the call

From his bramble in the thicket
  When the dew is on the fall.

Many times in lands far distant,
  In my dreams I hear him play
On his flute within the thicket,
  Ere the showers have passed away.

Years have passed since last I heard him,
  Since I said a sad adieu
To the early Irish morning
  With the rainbow-tinted dew.

And I still can hear him calling
  And the call comes clear and sweet,
And I still can see the mornings
  With the dew about my feet.

Wet your feet, wet your feet,
  Silver toned he sounds the call
From his bramble in the thicket
  When the dew is on the fall.

James MacAlpine

THE BLACKBIRD

In the far corner,
close by the swings,
every morning
a blackbird sings.

His bill's so yellow,
his coat's so black,
that he makes a fellow
whistle back.

Ann, my daughter,
thinks that he
sings for us two
especially.

Humbert Wolfe

BOB WHITE

There's a plump little chap in a speckled coat,
And he sings on the zigzag rails remote,
Where he whistles at breezy, bracing morn,
When the buckwheat is ripe, and stacked is the corn,
        "Bob White! Bob White! Bob White!"

Is he hailing some comrade as blithe as he?
Now I wonder where Robert White can be!
O'er the billows of gold and amber grain
There is no one in sight—but, hark again:
        "Bob White! Bob White! Bob White!"

Ah! I see why he calls; in the stubble there
Hide his plump little wife and babies fair!
So contented is he, and so proud of the same,
That he wants all the world to know his name:
        "Bob White! Bob White! Bob White!"

George Cooper

ROBERT OF LINCOLN

Merrily swinging on brier and weed,
    Near to the nest of his little dame,
Over the mountain-side or mead,
    Robert of Lincoln is telling his name:
        Bob-o'-link, bob-o'-link,
        Spink, spank, spink;

Snug and safe is that nest of ours,
Hidden among the summer flowers.
                    Chee, chee, chee.

Robert of Lincoln is gayly dressed,
    Wearing a bright black wedding-coat;
White are his shoulders and white his crest,
    Hear him call in his merry note:
        Bob-o'-link, bob-o'-link,
        Spink, spank, spink;
Look, what a nice new coat is mine,
Sure there was never a bird so fine.
                    Chee, chee, chee.

Robert of Lincoln's Quaker wife,
    Pretty and quiet, with plain brown wings,
Passing at home a patient life,
    Broods in the grass while her husband sings:
        Bob-o'-link, bob-o'-link,
        Spink, spank, spink;
Brood, kind creature; you need not fear
Thieves and robbers while I am here.
                    Chee, chee, chee.

Modest and shy as a nun is she;
    One weak chirp is her only note.
Braggart and prince of braggarts is he,
    Pouring boasts from his little throat:
        Bob-o'-link, bob-o'-link,
        Spink, spank, spink;
Never was I afraid of man;
Catch me, cowardly knaves, if you can!
                    Chee, chee, chee.

Six white eggs on a bed of hay,
    Flecked with purple, a pretty sight!
There as the mother sits all day,
    Robert is singing with all his might:

Bob-o'-link, bob-o'-link,
Spink, spank, spink;
Nice good wife, that never goes out,
Keeping house while I frolic about.
Chee, chee, chee.

Soon as the little ones chip the shell,
Six wide mouths are open for food;
Robert of Lincoln bestirs him well,
Gathering seeds for the hungry brood.
Bob-o'-link, bob-o'-link,
Spink, spank, spink;
This new life is likely to be
Hard for a gay young fellow like me.
Chee, chee, chee.

Robert of Lincoln at length is made
Sober with work, and silent with care;
Off is his holiday garment laid,
Half forgotten that merry air:
Bob-o'-link, bob-o'-link,
Spink, spank, spink;
Nobody knows but my mate and I
Where our nest and our nestlings lie.
Chee, chee, chee.

Summer wanes; the children are grown;
Fun and frolic no more he knows;
Robert of Lincoln's a humdrum crone;
Off he flies, and we sing as he goes:
Bob-o'-link, bob-o'-link,
Spink, spank, spink;
When you can pipe that merry old strain,
Robert of Lincoln, come back again.
Chee, chee, chee.
William Cullen Bryant

THE O'LINCON FAMILY

A flock of merry singing-birds were sporting in the grove;
Some were warbling cheerily, and some were making love:
There were Bobolincon, Wadolincon, Winterseeble, Con-
    quedle,—
A livelier set was never led by tabor, pipe, or fiddle,—
Crying, "Phew, shew, Wadolincon, see, see, Bobolincon,
Down among the tickletops, hiding in the buttercups!
I know a saucy chap, I see his shining cap
Bobbing in the clover there—see, see, see!"

Up flies Bobolincon, perching on an apple-tree,
Startled by his rival's song, quickened by his raillery,
Soon he spies the rogue afloat, curveting in the air,
And merrily he turns about, and warns him to beware!
" 'Tis you that would a-wooing go, down among the rushes
    O!
But wait a week, till flowers are cheery,—wait a week, and,
    ere you marry,
Be sure of a house wherein to tarry!
Wadolink, Whiskodink, Tom Denny, wait, wait, wait!"

Every one's a funny fellow; every one's a little mellow;
Follow, follow, follow, follow, o'er the hill and in the
    hollow!
Merrily, merrily, there they hie; now they rise and now
    they fly;
They cross and turn, and in and out, and down in the mid-
    dle and wheel about,—
With a "Phew, shew, Wadolincon! listen to me, Bobo-
    lincon!—
Happy's the wooing that's speedily doing, that's speedily
    doing,

That's merry and over with the bloom of the clover!
Bobolincon, Wadolincon, Winterseeble, follow, follow, follow me!"

Wilson Flagg

WILD GEESE

How oft against the sunset sky or moon
   I watched that moving zigzag of spread wings
In unforgotten Autumns gone too soon,
   In unforgotten Springs!

Creatures of desolation, far they fly
   Above all lands bound by the curling foam;
In misty fens, wild moors and trackless sky
   These wild things have their home.

They know the tundra of Siberian coasts.
   And tropic marshes by the Indian seas;
They know the clouds and night and starry hosts
   From Crux to Pleiades.

Dark flying rune against the western glow—
   It tells the sweep and loneliness of things,
Symbol of Autumns vanished long ago.
   Symbol of coming Springs!

Frederick Peterson

THE JACKDAW

There is a bird, who by his coat,
And by the hoarseness of his note,
   Might be supposed a crow;
A great frequenter of the church,
Where bishop-like he finds a perch,
   And dormitory too.

Above the steeple shines a plate,
That turns and turns, to indicate
   From what point blows the weather;
Look up—your brains begin to swim,
'Tis in the clouds—that pleases him,
   He chooses it the rather.

Fond of the speculative height,
Thither he wings his airy flight,
   And thence securely sees
The bustle and the raree-show,
That occupy mankind below,
   Secure and at his ease.

You think, no doubt, he sits and muses
On future broken bones and bruises,
   If he should chance to fall.
No: not a single thought like that
Employs his philosophic pate,
   Or troubles it at all.

He sees that this great roundabout,
The world, with all its medley rout,
   Church, army, physic, law,
Its customs, and its businesses,
Is no concern at all of his,
   And says—what says he?—"Caw."

Thrice happy bird! I too have seen
Much of the vanities of men;
   And, sick of having seen 'em,
Would cheerfully these limbs resign
For such a pair of wings as thine,
   And such a head between 'em.

                    From the Latin of Vincent Bourne,
                              by William Cowper

ODE TO A NIGHTINGALE

My heart aches, and a drowsy numbness pains
  My sense, as though of hemlock I had drunk,
Or emptied some dull opiate to the drains
  One minute past, and Lethe-wards had sunk:
'Tis not through envy of thy happy lot,
  But being too happy in thy happiness,—
    That thou, light-wingèd Dryad of the trees,
      In some melodious plot
  Of beechen green, and shadows numberless,
    Singest of summer in full-throated ease.

O for a draught of vintage, that hath been
  Cooled a long age in the deep-delvèd earth,
Tasting of Flora and the country green,
  Dance, and Provençal song, and sunburnt mirth!
O for a beaker full of the warm South,
  Full of the true, the blushful Hippocrene,
    With beaded bubbles winking at the brim,
      And purple-stainèd mouth;
  That I might drink, and leave the world unseen,
    And with thee fade away into the forest dim:

Fade far away, dissolve, and quite forget
  What thou among the leaves hast never known,
The weariness, the fever, and the fret,
  Here, where men sit and hear each other groan;
Where palsy shakes a few, sad, last gray hairs,
  Where youth grows pale, and specter-thin, and dies;
    Where but to think is to be full of sorrow
      And leaden-eyed despairs;
  Where Beauty cannot keep her lustrous eyes
    Or new Love pine at them beyond tomorrow.

Away! away! for I will fly to thee,
  Not charioted by Bacchus and his pards,

But on the viewless wings of Poesy,
  Though the dull brain perplexes and retards:
Already with thee! tender is the night,
    And haply the Queen-Moon is on her throne,
      Clustered around by all her starry Fays;
          But here there is no light,
      Save what from heaven is with the breezes blown
        Through verdurous glooms and winding mossy
          ways.

I cannot see what flowers are at my feet,
    Nor what soft incense hangs upon the boughs,
But, in embalmèd darkness, guess each sweet
    Wherewith the seasonable month endows
The grass, the thicket, and the fruit-tree wild;
    White hawthorn, and the pastoral eglantine;
      Fast-fading violets covered up in leaves;
          And mid-May's eldest child,
    The coming musk-rose, full of dewy wine,
      The murmurous haunt of flies on summer eves.

Darkling I listen; and, for many a time
    I have been half in love with easeful Death,
Called him soft names in many a musèd rhyme,
    To take into the air my quiet breath;
Now more than ever seems it rich to die,
    To cease upon the midnight with no pain,
      While thou art pouring forth thy soul abroad
          In such an ecstasy!
      Still wouldst thou sing, and I have ears in vain—
        To thy high requiem become a sod.

Thou wast not born for death, immortal Bird!
    No hungry generations tread thee down;
The voice I hear this passing night was heard
    In ancient days by emperor and clown:

Perhaps the self-same song that found a path
   Through the sad heart of Ruth, when, sick for home,
      She stood in tears amid the alien corn;
        The same that oft-times hath
   Charmed magic casements, opening on the foam
      Of perilous seas, in faery lands forlorn.

Forlorn! the very word is like a bell
   To toll me back from thee to my soul self!
Adieu! the fancy cannot cheat so well
   As she is famed to do, deceiving elf.
Adieu! adieu! thy plaintive anthem fades
   Past the near meadows, over the still stream,
      Up the hill-side; and now 'tis buried deep
        In the next valley-glades:
   Was it a vision, or a waking dream?
      Fled is that music:—Do I wake or sleep?

                      John Keats

SONG: THE OWL

When cats run home and light is come,
    And dew is cold upon the ground,
And the far-off stream is dumb,
    And the whirring sail goes round,
    And the whirring sail goes round;
Alone and warming his five wits,
The white owl in the belfry sits.

When merry milkmaids click the latch,
    And rarely smells the new-mown hay,
And the cock hath sung beneath the thatch
    Twice or thrice his roundelay,
    Twice or thrice his roundelay;
Alone and warming his five wits,
The white owl in the belfry sits.

                      Alfred Tennyson

ROBIN REDBREAST

Sweet Robin, I have heard them say
That thou wert there upon the day
The Christ was crowned in cruel scorn
And bore away one bleeding thorn,—
That so the blush upon thy breast,
In shameful sorrow, was impressed;
And thence thy genial sympathy
With our redeemed humanity.

Sweet Robin, would that I might be
Bathed in my Saviour's blood, like thee;
Bear in my breast, whate'er the loss,
The bleeding blazon of the cross;
Live ever, with thy loving mind,
In fellowship with human-kind;
And take my pattern still from thee,
In gentleness and constancy.

George Washington Doane

THE ROBIN

The robin is the one
That interrupts the morn
With hurried, few, express reports
When March is scarcely on.

The robin is the one
That overflows the noon
With her cherubic quantity,
And April but begun.

The robin is the one
That speechless from her nest

Submits that home and certainty
And sanctity are best.

Emily Dickinson

THE SANDPIPER

Across the narrow beach we flit,
  One little sandpiper and I,
And fast I gather, bit by bit,
  The scattered driftwood bleached and dry.
The wild waves reach their hands for it,
  The wild wind raves, the tide runs high,
As up and down the beach we flit,—
  One little sandpiper and I.

Above our heads the sullen clouds
  Scud black and swift across the sky;
Like silent ghosts in misty shrouds
  Stand out the white lighthouses high.
Almost as far as eye can reach
  I see the close-reefed vessels fly,
As fast we flit along the beach,—
  One little sandpiper and I.

I watch him as he skims along,
  Uttering his sweet and mournful cry.
He starts not at my fitful song,
  Or flash of fluttering drapery.
He has no thought of any wrong;
  He scans me with a fearless eye:
Staunch friends are we, well tried and strong,
  The little sandpiper and I.

Comrade, where wilt thou be to-night
  When the loosed storm breaks furiously?

My driftwood fire will burn so bright!
  To what warm shelter canst thou fly?
I do not fear for thee, though wroth
  The tempest rushes through the sky:
For are we not God's children both,
  Thou, little sandpiper, and I?

Celia Thaxter

TO A SKYLARK

Ethereal minstrel! pilgrim of the sky!
Dost thou despise the earth where cares abound?
Or, while the wings aspire, are heart and eye
Both with thy nest upon the dewy ground?
Thy nest which thou canst drop into at will,
Those quivering wings composed, that music still!

To the last point of vision, and beyond,
Mount, daring warbler!—that love-prompted strain
—'Twixt thee and thine a never-failing bond—
Thrills not the less the bosom of the plain:
Yet might'st thou seem, proud privilege! to sing
All independent of the leafy spring.

Leave to the nightingale her shady wood;
A privacy of glorious light is thine,
Whence thou dost pour upon the world a flood
Of harmony, with instinct more divine:
Type of the wise, who soar, but never roam—
True to the kindred points of Heaven and Home!

William Wordsworth

THE SKYLARK

Bird of the wilderness,
  Blithesome and cumberless,
Sweet be thy matin o'er moorland and lea!

Emblem of happiness,
Blest is thy dwelling-place—
O to abide in the desert with thee!

Wild is thy lay and loud,
Far in the downy cloud,
Love gives it energy, love gave it birth.
Where, on thy dewy wing,
Where art thou journeying?
Thy lay is in heaven, thy love is on earth.

O'er fell and fountain sheen,
O'er moor and mountain green,
O'er the red streamer that heralds the day,
Over the cloudlet dim,
Over the rainbow's rim,
Musical cherub, soar, singing, away!

Then, when the gloaming comes,
Low in the heather blooms
Sweet will thy welcome and bed of love be!
Emblem of happiness,
Blest is thy dwelling-place—
O to abide in the desert with thee!

James Hogg

TO A SKYLARK

Hail to thee, blithe spirit!
Bird thou never wert,
That from heaven, or near it,
Pourest thy full heart
In profuse strains of unpremeditated art.

Higher still and higher,
From the earth thou springest

Like a cloud of fire;
    The blue deep thou wingest,
And singing still dost soar, and soaring ever singest.

In the golden light'ning
    Of the sunken sun,
O'er which clouds are bright'ning,
    Thou dost float and run;
Like an unbodied joy whose race is just begun.

The pale purple even
    Melts around thy flight;
Like a star of heaven,
    In the broad daylight
Thou art unseen,—but yet I hear thy shrill delight,

Keen as are the arrows
    Of that silver sphere,
Whose intense lamp narrows
    In the white dawn clear,
Until we hardly see—we feel that it is there.

All the earth and air
    With thy voice is loud,
As, when night is bare,
    From one lonely cloud
The moon rains out her beams, and heaven is overflowed.

What thou art we know not;
    What is most like thee?
From rainbow-clouds there flow not
    Drops so bright to see
As from thy presence showers a rain of melody.

Like a Poet hidden
    In the light of thought,

Singing hymns unbidden
   Till the world is wrought
To sympathy with hopes and fears it heeded not:

   Like a high-born maiden
     In a palace-tower,
   Soothing her love-laden
     Soul in secret hour
With music sweet as love, which overflows her bower:

   Like a glow-worm golden
     In a dell of dew,
   Scattering unbeholden
     Its aërial hue
Among the flowers and grass, which screen it from the
   view:

   Like a rose embowered
     In its own green leaves,
   By warm winds deflowered,
     Till the scent it gives
Makes faint with too much sweet these heavy-wingèd
   thieves:

   Sound of vernal showers
     On the twinkling grass,
   Rain-awakened flowers,
     All that ever was
Joyous and clear and fresh, thy music doth surpass.

   Teach us, Sprite or Bird,
     What sweet thoughts are thine:
   I have never heard
     Praise of love or wine
That panted forth a flood of rapture so divine:

   Chorus hymeneal,
     Or triumphal chaunt,

Matched with thine would be all
     But an empty vaunt,
A thing wherein we feel there is some hidden want.

     What objects are the fountains
          Of thy happy strain?
     What fields, or waves, or mountains?
          What shapes of sky or plain?
What love of thine own kind? what ignorance of pain?

     With thy clear keen joyance
          Languor cannot be:
     Shadow of annoyance
          Never came near thee:
Thou lovest—but ne'er knew love's sad satiety.

     Waking or asleep
          Thou of death must deem
     Things more true and deep
          Than we mortals dream,
Or how could thy notes flow in such a crystal stream?

     We look before and after,
          And pine for what is not:
     Our sincerest laughter
          With some pain is fraught;
Our sweetest songs are those that tell of saddest thought.

     Yet, if we could scorn
          Hate, and pride, and fear;
     If we were things born
          Not to shed a tear,
I know not how thy joy we ever should come near.

     Better than all measures
          Of delightful sound—

Better than all treasures
That in books are found,
Thy skill to poet were, thou scorner of the ground!

Teach me half the gladness
That thy brain must know,
Such harmonious madness
From my lips would flow,
The world should listen then—as I am listening now.

Percy Bysshe Shelley

THE THROSTLE

"Summer is coming, summer is coming,
I know it, I know it, I know it.
Light again, leaf again, life again, love again,"
Yes, my wild little Poet.

Sing the new year in under the blue.
Last year you sang it as gladly.
"New, new, new, new!" Is it then *so* new
That you should carol so madly?

"Love again, song again, nest again, young again,"
Never a prophet so crazy!
And hardly a daisy as yet, little friend,
See, there is hardly a daisy.

"Here again, here, here, here, happy year!"
O warble unchidden, unbidden!
Summer is coming, is coming, my dear,
And all the winters are hidden.

Alfred Tennyson

CHANTICLEER

Of all the birds from East to West
  That tuneful are and dear,
I love that farmyard bird the best,
  They call him Chanticleer.

Gold plume and copper plume,
  Comb of scarlet gay;
'Tis he that scatters night and gloom,
  And whistles back the day!

He is the sun's brave herald
  That, ringing his blithe horn,
Calls round a world dew-pearled
  The heavenly airs of morn.

O clear gold, shrill and bold!
  He calls through creeping mist
The mountains from the night and cold
  To rose and amethyst.

He sets the birds to singing,
  And calls the flowers to rise;
The morning cometh, bringing
  Sweet sleep to heavy eyes.

Gold plume and silver plume,
  Comb of coral gay;
'Tis he packs off the night and gloom,
  And summons home the day!

Black fear he sends it flying,
  Black care he drives afar;
And creeping shadows sighing
  Before the morning star.

The birds of all the forest
  Have dear and pleasant cheer,
But yet I hold the rarest
  The farmyard Chanticleer.

Red cock or black cock,
  Gold cock or white,
The flower of all the feathered flock,
  He whistles back the light!
                    Katharine Tynan Hinkson

FIREFLIES

Little lamps of the dusk,
  You fly low and gold
When the summer evening
  Starts to unfold,
So that all the insects,
  Now, before you pass,
Will have light to see by
  Undressing in the grass.

But when night has flowered
  Little lamps a-gleam,
You fly over tree-tops
  Following a dream.
Men wonder from their windows
  That a firefly goes so far—
They do not know your longing
  To be a shooting star.
                    Carolyn Hall

A WET SHEET AND A FLOWING SEA

A wet sheet and a flowing sea,
  A wind that follows fast,

And fills the white and rustling sail,
  And bends the gallant mast;
And bends the gallant mast, my boys,
  While, like the eagle free,
Away the good ship flies, and leaves
  Old England on the lee.

O for a soft and gentle wind!
  I heard a fair one cry;
But give to me the snoring breeze
  And white waves heaving high;
And white waves heaving high, my boys,
  The good ship tight and free—
The world of waters is our home,
  And merry men are we.

There's tempest in yon hornèd moon,
  And lightning in yon cloud;
And hark the music, mariners!
  The wind is piping loud;
The wind is piping loud, my boys,
  The lightning flashes free—
While the hollow oak our palace is,
  Our heritage the sea.

                                Allan Cunningham

THE SEA

The sea! the sea! the open sea!
The blue, the fresh, the ever free!
Without a mark, without a bound,
It runneth the earth's wide regions round;
It plays with the clouds; it mocks the skies;
Or like a cradled creature lies.

I'm on the sea! I'm on the sea!
I am where I would ever be;

With the blue above, and the blue below,
And silence wheresoe'er I go;
If a storm should come and awake the deep,
What matter? *I* shall ride and sleep.

I love, O, how I love to ride
On the fierce, foaming, bursting tide,
When every mad wave drowns the moon
Or whistles aloft his tempest tune,
And tells how goeth the world below,
And why the sou'west blasts do blow.

I never was on the dull, tame shore,
But I loved the great sea more and more,
And backwards flew to her billowy breast,
Like a bird that seeketh its mother's nest;
And a mother she *was*, and *is*, to me;
For I was born on the open sea!

The waves were white, and red the morn,
In the noisy hour when I was born;
And the whale it whistled, the porpoise rolled,
And the dolphins bared their backs of gold;
And never was heard such an outcry wild
As welcomed to life the ocean-child!

I've lived since then, in calm and strife,
Full fifty summers, a sailor's life,
With wealth to spend and power to range,
But never have sought nor sighed for change;
And Death, whenever he comes to me,
Shall come on the wild, unbounded sea!

Bryan Waller Procter

HOMEWARD BOUND

Head the ship for England!
Shake out every sail!

Blithe leap the billows,
   Merry sings the gale.
Captain, work the reckoning;
   How many knots a day?—
Round the world and home again,
   That's the sailor's way!

We've traded with the Yankees,
   Brazilians and Chinese;
We've laughed with dusky beauties
   In shade of tall palm-trees;
Across the line and Gulf-Stream—
   Round by Table Bay—
Everywhere and home again,
   That's the sailor's way!

Nightly stands the North Star
   Higher on our bow;
Straight we run for England;
   Our thoughts are in it now.
Jolly times with friends ashore,
   When we've drawn our pay!—
All about and home again,
   That's the sailor's way!

William Allingham

SONG FOR ALL SEAS, ALL SHIPS

I

To-day a rude brief recitative,
Of ships sailing the seas, each with its special flag or ship-
      signal,
Of unnamed heroes in the ships—of waves spreading and
      spreading far as the eye can reach,
Of dashing spray, and the winds piping and blowing,
And out of these a chant for the sailors of all nations,
Fitful, like a surge.

Of sea-captains young or old, and the mates, and of all in-
trepid sailors,
Of the few, very choice, taciturn, whom fate can never
surprise nor death dismay,
Picked sparingly without noise by thee, old ocean, chosen
by thee,
Thou sea that pickest and cullest the race in time, and
unitest nations,
Suckled by thee, old husky nurse, embodying thee,
Indomitable, untamed as thee.

(Ever the heroes on water or on land, by ones or twos ap-
pearing,
Ever the stock preserved and never lost, though rare,
enough for seed preserved.)

II

Flaunt out, O sea, your separate flags of nations!
Flaunt out visible as ever the various ship-signals!
But do you reserve especially for yourself and for the soul
of man one flag above all the rest,
A spiritual woven signal for all nations, emblem of man
elate above death,
Token of all brave captains and all intrepid sailors and
mates,
And all that went down doing their duty,
Reminiscent of them, twined from all intrepid captains
young or old,
A pennant universal, subtly waving all time, o'er all brave
sailors,
All seas, all ships.   *Walt Whitman*

THE LITTLE WAVES OF BREFFNY

The grand road from the mountain goes shining to the sea,
  And there is traffic in it, and many a horse and cart;

But the little roads of Cloonagh are dearer far to me,
    And the little roads of Cloonagh go rambling through
      my heart.

A great storm from the ocean goes shouting o'er the hill,
    And there is glory in it, and terror on the wind;
But the haunted air of twilight is very strange and still,
    And the little winds of twilight are dearer to my mind.

The great waves of the Atlantic sweep storming on their
      way,
    Shining green and silver with the hidden herring shoal;
But the little waves of Breffny have drenched my heart in
      spray,
    And the little waves of Breffny go stumbling through
      my soul.

Eva Gore-Booth

THE SEA GIPSY

I am fevered with the sunset,
I am fretful with the bay,
For the wander-thirst is on me
And my soul is in Cathay.

There's a schooner in the offing,
With her topsails shot with fire,
And my heart has gone aboard her
For the Islands of Desire.

I must forth again to-morrow!
With the sunset I must be
Hull down on the trail of rapture
In the wonder of the Sea.

Richard Hovey

SEA FEVER

I must go down to the seas again, to the lonely sea and the
    sky,
And all I ask is a tall ship and a star to steer her by;
And the wheel's kick and the wind's song and the white
    sail's shaking,
And the gray mist on the sea's face, and a gray dawn
    breaking.

I must go down to the seas again, for the call of the run-
    ning tide
Is a wild call and a clear call that may not be denied;
And all I ask is a windy day with the white clouds flying,
And the flung spray and the blown spume, and the sea-
    gulls crying.

I must go down to the seas again, to the vagrant gipsy life,
To the gull's way and the whale's way where the wind's
    like a whetted knife;
And all I ask is a merry yarn from a laughing fellow-rover,
And a quiet sleep and a sweet dream when the long trick's
    over.

John Masefield

THE VAGABOND

Give to me the life I love,
  Let the lave go by me,
Give the jolly heaven above
  And the byway nigh me.
Bed in the bush with stars to see,
  Bread I dip in the river—
There's the life for a man like me,
  There's the life for ever.

Or let autumn fall on me
 Where afield I linger,
Silencing the bird on tree,
 Biting the blue finger.
White as meal the frosty field—
 Warm the fireside haven—
Not to autumn will I yield,
 Not to winter even!

Let the blow fall soon or late,
 Let what will be o'er me;
Give the face of earth around,
 And the road before me.
Wealth I ask not, hope nor love,
 Nor a friend to know me;
All I ask, the heaven above
 And the road below me.

Robert Louis Stevenson

OVER THE HILLS AND FAR AWAY

Where forlorn sunsets flare and fade
 On desolate sea and lonely sand,
Out of the silence and the shade
 What is the voice of strange command
Calling you still, as friend calls friend
 With love that cannot brook delay,
To rise and follow the ways that wend
 Over the hills and far away?

Hark in the city, street on street
 A roaring reach of death and life,
Of vortices that clash and fleet
 And ruin in appointed strife,
Hark to it calling, calling clear,
 Calling until you cannot stay

From dearer things than your own most dear
  Over the hills and far away.

Out of the sound of the ebb-and-flow,
  Out of the sight of lamp and star,
It calls you where the good winds blow,
  And the unchanging meadows are:
From faded hopes and hopes agleam,
  It calls you, calls you night and day
Beyond the dark into the dream
  Over the hills and far away.

William Ernest Henley

AFOOT AND LIGHT-HEARTED

From "Song of the Open Road"

Afoot and light-hearted I take to the open road,
Healthy, free, the world before me,
The long brown path before me leading wherever I choose.

Henceforth I ask not good-fortune, I myself am good-for-
    tune,
Henceforth I whimper no more, postpone no more, need
    nothing,
Done with indoor complaints, libraries, querulous criticisms,
Strong and content I travel the open road.

Walt Whitman

THE JOYS OF THE ROAD

Now the joys of the road are chiefly these:
A crimson touch on the hard-wood trees;

A vagrant's morning wide and blue,
In early fall, when the wind walks, too;

A shadowy highway cool and brown
Alluring up and enticing down

From rippled water to dappled swamp,
From purple glory to scarlet pomp;

The outward eye, the quiet will,
And the striding heart from hill to hill;

The tempter apple over the fence;
The cobweb bloom on the yellow quince;

The palish asters along the wood,—
A lyric touch of the solitude;

An open hand, an easy shoe,
And a hope to make the day go through,—

Another to sleep with, and a third
To wake me up at the voice of a bird;

The resonant far-listening morn,
And the hoarse whisper of the corn;

The crickets mourning their comrades lost,
In the night's retreat from the gathering frost;

(Or is it their slogan, plaintive and shrill,
As they beat on their corselets, valiant still?)

A hunger fit for the kings of the sea,
And a loaf of bread for Dickon and me;

A thirst like that of the Thirsty Sword,
And a jug of cider on the board;

An idle noon, a bubbling spring,
The sea in the pine-tops murmuring;

A scrap of gossip at the ferry;
A comrade neither glum nor merry,

Asking nothing, revealing naught,
But minting his words from a fund of thought,

A keeper of silence eloquent,
Needy, yet royally well content,

Of the mettled breed, yet abhorring strife,
And full of the mellow juice of life,

No fidget and no reformer, just
A calm observer of ought and must,

A lover of books, but a reader of man,
No cynic and no charlatan,

Who never defers and never demands,
But, smiling, takes the world in his hands,—

Seeing it good as when God first saw
And gave it the weight of His will for law.

And O the joy that is never won,
But follows and follows the journeying sun,

By marsh and tide, by meadow and stream,
A will-o'-the-wind, a light-o'-dream,

Delusion afar, delight anear,
From morrow to morrow, from year to year,

A jack-o'-lantern, a fairy fire,
A dare, a bliss, and a desire!

The racy smell of the forest loam,
When the stealthy, sad-heart leaves go home;

(O leaves, O leaves, I am one with you,
Of the mould and the sun and the wind and the dew!)

The broad gold wake of the afternoon;
The silent fleck of the cold new moon;

The sound of the hollow sea's release
From stormy tumult to starry peace;

With only another league to wend;
And two brown arms at the journey's end!

These are the joys of the open road—
For him who travels without a load.

Bliss Carman

VIII. Stories in Rhyme

THE LAND OF STORY-BOOKS

At evening when the lamp is lit,
Around the fire my parents sit;
They sit at home and talk and sing,
And do not play at anything.

Now, with my little gun, I crawl
All in the dark along the wall,
And follow round the forest track
Away behind the sofa back.

There, in the night, where none can spy,
All in my hunter's camp I lie,
And play at books that I have read
Till it is time to go to bed.

These are the hills, these are the woods,
These are my starry solitudes;
And there the river by whose brink
The roaring lions come to drink.

I see the others far away
As if in firelit camp they lay,
And I, like to an Indian scout,
Around their party prowled about,

So, when my nurse comes in for me,
Home I return across the sea,
And go to bed with backward looks
At my dear land of Story-books.

Robert Louis Stevenson

STORIES IN RHYME

GOD'S JUDGMENT ON A WICKED BISHOP

The summer and autumn had been so wet,
That in winter the corn was growing yet;
'Twas a piteous sight to see, all around,
The grain lie rotting on the ground.

Every day the starving poor
Crowded around Bishop Hatto's door;
For he had a plentiful last-year's store,
And all the neighborhood could tell
His granaries were furnished well.

At last Bishop Hatto appointed a day
To quiet the poor without delay;
He bade them to his great barn repair,
And they should have food for the winter there.

Rejoiced such tidings good to hear,
The poor folk flocked from far and near;
The great barn was full as it could hold
Of women and children, and young and old.

Then, when he saw it could hold no more,
Bishop Hatto he made fast the door;
And, while for mercy on Christ they call,
He set fire to the barn, and burnt them all.

"I' faith, 'tis an excellent bonfire!" quoth he;
"And the country is greatly obliged to me
For ridding it, in these times forlorn,
Of rats that only consume the corn."

So then to his palace returnèd he,
And he sat down to supper merrily,
And he slept that night like an innocent man;
But Bishop Hatto never slept again.

In the morning, as he entered the hall,
Where his picture hung against the wall,
A sweat like death all over him came,
For the rats had eaten it out of the frame.

As he looked, there came a man from his farm,—
He had a countenance white with alarm:
"My Lord, I opened your granaries this morn,
And the rats had eaten all your corn."

Another came running presently,
And he was pale as pale could be.
"Fly! my Lord Bishop, fly!" quoth he,
"Ten thousand rats are coming this way,—
The Lord forgive you for yesterday!"

"I'll go to my tower in the Rhine," replied he;
" 'Tis the safest place in Germany,—
The walls are high, and the shores are steep,
And the tide is strong, and the water deep."

Bishop Hatto fearfully hastened away,
And he crossed the Rhine without delay,
And reached his tower, and barred with care
All the windows, and doors, and loop-holes there.

He laid him down and closed his eyes,
But soon a scream made him arise;
He started, and saw two eyes of flame
On his pillow, from whence the screaming came.

He listened and looked,—it was only the cat;
But the Bishop he grew more fearful for that,
For she sat screaming, mad with fear,
At the army of rats that were drawing near.

For they have swum over the river so deep,
And they have climbed the shores so steep,
And now by thousands up they crawl
To the holes and the windows in the wall.

Down on his knees the Bishop fell,
And faster and faster his beads did he tell,
As, louder and louder, drawing near,
The gnawing of their teeth he could hear.

And in at the windows, and in at the door,
And through the walls helter-skelter they pour;
And down from the ceiling and up through the floor,
From the right and the left, from behind and before,
From within and without, from above and below,—
And all at once to the Bishop they go.

They have whetted their teeth against the stones,
And now they pick the Bishop's bones;
They gnawed the flesh from every limb,
For they were sent to do judgment on him!

Robert Southey

THE INCHCAPE ROCK

No stir in the air, no stir in the sea,
The ship was still as she could be;
Her sails from heaven received no motion,
Her keel was steady in the ocean.

Without either sign or sound of their shock,
The waves flowed over the Inchcape Rock;

So little they rose, so little they fell,
They did not move the Inchcape Bell.

The holy Abbot of Aberbrothok
Had placed that bell on the Inchcape Rock;
On a buoy in the storm it floated and swung,
And over the waves its warning rung.

When the rock was hid by the surge's swell,
The mariners heard the warning Bell;
And then they knew the perilous Rock,
And blessed the Abbot of Aberbrothok.

The Sun in heaven was shining gay,
All things were joyful on that day;
The sea-birds screamed as they wheeled around,
And there was joyance in their sound.

The buoy of the Inchcape Bell was seen,
A darker speck on the ocean green;
Sir Ralph, the Rover, walked his deck,
And he fixed his eye on the darker speck.

He felt the cheering power of spring,
It made him whistle, it made him sing;
His heart was mirthful to excess;
But the Rover's mirth was wickedness.

His eye was on the Inchcape float;
Quoth he, "My men, put out the boat;
And row me to the Inchcape Rock,
And I'll plague the Abbot of Aberbrothok."

The boat is lowered, the boatmen row,
And to the Inchcape Rock they go;
Sir Ralph bent over from the boat,
And cut the Bell from the Inchcape float.

Down sank the Bell with a gurgling sound;
The bubbles rose, and burst around.
Quoth Sir Ralph, "The next who comes to the Rock
Won't bless the Abbot of Aberbrothok."

Sir Ralph, the Rover, sailed away,
He scoured the seas for many a day;
And now, grown rich with plundered store,
He steers his course for Scotland's shore.

So thick a haze o'erspreads the sky
They cannot see the Sun on high;
The wind hath blown a gale all day;
At evening it hath died away.

On the deck the Rover takes his stand;
So dark it is they see no land.
Quoth Sir Ralph, "It will be lighter soon,
For there is the dawn of the rising moon."

"Canst hear," said one, "the breakers roar?
For yonder, methinks, should be the shore."
"Now where we are I cannot tell,
But I wish I could hear the Inchcape Bell."

They hear no sound; the swell is strong;
Though the wind hath fallen, they drift along,
Till the vessel strikes with a shivering shock,—
"O Christ! it is the Inchcape Rock!"

Sir Ralph, the Rover, tore his hair;
He cursed himself in his despair.
The waves rush in on every side;
The ship is sinking beneath the tide.

But, even in his dying fear,
One dreadful sound could the Rover hear,—

A sound as if, with the Inchcape Bell,
The Devil below was ringing his knell.

Robert Southey

LORD ULLIN'S DAUGHTER

A chieftain, to the Highlands bound,
    Cries, "Boatman, do not tarry!
And I'll give thee a silver pound,
    To row us o'er the ferry."

"Now who be ye, would cross Lochgyle,
    This dark and stormy water?"
"O, I'm the chief of Ulva's Isle,
    And this Lord Ullin's daughter.

"And fast before her father's men
    Three days we've fled together,
For should he find us in the glen,
    My blood would stain the heather.

"His horsemen hard behind us ride;
    Should they our steps discover,
Then who will cheer my bonny bride
    When they have slain her lover?"

Outspoke the hardy Highland wight,
    "I'll go, my chief,—I'm ready:—
It is not for your silver bright;
    But for your winsome lady:

"And by my word! the bonny bird
    In danger shall not tarry:
So, though the waves are raging white,
    I'll row you o'er the ferry."

By this the storm grew loud apace,
  The water-wraith was shrieking;
And in the scowl of heaven each face
  Grew dark as they were speaking.

But still as wilder blew the wind,
  And as the night grew drearer,
Adown the glen rode armèd men,—
  Their trampling sounded nearer.

"O, haste thee, haste!" the lady cries,
  "Though tempests round us gather;
I'll meet the raging of the skies,
  But not an angry father."

The boat has left a stormy land,
  A stormy sea before her,—
When, O, too strong for human hand,
  The tempest gathered o'er her.

And still they rowed amidst the roar
  Of waters fast prevailing:
Lord Ullin reached that fatal shore,—
  His wrath was changed to wailing.

For sore dismayed, through storm and shade,
  His child he did discover:
One lovely hand she stretched for aid,
  And one was round her lover.

"Come back! come back!" he cried in grief,
  "Across this stormy water:
And I'll forgive your Highland chief,
  My daughter!—O my daughter!"

'Twas vain;—the loud waves lashed the shore,
    Return or aid preventing;—
The waters wild went o'er his child,
    And he was left lamenting.
                                    Thomas Campbell

THE PIED PIPER OF HAMELIN

Hamelin Town's in Brunswick,
By famous Hanover city;
    The river Weser, deep and wide,
    Washes its wall on the southern side;
    A pleasanter spot you never spied;
But, when begins my ditty,
    Almost five hundred years ago,
    To see the townsfolk suffer so
From vermin was a pity.

    Rats!
They fought the dogs and killed the cats,
    And bit the babies in the cradles,
And ate the cheeses out of the vats,
    And licked the soup from the cooks' own ladles,
Split open the kegs of salted sprats,
Made nests inside men's Sunday hats,
And even spoiled the women's chats
    By drowning their speaking
    With shrieking and squeaking
In fifty different sharps and flats.

At last the people in a body
    To the Town Hall came flocking:
" 'Tis clear," cried they, "our Mayor's a noddy;
    And as for our Corporation,—shocking
To think we buy gowns lined with ermine
For dolts that can't or won't determine

What's best to rid us of our vermin!
You hope, because you're old and obese,
To find in the furry civic robe ease?
Rouse up, sirs! Give your brains a racking,
To find the remedy we're lacking,
Or, sure as fate, we'll send you packing!"
At this the Mayor and Corporation
Quaked with a mighty consternation.

An hour they sat in council,—
    At length the Mayor broke silence:
"For a guilder I'd my ermine gown sell;
    I wish I were a mile hence!
It's easy to bid one rack one's brain,—
I'm sure my poor head aches again,
I've scratched it so, and all in vain.
Oh for a trap, a trap, a trap!"
Just as he said this, what should hap
At the chamber-door but a gentle tap?
"Bless us," cried the Mayor, "what's that?"
(With the Corporation as he sat,
Looking little though wondrous fat;
Nor brighter was his eye, nor moister
Than a too-long-opened oyster,
Save when at noon his paunch grew mutinous
For a plate of turtle green and glutinous)
"Only a scraping of shoes on the mat?
Anything like the sound of a rat
Makes my heart go pit-a-pat!"

"Come in!" the Mayor cried, looking bigger:
And in did come the strangest figure!
His queer long coat from heel to head
Was half of yellow and half of red,
And he himself was tall and thin,
With sharp blue eyes, each like a pin,

And light loose hair, yet swarthy skin,
No tuft on cheek nor beard on chin,
But lips where smiles went out and in;
There was no guessing his kith and kin:
And nobody could enough admire
The tall man and his quaint attire.
Quoth one: "It's as my great-grandsire,
Starting up at the Trump of Doom's tone,
Had walked this way from his painted tombstone!"

He advanced to the council-table:
And, "Please your honors," said he, "I'm able,
By means of a secret charm, to draw
All creatures living beneath the sun,
That creep or swim or fly or run,
After me so as you never saw!
And I chiefly use my charm
On creatures that do people harm,
The mole and toad and newt and viper;
And people call me the Pied Piper."
(And here they noticed round his neck
A scarf of red and yellow stripe,
To match with his coat of the self-same check,
And at the scarf's end hung a pipe;
And his fingers, they noticed, were ever straying
As if impatient to be playing
Upon this pipe, as low it dangled
Over his vesture so old-fangled.)
"Yet," said he, "poor piper as I am,
In Tartary I freed the Cham,
Last June, from his huge swarms of gnats;
I eased in Asia the Nizam
Of a monstrous brood of vampire-bats;
And as for what your brain bewilders,—
If I can rid your town of rats,
Will you give me a thousand guilders?"

"One? fifty thousand!" was the exclamation
Of the astonished Mayor and Corporation.

Into the street the Piper stepped,
    Smiling first a little smile,
As if he knew what magic slept
    In his quiet pipe the while;
Then, like a musical adept,
To blow the pipe his lips he wrinkled,
And green and blue his sharp eyes twinkled,
Like a candle-flame where salt is sprinkled;
And ere three shrill notes the pipe uttered,
You heard as if an army muttered;
And the muttering grew to a grumbling;
And the grumbling grew to a mighty rumbling;
And out of the houses the rats came tumbling.
Great rats, small rats, lean rats, brawny rats,
Brown rats, black rats, gray rats, tawny rats,
Grave old plodders, gay young friskers,
    Fathers, mothers, uncles, cousins,
Cocking tails and pricking whiskers;
    Families by tens and dozens,
Brothers, sisters, husbands, wives,—
Followed the Piper for their lives.
From street to street he piped advancing,
And step for step they followed dancing,
Until they came to the river Weser,
Wherein all plunged and perished!
—Save one who, stout as Julius Cæsar,
Swam across and lived to carry
(As he, the manuscript he cherished)
To Rat-land home his commentary,
Which was: "At the first shrill notes of the pipe,
I heard a sound as of scraping tripe,
And putting apples, wondrous ripe,
Into a cider-press's gripe,—

And a moving away of pickle-tub-boards,
And a leaving ajar of conserve-cupboards,
And a drawing the corks of train-oil-flasks,
And a breaking the hoops of butter-casks;
And it seemed as if a voice
(Sweeter far than by harp or by psaltery
Is breathed) called out, 'Oh rats, rejoice!
The world is grown to one vast drysaltery!
So munch on, crunch on, take your nuncheon!
Breakfast, supper, dinner, luncheon!'
And just as a bulky sugar-puncheon,
All ready staved, like a great sun shone
Glorious scarce an inch before me,
Just as methought it said, 'Come, bore me!'—
I found the Weser rolling o'er me."

You should have heard the Hamelin people
Ringing the bells till they rocked the steeple.
"Go," cried the Mayor, "and get long poles!
Poke out the nests and block up the holes!
Consult with carpenters and builders,
And leave in our town not even a trace
Of the rats!"—when suddenly, up the face
Of the Piper perked in the market-place,
With a "First, if you please, my thousand guilders!"

A thousand guilders! The Mayor looked blue;
So did the Corporation too.
For council-dinners made rare havoc
With Claret, Moselle, Vin-de-Grave, Hock;
And half the money would replenish
Their cellar's biggest butt with Rhenish.
To pay this sum to a wandering fellow
With a gypsy coat of red and yellow!
"Beside," quoth the Mayor, with a knowing wink,
"Our business was done at the river's brink;

We saw with our eyes the vermin sink,
And what's dead can't come to life, I think.
So, friend, we're not the folks to shrink
From the duty of giving you something for drink,
And a matter of money to put in your poke;
But as for the guilders, what we spoke
Of them, as you very well know, was in joke.
Beside, our losses have made us thrifty;
A thousand guilders! Come, take fifty!"

The Piper's face fell, and he cried,
"No trifling! I can't wait, beside!
I've promised to visit by dinner time
Bagdat, and accept the prime
Of the Head Cook's pottage, all he's rich in,
For having left, in the Caliph's kitchen,
Of a nest of scorpions no survivor:
With him I proved no bargain-driver;
With you, don't think I'll bate a stiver!
And folks who put me in a passion
May find me pipe after another fashion."

"How?" cried the Mayor, "d'ye think I brook
Being worse treated than a Cook?
Insulted by a lazy ribald
With idle pipe and vesture piebald?
You threaten us, fellow? Do your worst,
Blow your pipe there till you burst!"

Once more he stepped into the street;
    And to his lips again
    Laid his long pipe of smooth straight cane;
And ere he blew three notes (such sweet
Soft notes as yet musician's cunning
Never gave the enraptured air)

There was a rustling that seemed like a bustling
Of merry crowds justling at pitching and hustling;
Small feet were pattering, wooden shoes clattering,
Little hands clapping, and little tongues chattering;
And, like fowls in a farm-yard when barley is scattering,
Out came the children running:
All the little boys and girls,
With rosy cheeks and flaxen curls,
And sparkling eyes and teeth like pearls,
Tripping and skipping, ran merrily after
The wonderful music with shouting and laughter.

The mayor was dumb, and the Council stood
As if they were changed into blocks of wood,
Unable to move a step, or cry
To the children merrily skipping by,—
Could only follow with the eye
That joyous crowd at the Piper's back.
But how the Mayor was on the rack,
And the wretched Council's bosoms beat,
As the Piper turned from the High Street
To where the Weser rolled its waters
Right in the way of their sons and daughters!
However, he turned from South to West,
And to Koppelberg Hill his steps addressed,
And after him the children pressed;
Great was the joy in every breast.
"He never can cross that mighty top!
He's forced to let the piping drop,
And we shall see our children stop!"
When, lo, as they reached the mountain-side,
A wondrous portal opened wide,
As if a cavern was suddenly hollowed;
And the Piper advanced and the children followed;
And when all were in, to the very last,
The door in the mountain-side shut fast.

Did I say, all? No! One was lame,
And could not dance the whole of the way;
And in after years, if you would blame
His sadness, he was used to say,—
"It's dull in our town since my playmates left!
I can't forget that I'm bereft
Of all the pleasant sights they see,
Which the Piper also promised me;
For he led us, he said, to a joyous land,
Joining the town and just at hand,
Where waters gushed, and fruit-trees grew,
And flowers put forth a fairer hue,
And everything was strange and new;
The sparrows were brighter than peacocks here,
And their dogs outran our fallow deer,
And honey-bees had lost their stings,
And horses were born with eagles' wings;
And just as I became assured
My lame foot would be speedily cured,
The music stopped and I stood still,
And found myself outside the hill,
Left alone against my will,
To go now limping as before,
And never hear of that country more!"

Alas, alas for Hamelin!
   There came into many a burgher's pate
   A text which says that heaven's gate
   Opes to the rich at as easy rate
As the needle's eye takes a camel in!
The Mayor sent East, West, North and South,
   To offer the Piper, by word of mouth,
   Wherever it was men's lot to find him,
Silver and gold to his heart's content,
If he'd only return the way he went,
   And bring the children behind him.

But when they saw 'twas a lost endeavor,
And Piper and dancers were gone forever,
They made a decree that lawyers never
  Should think their records dated duly
If, after the day of the month and year,
These words did not as well appear,
"And so long after what happened here
  On the Twenty-second of July,
Thirteen hundred and seventy-six:"
And the better in memory to fix
The place of the children's last retreat,
They called it, the Pied Piper's Street—
Where any one playing on pipe or tabor
Was sure for the future to lose his labor.
Nor suffered they hostlery or tavern
  To shock with mirth a street so solemn,
But opposite the place of the cavern
  They wrote the story on a column,
And on the great church-window painted
The same, to make the world acquainted
How their children were stolen away,
And there it stands to this very day.
And I must not omit to say
That in Transylvania there's a tribe
Of alien people who ascribe
The outlandish ways and dress
On which their neighbors lay such stress,
To their fathers and mothers having risen
Out of some subterraneous prison
Into which they were trepanned
Long time ago in a mighty band
Out of Hamelin town in Brunswick land,
But how or why, they don't understand.

So, Willy, let me and you be wipers
Of scores out with all men—especially pipers!

And, whether they pipe us free fróm rats or fróm mice,
If we've promised them aught, let us keep our promise!

Robert Browning

HERVÉ RIEL

On the sea and at the Hogue, sixteen hundred ninety-two,
  Did the English fight the French,—woe to France!
And, the thirty-first of May, helter-skelter through the
    blue,
Like a crowd of frightened porpoises a shoal of sharks pur-
    sue,
  Came crowding ship on ship to Saint Malo on the Rance,
With the English fleet in view.

'Twas the squadron that escaped, with the victor in full
    chase;
  First and foremost of the drove, in his great ship, Dam-
    freville;
    Close on him fled, great and small,
    Twenty-two good ships in all;
And they signalled to the place
"Help the winners of a race!
  Get us guidance, give us harbor, take us quick—or,
    quicker still,
  Here's the English can and will!"

Then the pilots of the place put out brisk and leapt on
    board;
  "Why, what hope or chance have ships like these to
    pass?" laughed they:
"Rocks to starboard, rocks to port, all the passage scarred
    and scored,
Shall the *Formidable* here, with her twelve-and-eighty guns,
  Think to make the river-mouth by the single narrow
    way,

Trust to enter where 'tis ticklish for a craft of twenty tons,
  And with flow at full beside?
  Now, 'tis slackest ebb of tide.
  Reach the mooring? Rather say,
While rock stands or water runs,
  Not a ship will leave the bay!"

Then was called a council straight.
Brief and bitter the debate:
"Here's the English at our heels; would you have them
  take in tow
All that's left us of the fleet, linked together stern and bow,
For a prize to Plymouth Sound?
Better run the ships aground!"
 (Ended Damfreville his speech).
"Not a minute more to wait!
  Let the captains all and each
  Shove ashore, then blow up, burn the vessels on the
  beach!
France must undergo her fate.

"Give the word!" But no such word
Was ever spoke or heard;
For up stood, for out stepped, for in struck amid all these
—A Captain? A Lieutenant? A Mate—first, second,
  third?
  No such man of mark, and meet
  With his betters to compete!
  But a simple Breton sailor pressed by Tourville for the
  fleet,
A poor coasting pilot he, Hervé Riel the Croisickese.

And "What mockery or malice have we here?" cries Hervé
  Riel:
"Are you mad, you Malouins? Are you cowards, fools, or
  rogues?

Talk to me of rocks and shoals, me who took the soundings,
    tell
On my fingers every bank, every shallow, every swell
  'Twixt the offing here and Grève where the river disem-
    bogues?
Are you bought by English gold? Is it love the lying's
    for?
    Morn and eve, night and day,
    Have I piloted your bay,
Entered free and anchored fast at the foot of Solidor.
  Burn the fleet and ruin France? That were worse than
    fifty Hogues!
    Sirs, they know I speak the truth! Sirs, believe me
    there's a way!
Only let me lead the line,
  Have the biggest ship to steer,
  Get this *Formidable* clear,
Make the others follow mine,
And I lead them, most and least, by a passage I know well,
  Right to Solidor past Grève,
    And there lay them safe and sound;
  And if one ship misbehave,—
    —Keel so much as grate the ground,
Why, I've nothing but my life,—here's my head!" cries
    Hervé Riel.

Not a minute more to wait.
"Steer us in, then, small and great!
  Take the helm, lead the line, save the squadron!" cried
    its chief.
Captains, give the sailor place!
  He is Admiral, in brief.
Still the north-wind, by God's grace!
See the noble fellow's face
As the big ship, with a bound,
Clears the entry like a hound,

Keeps the passage, as its inch of way were the wide seas
     profound!
  See, safe through shoal and rock,
  How they follow in a flock,
Not a ship that misbehaves, not a keel that grates the
     ground,
  Not a spar that comes to grief!
The peril, see, is past.
All are harbored to the last,
And just as Hervé Riel hollas "Anchor!"—sure as fate,
Up the English come,—too late!

So, the storm subsides to calm:
  They see the green trees wave
  On the heights o'erlooking Grève.
Hearts that bled are stanched with balm.
"Just our rapture to enhance,
  Let the English rake the bay,
Gnash their teeth and glare askance
  As they cannonade away!
'Neath rampired Solidor pleasant riding on the Rance!"
How hope succeeds despair on each Captain's counte-
     nance!
Out burst all with one accord,
  "This is Paradise for Hell!
    Let France, let France's King
    Thank the man that did the thing!"
What a shout, and all one word,
  "Hervé Riel!"
As he stepped in front once more,
  Not a symptom of surprise
  In the frank blue Breton eyes,
Just the same man as before.

Then said Damfreville, "My friend,
I must speak out at the end,

Though I find the speaking hard.
Praise is deeper than the lips:
You have saved the King his ships,
　You must name your own reward.
'Faith, our sun was near eclipse!
Demand whate'er you will,
France remains your debtor still.
Ask to heart's content and have! or my name's not Dam-
　　freville."

Then a beam of fun outbroke
On the bearded mouth that spoke,
As the honest heart laughed through
Those frank eyes of Breton blue:
"Since I needs must say my say,
　Since on board the duty's done,
　And from Malo Roads to Croisic Point, what is it but a
　　run?—
Since 'tis ask and have, I may—
　Since the others go ashore—
Come! A good whole holiday!
　Leave to go and see my wife, whom I call the Belle
　　Aurore!"
　That he asked and that he got,—nothing more.

Name and deed alike are lost:
Not a pillar nor a post
　In his Croisic keeps alive the feat as it befell;
Not a head in white and black
On a single fishing-smack,
In memory of the man but for whom had gone to wrack
　All that France saved from the fight whence England
　　bore the bell:
Go to Paris: rank on rank
　Search the heroes flung pell-mell
On the Louvre, face and flank!

You shall look long enough ere you come to Hervé Riel
So, for better and for worse,
Hervé Riel, accept my verse!
In my verse, Hervé Riel, do thou once more
Save the squadron, honor France, love thy wife the Belle
      Aurore!

Robert Browning

HOW THEY BROUGHT THE GOOD NEWS FROM GHENT TO AIX

I sprang to the stirrup, and Joris, and he;
I galloped, Dirck galloped, we galloped all three;
"Good speed!" cried the watch, as the gate-bolts undrew;
"Speed!" echoed the wall to us galloping through;
Behind shut the postern, the lights sank to rest,
And into the midnight we galloped abreast.

Not a word to each other; we kept the great pace
Neck by neck, stride by stride, never changing our place;
I turned in my saddle and made its girths tight,
Then shortened each stirrup, and set the pique right,
Rebuckled the cheek-strap, chained slacker the bit,
Nor galloped less steadily Roland a whit.

'Twas moonset at starting; but while we drew near
Lokeren, the cocks crew and twilight dawned clear;
At Boom, a great yellow star came out to see;
At Düffeld, 'twas morning as plain as could be;
And from Mecheln church-steeple we heard the half-
      chime,
So Joris broke silence with, "Yet there is time!"

At Aershot, up leaped of a sudden the sun,
And against him the cattle stood black every one,

To stare through the mist at us galloping past,
And I saw my stout galloper Roland at last,
With resolute shoulders, each butting away
The haze, as some bluff river headland its spray:

And his low head and crest, just one sharp ear bent back
For my voice, and the other pricked out on his track;
And one eye's black intelligence,—ever that glance
O'er its white edge at me, his own master, askance!
And the thick heavy spume-flakes which aye and anon
His fierce lips shook upwards in galloping on.

By Hasselt, Dirck groaned; and cried Joris "Stay spur!
Your Roos galloped bravely, the fault's not in her,
We'll remember at Aix"—for one heard the quick wheeze
Of her chest, saw the stretched neck and staggering knees,
And sunk tail, and horrible heave of the flank,
As down on her haunches she shuddered and sank.

So, we were left galloping, Joris and I,
Past Looze and past Tongres, no cloud in the sky;
The broad sun above laughed a pitiless laugh,
'Neath our feet broke the brittle bright stubble like chaff;
Till over by Dalhem a dome-spire sprang white,
And "Gallop," gasped Joris, "for Aix is in sight!

"How they'll greet us!"—and all in a moment his roan
Rolled neck and croup over, lay dead as a stone;
And there was my Roland to bear the whole weight
Of the news which alone could save Aix from her fate,
With his nostrils like pits full of blood to the brim,
And with circles of red for his eye-sockets' rim.

Then I cast loose my buffcoat, each holster let fall,
Shook off both my jack-boots, let go belt and all,

Stood up in the stirrup, leaned, patted his ear,
Called my Roland his pet-name, my horse without peer;
Clapped my hands, laughed and sang, any noise, bad or
　　good,
Till at length into Aix Roland galloped and stood.

And all I remember is,—friends flocking round
As I sat with his head 'twixt my knees on the ground;
And no voice but was praising this Roland of mine,
As I poured down his throat our last measure of wine,
Which (the burgesses voted by common consent)
Was no more than his due who brought good news from
　　Ghent.

Robert Browning

A STORY FOR A CHILD

Little one, come to my knee!
　　Hark, how the rain is pouring
Over the roof, in the pitch-black night,
　　And the wind in the woods a-roaring!

Hush, my darling, and listen,
　　Then pay for the story with kisses;
Father was lost in the pitch-black night,
　　In just such a storm as this is!

High up on the lonely mountains,
　　Where the wild men watched and waited;
Wolves in the forest, and bears in the bush,
　　And I on my path belated.

The rain and the night together
　　Came down, and the wind came after,
Bending the props of the pine-tree roof,
　　And snapping many a rafter.

I crept along in the darkness,
    Stunned, and bruised, and blinded,—
Crept to a fir with thick-set boughs,
    And a sheltering rock behind it.

There, from the blowing and raining,
    Crouching, I sought to hide me:
Something rustled, two green eyes shone,
    And a wolf lay down beside me.

Little one, be not frightened;
    I and the wolf together,
Side by side, through the long, long night,
    Hid from the awful weather.

His wet fur pressed against me;
    Each of us warmed the other;
Each of us felt, in the stormy dark,
    That beast and man was brother.

And when the falling forest
    No longer crashed in warning,
Each of us went from our hiding-place
    Forth in the wild, wet morning.

Darling, kiss me payment!
    Hark, how the wind is roaring;
Father's house is a better place
    When the stormy rain is pouring!

                                    Bayard Taylor

THE GLOVE AND THE LIONS

King Francis was a hearty king, and loved a royal sport,
And one day, as his lions fought, sat looking on the court.

The nobles filled the benches, with the ladies in their
        pride,
And 'mongst them sat the Count de Lorge, with one for
        whom he sighed:
And truly 'twas a gallant thing to see that crowning show,
Valor and love, and a king above, and the royal beasts
        below.

Ramped and roared the lions, with horrid laughing jaws;
They bit, they glared, gave blows like beams, a wind went
        with their paws;
With wallowing might and stifled roar they rolled on one
        another,
Till all the pit with sand and mane was in a thunderous
        smother;
The bloody foam above the bars came whisking through
        the air;
Said Francis then, "Faith, gentlemen, we're better here
        than there."

De Lorge's love o'erheard the king, a beauteous lively
        dame,
With smiling lips and sharp bright eyes, which always
        seemed the same;
She thought, "The Count, my lover, is brave as brave can
        be;
He surely would do wondrous things to show his love of
        me;
King, ladies, lovers, all look on; the occasion is divine;
I'll drop my glove, to prove his love; great glory will be
        mine."

She dropped her glove, to prove his love, then looked at
        him and smiled;
He bowed, and in a moment leaped among the lions wild;

The leap was quick, return was quick, he has regained his
    place,
Then threw the glove, but not with love, right in the lady's
    face.
"By heaven," said Francis, "rightly done!" and he rose
    from where he sat;
"No love," quoth he, "but vanity, sets love a task like
    that."

Leigh Hunt

YOUNG LOCHINVAR

From "Marmion"

O, young Lochinvar is come out of the west,
Through all the wide Border his steed was the best;
And, save his good broadsword, he weapon had none,
He rode all unarmed, and he rode all alone.
So faithful in love, and so dauntless in war,
There never was knight like the young Lochinvar.

He stayed not for brake, and he stopped not for stone,
He swam the Eske river where ford there was none;
But, ere he alighted at Netherby gate,
The bride had consented, the gallant came late;
For a laggard in love, and a dastard in war,
Was to wed the fair Ellen of brave Lochinvar.

So boldly he entered the Netherby Hall,
Among bridesmen, and kinsmen, and brothers, and all.
Then spoke the bride's father, his hand on his sword,
(For the poor craven bridegroom said never a word),
"O come ye in peace here, or come ye in war,
Or to dance at our bridal, young Lord Lochinvar?"

"I long wooed your daughter, my suit you denied;—
Love swells like the Solway, but ebbs like its tide,—

And now am I come, with this lost love of mine,
To lead but one measure, drink one cup of wine.
There are maidens in Scotland more lovely by far,
That would gladly be bride to the young Lochinvar."

The bride kissed the goblet; the knight took it up,
He quaffed off the wine, and he threw down the cup.
She looked down to blush, and she looked up to sigh,
With a smile on her lips, and a tear in her eye.
He took her soft hand, ere her mother could bar,—
"Now tread we a measure!" said young Lochinvar.

So stately his form, and so lovely her face,
That never a hall such a galliard did grace;
While her mother did fret, and her father did fume,
And the bridegroom stood dangling his bonnet and plume;
And the bride-maidens whispered, "'Twere better by far
To have matched our fair cousin with young Lochinvar."

One touch to her hand, and one word in her ear,
When they reached the hall-door, and the charger stood
        near:
So light to the croupe the fair lady he swung,
So light to the saddle before her he sprung!
"She is won! we are gone! over bank, bush, and scaur;
They'll have fleet steeds that follow," quoth young Loch-
        invar.

There was mounting 'mong Græmes of the Netherby clan;
Forsters, Fenwicks, and Musgraves, they rode and they
        ran:
There was racing and chasing on Cannobie Lee,
But the lost bride of Netherby ne'er did they see.
So daring in love, and so dauntless in war,
Have ye e'er heard of gallant like young Lochinvar?

                                        Walter Scott

A DUTCH PICTURE

Simon Danz has come home again,
  From cruising about with his buccaneers;
He has singed the beard of the King of Spain
And carried away the Dean of Jaen
  And sold him in Algiers.

In his house by the Maese, with its roof of tiles,
  And weathercocks flying aloft in air,
There are silver tankards of antique styles,
Plunder of convent and castle, and piles
  Of carpets rich and rare.

In his tulip-garden there by the town,
  Overlooking the sluggish stream,
With his Moorish cap and dressing-gown,
The old sea-captain, hale and brown,
  Walks in a waking dream.

A smile in his gray mustachio lurks
  Whenever he thinks of the King of Spain,
And the listed tulips look like Turks,
And the silent gardener as he works
  Is changed to the Dean of Jaen.

The windmills on the outermost
  Verge of the landscape in the haze,
To him are towers on the Spanish coast,
With whiskered sentinels at their post,
  Though this is the river Maese.

But when the winter rains begin,
  He sits and smokes by the blazing brands,
And old seafaring men come in,
Goat-bearded, gray, and with double chin,
  And rings upon their hands.

They sit there in the shadow and shine
 Of the flickering fire of the winter night;
Figures in color and design
Like those by Rembrandt of the Rhine,
 Half darkness and half light.

And they talk of ventures lost or won,
 And their talk is ever and ever the same,
While they drink the red wine of Tarragon,
From the cellars of some Spanish Don,
 Or convent set on flame.

Restless at times with heavy strides
 He paces his parlor to and fro;
He is like a ship that at anchor rides,
And swings with the rising and falling tides,
 And tugs at her anchor-tow.

Voices mysterious far and near,
 Sound of the wind and sound of the sea,
Are calling and whispering in his ear,
"Simon Danz! Why stayest thou here?
 Come forth and follow me!"

So he thinks he shall take to the sea again
 For one more cruise with his buccaneers,
To singe the beard of the King of Spain,
And capture another Dean of Jaen
 And sell him in Algiers.

     Henry Wadsworth Longfellow

THE DIVERTING HISTORY OF JOHN GILPIN

SHOWING HOW HE WENT FARTHER THAN HE INTENDED AND
CAME SAFE HOME AGAIN

John Gilpin was a citizen
 Of credit and renown,

A train-band captain eke was he
  Of famous London town.

John Gilpin's spouse said to her dear,
  "Though wedded we have been
These twice ten tedious years, yet we
  No holiday have seen.

"To-morrow is our wedding-day,
  And we will then repair
Unto the Bell at Edmonton,
  All in a chaise and pair.

"My sister, and my sister's child,
  Myself, and children three,
Will fill the chaise; so you must ride
  On horseback after we."

He soon replied, "I do admire
  Of womankind but one,
And you are she, my dearest dear,
  Therefore it shall be done.

"I am a linen-draper bold,
  As all the world doth know,
And my good friend the calender
  Will lend his horse to go."

Quoth Mrs. Gilpin, "That's well said;
  And for that wine is dear,
We will be furnished with our own,
  Which is both bright and clear."

John Gilpin kissed his loving wife;
  O'erjoyed was he to find,
That though on pleasure she was bent,
  She had a frugal mind.

The morning came, the chaise was brought,
   But yet was not allowed
To drive up to the door, lest all
   Should say that she was proud.

So three doors off the chaise was stayed,
   Where they did all get in;
Six precious souls, and all agog
   To dash through thick and thin.

Smack went the whip, round went the wheels,
   Were never folks so glad,
The stones did rattle underneath,
   As if Cheapside were mad.

John Gilpin at his horse's side
   Seized fast the flowing mane,
And up he got, in haste to ride,
   But soon came down again;

For saddle-tree scarce reached had he,
   His journey to begin,
When, turning round his head, he saw
   Three customers come in.

So down he came; for loss of time,
   Although it grieved him sore,
Yet loss of pence, full well he knew,
   Would trouble him much more.

'Twas long before the customers
   Were suited to their mind,
When Betty screaming came downstairs,
   "The wine is left behind!"

"Good lack!" quoth he—"yet bring it me,
   My leathern belt likewise,

In which I bear my trusty sword,
　　When I do exercise."

Now Mistress Gilpin (careful soul!)
　　Had two stone bottles found,
To hold the liquor that she loved,
　　And keep it safe and sound.

Each bottle had a curling ear,
　　Through which the belt he drew,
And hung a bottle on each side,
　　To make his balance true.

Then over all, that he might be
　　Equipped from top to toe,
His long red cloak, well brushed and neat,
　　He manfully did throw.

Now see him mounted once again
　　Upon his nimble steed,
Full slowly pacing o'er the stones,
　　With caution and good heed.

But finding soon a smoother road
　　Beneath his well-shod feet,
The snorting beast began to trot,
　　Which galled him in his seat.

So, "Fair and softly," John he cried,
　　But John he cried in vain;
That trot became a gallop soon,
　　In spite of curb and rein.

So stooping down, as needs he must
　　Who cannot sit upright,
He grasped the mane with both his hands,
　　And eke with all his might.

His horse, who never in that sort
    Had handled been before,
What thing upon his back had got
    Did wonder more and more.

Away went Gilpin, neck or naught;
    Away went hat and wig:
He little dreamt, when he set out,
    Of running such a rig.

The wind did blow, the cloak did fly,
    Like streamer long and gay,
Till, loop and button failing both,
    At last it flew away.

Then might all people well discern
    The bottles he had slung;
A bottle swinging at each side,
    As hath been said or sung.

The dogs did bark, the children screamed,
    Up flew the windows all;
And every soul cried out, "Well done!"
    As loud as he could bawl.

Away went Gilpin—who but he?
    His fame soon spread around;
"He carries weight!" "He rides a race!"
    "'Tis for a thousand pound!"

And still, as fast as he drew near,
    'Twas wonderful to view
How in a trice the turnpike-men
    Their gates wide open threw.

And now, as he went bowing down
    His reeking head full low,

The bottles twain behind his back
  Were shattered at a blow.

Down ran the wine into the road,
  Most piteous to be seen,
Which made his horse's flanks to smoke
  As they had basted been.

But still he seemed to carry weight,
  With leathern girdle braced;
For all might see the bottle-necks
  Still dangling at his waist.

Thus all through merry Islington
  These gambols he did play,
Until he came unto the Wash
  Of Edmonton so gay;

And there he threw the Wash about
  On both sides of the way,
Just like unto a trundling mop,
  Or a wild goose at play.

At Edmonton his loving wife
  From the balcony spied
Her tender husband, wondering much
  To see how he did ride.

"Stop, stop, John Gilpin!—Here's the house!"
  They all at once did cry:
"The dinner waits, and we are tired;"—
  Said Gilpin—"So am I."

But yet his horse was not a whit
  Inclined to tarry there!
For why?—his owner had a house
  Full ten miles off, at Ware,

So like an arrow swift he flew,
   Shot by an archer strong;
So did he fly—which brings me to
   The middle of my song.

Away went Gilpin, out of breath,
   And sore against his will,
Till at his friend the calender's
   His horse at last stood still.

The calender, amazed to see
   His neighbor in such trim,
Laid down his pipe, flew to the gate,
   And thus accosted him:

"What news? what news? your tidings tell;
   Tell me you must and shall—
Say why bareheaded you are come,
   Or why you come at all?"

Now Gilpin had a pleasant wit
   And loved a timely joke;
And thus unto the calender
   In merry guise he spoke:

"I came because your horse would come,
   And, if I well forebode,
My hat and wig will soon be here.—
   They are upon the road."

The calender, right glad to find
   His friend in merry pin,
Returned him not a single word
   But to the house went in;

Whence straight he came with hat and wig;
   A wig that flowed behind,

A hat not much the worse for wear,
   Each comely in its kind.

He held them up, and in his turn
   Thus showed his ready wit,
"My head is twice as big as yours,
   They therefore needs must fit.

"But let me scrape the dirt away
   That hangs upon your face;
And stop and eat, for well you may
   Be in a hungry case."

Said John, "It is my wedding-day,
   And all the world would stare,
If wife should dine at Edmonton,
   And I should dine at Ware."

So turning to his horse, he said,
   "I am in haste to dine;
'Twas for your pleasure you came here,
   You shall go back for mine."

Ah, luckless speech, and bootless boast!
   For which he paid full dear;
For, while he spake, a braying ass
   Did sing most loud and clear;

Whereat his horse did snort, as he
   Had heard a lion roar,
And galloped off with all his might
   As he had done before.

Away went Gilpin, and away
   Went Gilpin's hat and wig:
He lost them sooner than at first;
   For why?—they were too big.

Now Mistress Gilpin, when she saw
  Her husband posting down
Into the country far away,
  She pulled out half-a-crown;

And thus unto the youth she said
  That drove them to the Bell,
"This shall be yours, when you bring back
  My husband safe and well."

The youth did ride, and soon did meet
  John coming back amain:
Whom in a trice he tried to stop,
  By catching at his rein;

But not performing what he meant,
  And gladly would have done,
The frighted steed he frighted more,
  And made him faster run.

Away went Gilpin, and away
  Went postboy at his heels,
The postboy's horse right glad to miss
  The lumbering of the wheels.

Six gentlemen upon the road,
  Thus seeing Gilpin fly,
With postboy scampering in the rear,
  They raised the hue and cry:

"Stop thief! stop thief!—a highwayman!"
  Not one of them was mute;
And all and each that passed that way
  Did join in the pursuit.

And now the turnpike gates again
  Flew open in short space;

The toll-men thinking, as before,
   That Gilpin rode a race.

And so he did, and won it too,
   For he got first to town;
Nor stopped till where he had got up
   He did again get down.

Now let us sing, Long live the king!
   And Gilpin, long live he!
And when he next doth ride abroad
   May I be there to see!

William Cowper

THE DEACON'S MASTERPIECE

OR, THE WONDERFUL "ONE-HOSS SHAY"
A LOGICAL STORY

Have you heard of the wonderful one-hoss shay,
That was built in such a logical way
It ran a hundred years to a day,
And then, of a sudden, it—ah, but stay,
I'll tell you what happened without delay,
Scaring the parson into fits,
Frightening people out of their wits,—
Have you ever heard of that, I say?

Seventeen hundred and fifty-five.
Georgius Secundus was then alive,—
Snuffy old drone from the German hive.
That was the year when Lisbon-town
Saw the earth open and gulp her down,
And Braddock's army was done so brown,
Left without a scalp to its crown.
It was on the terrible Earthquake-day
That the Deacon finished the one-hoss shay.

Now in building of chaises, I tell you what,
There is always *somewhere* a weakest spot,—
In hub, tire, felloe, in spring or thill,
In panel, or crossbar, or floor, or sill,
In screw, bolt, throughbrace,—lurking still,
Find it somewhere you must and will,—
Above or below, or within or without,—
And that's the reason, beyond a doubt,
That a chaise *breaks down*, but doesn't *wear out*.

But the Deacon swore (as Deacons do,
With an "I dew vum," or an "I tell *yeou*")
He would build one shay to beat the taown
'N' the keounty 'n' all the kentry raoun';
It should be so built that it *couldn't* break daown:
"Fur," said the Deacon, "'t's mighty plain
Thut the weakes' place mus' stan' the strain;
'N' the way t' fix it, uz I maintain,
Is only jest
T' make *that* place uz strong uz the rest."

So the Deacon inquired of the village folk
Where he could find the strongest oak,
That couldn't be split nor bent nor broke,—
That was for spokes and floor and sills;
He sent for lancewood to make the thills;
The crossbars were ash, from the straightest trees,
The panels of white-wood, that cuts like cheese,
But lasts like iron for things like these;
The hubs of logs from the "Settler's ellum,"—
Last of its timber,—they couldn't sell 'em,
Never an axe had seen their chips,
And the wedges flew from between their lips
Their blunt ends frizzled like celery-tips;
Step and prop-iron, bolt and screw,
Spring, tire, axle, and linchpin too,

Steel of the finest, bright and blue;
Throughbrace bison-skin, thick and wide;
Boot, top, dasher, from tough old hide
Found in the pit when the tanner died.
That was the way he "put her through."
"There!" said the Deacon, "naow she'll dew!"

Do! I tell you, I rather guess
She was a wonder, and nothing less!
Colts grew horses, beards turned gray,
Deacon and deaconess dropped away,
Children and grandchildren—where were they?
But there stood the stout old one-hoss shay
As fresh as on Lisbon-earthquake-day!

EIGHTEEN HUNDRED; —it came and found
The Deacon's masterpiece strong and sound.
Eighteen hundred increased by ten;—
"Hahnsum kerridge" they called it then.
Eighteen hundred and twenty came;—
Running as usual; much the same.
Thirty and forty at last arrive,
And then come fifty, and FIFTY-FIVE.

Little of all we value here
Wakes on the morn of its hundredth year
Without both feeling and looking queer.
In fact, there's nothing that keeps its youth,
So far as I know, but a tree and truth.
(This is a moral that runs at large;
Take it.—You're welcome.—No extra charge.)

FIRST OF NOVEMBER,—the Earthquake-day,—
There are traces of age in the one-hoss shay,
A general flavor of mild decay,
But nothing local, as one may say.

There couldn't be,—for the Deacon's art
Had made it so like in every part
That there wasn't a chance for one to start.

For the wheels were just as strong as the thills,
And the floor was just as strong as the sills,
And the panels just as strong as the floor.
And the whipple-tree neither less nor more,
And the black crossbar as strong as the fore,
And spring and axle and hub *encore*.
And yet, *as a whole*, it is past a doubt
In another hour it will be *worn out!*

First of November, 'Fifty-five!
This morning the parson takes a drive.
Now, small boys, get out of the way!
Here comes the wonderful one-hoss shay,
Drawn by a rat-tailed, ewe-necked bay.
"Huddup!" said the parson.—Off went they.
The parson was working his Sunday's text,—
Had got to *fifthly*, and stopped perplexed
At what the—Moses—was coming next.

All at once the horse stood still,
Close by the meet'n'-house on the hill.
First a shiver, and then a thrill,
Then something decidedly like a spill,—
And the parson was sitting upon a rock,
At half past nine by the meet'n'-house clock,—
Just the hour of the Earthquake shock!
What do you think the parson found,
When he got up and stared around?
The poor old chaise in a heap or mound,
As if it had been to the mill and ground!
You see, of course, if you're not a dunce,
How it went to pieces all at once,—

All at once, and nothing first,—
Just as bubbles do when they burst.

End of the wonderful one-hoss shay.
Logic is logic.   That's all I say.

Oliver Wendell Holmes

DARIUS GREEN AND HIS FLYING-MACHINE

If ever there lived a Yankee lad,
Wise or otherwise, good or bad,
Who, seeing the birds fly, didn't jump
With flapping arms from stake or stump,
Or, spreading the tail of his coat for a sail,
Take a soaring leap from post or rail,
And wonder why *he* couldn't fly,
And flap and flutter and wish and try,—
If ever you knew a country dunce
Who didn't try that as often as once,
All I can say is, that's a sign
He never would do for a hero of mine.

An aspiring genius was D. Green:
The son of a farmer,—age fourteen;
His body was long and lank and lean,—
Just right for flying, as will be seen;
He had two eyes as bright as a bean,
And a freckled nose that grew between,
A little awry;—for I must mention
That he had riveted his attention
Upon his wonderful invention,
Twisting his tongue as he twisted the strings,
And working his face as he worked the wings,
And with every turn of gimlet and screw
Turning and screwing his mouth round too,
Till his nose seemed bent to catch the scent,

Around some corner, of new-baked pies,
And his wrinkled cheeks and his squinting eyes
Grew puckered into a queer grimace,
That made him look very droll in the face,
    And also very wise.

And wise he must have been, to do more
Than ever a genius did before,
Excepting Dædalus of yore
And his son Icarus, who wore
Upon their backs those wings of wax
He had read of in the old almanacs.
Darius was clearly of the opinion,
That the air was also man's dominion,
And that, with paddle or fin or pinion,
We soon or late should navigate
The azure as now we sail the sea.
The thing looks simple enough to me;
    And, if you doubt it,
Hear how Darius reasoned about it:

"The birds can fly, an' why can't I?
Must we give in," says he with a grin,
"'T the bluebird an' phœbe are smarter'n we be?
Jest fold our hands, an' see the swaller
An' blackbird an' catbird beat us holler?
Does the leetle, chatterin', sassy wren,
No bigger'n my thumb, know more than men?
Jest show me that! er prove 't the bat
Hez got more brains than's in my hat,
An' I'll back down, an' not till then!"

He argued further: "Ner I can't see
What's th' use o' wings to a bumble-bee,
Fer to git a livin' with, more'n to me;—
Ain't my business importanter'n his'n is?

That Icarus was a silly cuss,—
Him an' his daddy Dædalus;
They might 'a' knowed wings made o' wax
Wouldn't stan' sun-heat an' hard whacks:
I'll make mine o' luther, er suthin' er other."
And he said to himself, as he tinkered and planned:
"But I ain't goin' to show my hand
To nummies that never can understand
The fust idee that's big an' grand.
They'd 'a' laft an' made fun
O' Creation itself afore 'twas done!"
So he kept his secret from all the rest,
Safely buttoned within his vest;
And in the loft above the shed
Himself he locks, with thimble and thread
And wax and hammer and buckles and screws,
And all such things as geniuses use;—
Two bats for patterns, curious fellows!
A charcoal-pot and a pair of bellows;
An old hoop-skirt or two, as well as
Some wire, and several old umbrellas;
A carriage-cover, for tail and wings;
A piece of harness; and straps and strings;
And a big strong box, in which he locks
These and a hundred other things.

His grinning brothers, Reuben and Burke
And Nathan and Jotham and Solomon, lurk
Around the corner to see him work,—
Sitting cross-leggèd, like a Turk,
Drawing the waxed-end through with a jerk,
And boring the holes with a comical quirk
Of his wise old head, and a knowing smirk.
But vainly they mounted each other's backs,
And poked through knot-holes and pried through cracks;
With wood from the pile and straw from the stacks

He plugged the knot-holes and calked the cracks;
And a bucket of water, which one would think
He had brought up into the loft to drink
When he chanced to be dry,
Stood always nigh, for Darius was sly!
And, whenever at work he happened to spy
At chink or crevice a blinking eye,
He let a dipper of water fly:
"Take that! an', ef ever ye git a peep,
Guess ye'll ketch a weasel asleep!"
And he sings as he locks his big strong box:
"The weasel's head is small an' trim,
An' he is leetle an' long an' slim,
An' quick of motion an' nimble of limb,
An', ef yeou'll be advised by me,
Keep wide awake when ye're ketchin' him!"

    So day after day
He stitched and tinkered and hammered away,
    Till at last 'twas done,—
The greatest invention under the sun!
"An' now," says Darius, "hooray fer some fun!"

'Twas the Fourth of July, and the weather was dry,
And not a cloud was on all the sky,
Save a few light fleeces, which here and there,
    Half mist, half air,
Like foam on the ocean went floating by,—
Just as lovely a morning as ever was seen
For a nice little trip in a flying-machine.

Thought cunning Darius, "Now I shan't go
Along 'ith the fellers to see the show:
I'll say I've got sich a terrible cough!
An' then, when the folks 'ave all gone off,
I'll hev full swing fer to try the thing,
An' practyse a little on the wing."

"Ain't goin' to see the celebration?"
Says brother Nate. "No; botheration!
I've got sich a cold—a toothache—I—
My gracious!—feel's though I should fly!"
Said Jotham, "'Sho! guess ye better go."
    But Darius said, "No!
Shouldn't wonder 'f yeou might see me, though,
'Long 'bout noon, ef I git red
O' this jumpin', thumpin' pain 'n my head."
For all the while to himself he said,—
    "I tell ye what!
I'll fly a few times around the lot,
To see how 't seems, then soon's I've got
The hang o' the thing, ez likely's not,
I'll astonish the nation, an' all creation,
By flyin' over the celebration!
Over their heads I'll sail like an eagle;
I'll balance myself on my wings like a sea-gull;
I'll dance on the chimbleys; I'll stan' on the steeple;
I'll flop up to winders an' scare the people!
I'll light on the libbe'ty-pole, an' crow;
An' I'll say to the gawpin' fools below,
'What world's this 'ere that I've come near?'
Fer I'll make 'em b'lieve I'm a chap f'm the moon;
An' I'll try a race 'ith their ol' balloon!"

    He crept from his bed;
And, seeing the others were gone, he said,
"I'm a-gittin' over the cold 'n my head."
    And away he sped,
To open the wonderful box in the shed.

His brothers had walked but a little way,
When Jotham to Nathan chanced to say,
"What on airth is he up to, hey?"
"Don'o',—the' 's suthin' er other to pay,

Er he wouldn't 'a' stayed to hum to-day."
Says Burke, "His toothache's all 'n his eye!
He never'd miss a Fo'th-o'-July,
Ef he hedn't got some machine to try."
Then Sol, the little one, spoke: "By darn!
Le's hurry back, an' hide 'n the barn,
An' pay him fer tellin' us that yarn!"
"Agreed!"   Through the orchard they creep back,
Along by the fences, behind the stack,
And one by one, through a hole in the wall,
In under the dusty barn they crawl,
Dressed in their Sunday garments all;
And a very astonishing sight was that,
When each in his cobwebbed coat and hat
Came up through the floor like an ancient rat.
And there they hid; and Reuben slid
The fastenings back, and the door undid.
        "Keep dark!" said he,
"While I squint an' see what the' is to see."

As knights of old put on their mail,—
From head to foot an iron suit,
Iron jacket and iron boot,
Iron breeches, and on the head
No hat, but an iron pot instead,
And under the chin the bail,—
(I believe they called the thing a helm,)—
And, thus accoutred, they took the field,
Sallying forth to overwhelm
The dragons and pagans that plagued the realm;
So this modern knight prepared for flight,
Put on his wings and strapped them tight,—
Jointed and jaunty, strong and light,—
Buckled them fast to shoulder and hip,—

Ten feet they measured from tip to tip!
And a helm had he, but that he wore,
Not on his head, like those of yore,
    But more like the helm of a ship.

"Hush!" Reuben said, "he's up in the shed!
He's opened the winder,—I see his head!
He stretches it out, an' pokes it about,
Lookin' to see 'f the coast is clear,
    An' nobody near;—
Guess he don'o' who's hid in here!
He's riggin' a spring-board over the sill!
Stop laffin', Solomon! Burke, keep still!
He's a climbin' out now—Of all the things!
What's he got on? I van, it's wings!
An' that t'other thing? I vum, it's a tail!
An' there he sets like a hawk on a rail!
Steppin' careful, he travels the length
Of his spring-board, and teeters to try its strength.
Now he stretches his wings, like a monstrous bat;
Peeks over his shoulder, this way an' that,
Fer to see 'f the' 's any one passin' by;
But the' 's on'y a ca'f an' a goslin' nigh.
They turn up at him a wonderin' eye,
To see—The dragon! he's goin' to fly!
Away he goes! Jimminy! what a jump!
Flop—flop—an' plump to the ground with a thump!
Flutt'rin' an' flound'rin', all 'n a lump!"

As a demon is hurled by an angel's spear,
Heels over head, to his proper sphere,—
Heels over head, and head over heels,
Dizzily down the abyss he wheels,—
So fell Darius. Upon his crown,
In the midst of the barn-yard, he came down,

In a wonderful whirl of tangled strings,
Broken braces and broken springs,
Broken tail and broken wings,
Shooting-stars, and various things,—
Barn-yard litter of straw and chaff,
And much that wasn't so sweet by half.
Away with a bellow fled the calf,
And what was that? Did the gosling laugh?
'Tis a merry roar from the old barn-door,
And he hears the voice of Jotham crying;
"Say, D'rius! how de yeou like flyin'?"

Slowly, ruefully, where he lay,
Darius just turned and looked that way,
As he stanched his sorrowful nose with his cuff,
"Wal, I like flyin' well enough,"
He said; "but the' ain't sich a thunderin' sight
O' fun in 't when ye come to light."

I just have room for the MORAL here:
And this is the moral,—Stick to your sphere;
Or, if you insist, as you have the right,
On spreading your wings for a loftier flight,
The moral is,—Take care how you light.

John Townsend Trowbridge

THE SKELETON IN ARMOR

"Speak! speak! thou fearful guest!
Who, with thy hollow breast
Still in rude armor dressed,
    Comest to daunt me!
Wrapped not in Eastern balms,
But with thy fleshless palms
Stretched, as if asking alms,
    Why dost thou haunt me?"

Then, from those cavernous eyes
Pale flashes seemed to rise,
As when the Northern skies
 Gleam in December;
And, like the water's flow
Under December's snow,
Came a dull voice of woe
 From the heart's chamber.

"I was a viking old!
My deeds, though manifold,
No Skald in song has told,
 No Saga taught thee!
Take heed, that in thy verse
Thou dost the tale rehearse,
Else dread a dead man's curse;
 For this I sought thee.

"Far in the Northern Land,
By the wild Baltic's strand,
I, with my childish hand,
 Tamed the gerfalcon;
And, with my skates fast-bound,
Skimmed the half-frozen Sound,
That the poor whimpering hound
 Trembled to walk on.

"Oft to his frozen lair
Tracked I the grisly bear,
While from my path the hare
 Fled like a shadow;
Oft through the forest dark
Followed the were-wolf's bark,
Until the soaring lark
 Sang from the meadow.

"But when I older grew,
Joining a corsair's crew,
O'er the dark sea I flew
    With the marauders.
Wild was the life we led;
Many the souls that sped,
Many the hearts that bled,
    By our stern orders.

"Many a wassail-bout
Wore the long Winter out;
Often our midnight shout
    Set the cocks crowing,
As we the Berserk's tale
Measured in cups of ale,
Draining the oaken pail,
    Filled to o'erflowing.

"Once as I told in glee
Tales of the stormy sea,
Soft eyes did gaze on me,
    Burning yet tender;
And as the white stars shine
On the dark Norway pine,
On that dark heart of mine
    Fell their soft splendor.

"I wooed the blue-eyed maid,
Yielding, yet half afraid,
And in the forest's shade
    Our vows were plighted.
Under its loosened vest
Fluttered her little breast,
Like birds within their nest
    By the hawk frighted.

"Bright in her father's hall
Shields gleamed upon the wall,
Loud sang the minstrels all,
    Chanting his glory;
When of old Hildebrand
I asked his daughter's hand,
Mute did the minstrels stand
    To hear my story.

"While the brown ale he quaffed,
Loud then the champion laughed,
And as the wind-gusts waft
    The sea-foam brightly,
So the loud laugh of scorn,
Out of those lips unshorn,
From the deep drinking-horn
    Blew the foam lightly.

"She was a Prince's child,
I but a Viking wild,
And though she blushed and smiled,
    I was discarded!
Should not the dove so white
Follow the sea-mew's flight,
Why did they leave that night
    Her nest unguarded?

"Scarce had I put to sea,
Bearing the maid with me,
Fairest of all was she
    Among the Norsemen!
When on the white sea-strand,
Waving his armèd hand,
Saw we old Hildebrand,
    With twenty horsemen.

"Then launched they to the blast,
Bent like a reed each mast,
Yet we were gaining fast,
    When the wind failed us;
And with a sudden flaw
Came round the gusty Skaw,
So that our foe we saw
    Laugh as he hailed us.

"And as to catch the gale
Round veered the flapping sail,
'Death!' was the helmsman's hail,
    'Death without quarter!'
Mid-ships with iron keel
Struck we her ribs of steel;
Down her black hulk did reel
    Through the black water!

"As with his wings aslant,
Sails the fierce cormorant,
Seeking some rocky haunt,
    With his prey laden,—
So toward the open main,
Beating to sea again,
Through the wild hurricane,
    Bore I the maiden.

"Three weeks we westward bore,
And when the storm was o'er,
Cloud-like we saw the shore
    Stretching to leeward;
There for my lady's bower
Built I the lofty tower,
Which, to this very hour,
    Stands looking seaward.

"There lived we many years;
Time dried the maiden's tears;
She had forgot her fears,
    She was a mother;
Death closed her mild blue eyes,
Under that tower she lies;
Ne'er shall the sun arise
    On such another!

"Still grew my bosom then,
Still as a stagnant fen!
Hateful to me were men,
    The sunlight hateful!
In the vast forest here,
Clad in my warlike gear,
Fell I upon my spear,
    Oh, death was grateful!

"Thus, seamed with many scars,
Bursting these prison bars,
Up to its native stars
    My soul ascended!
There from the flowing bowl
Deep drinks the warrier's soul,
Skoal! to the Northland! *skoal!*"
    Thus the tale ended.

                    Henry Wadsworth Longfellow

HORATIUS AT THE BRIDGE

[c. 496 B. C.]

Lars Porsena of Clusium
    By the Nine Gods he swore
That the great house of Tarquin
    Should suffer wrong no more.

By the Nine Gods he swore it,
  And named a trysting-day,
And bade his messengers ride forth,
East and west and south and north,
  To summon his array.

East and west and south and north
  The messengers ride fast,
And tower and town and cottage
  Have heard the trumpet's blast.
Shame on the false Etruscan
  Who lingers in his home,
When Porsena of Clusium
  Is on the march for Rome.

The horsemen and the footmen
  Are pouring in amain
From many a stately market-place,
  From many a fruitful plain,
From many a lonely hamlet,
  Which, hid by beach and pine,
Like an eagle's nest, hangs on the crest
  Of purple Apennine. . . .

And now hath every city
  Sent up her tale of men;
The foot are fourscore thousand,
  The horse are thousands ten.
Before the gates of Sutrium
  Is met the great array;
A proud man was Lars Porsena
  Upon the trysting-day. . . .

But by the yellow Tiber
  Was tumult and affright:
From all the spacious champaign
  To Rome men took their flight.

A mile around the city,
  The throng stopped up the ways;
A fearful sight it was to see
  Through two long nights and days. . . .

Now, from the rock Tarpeian,
  Could the wan burghers spy
The line of blazing villages
  Red in the midnight sky.
The Fathers of the City,
  They sat all night and day,
For every hour some horseman came
  With tidings of dismay.

To eastward and to westward
  Have spread the Tuscan bands,
Nor house, nor fence, nor dovecote
  In Crustumerium stands.
Verbenna down to Ostia
  Hath wasted all the plain;
Astur hath stormed Janiculum,
  And the stout guards are slain.

I wis, in all the Senate
  There was no heart so bold
But sore it ached, and fast it beat,
  When that ill news was told.
Forthwith up rose the Consul,
  Up rose the Fathers all;
In haste they girded up their gowns,
  And hied them to the wall.

They held a council, standing
  Before the River-Gate;
Short time was there, ye well may guess,
  For musing or debate.

Out spake the Consul roundly:
   "The bridge must straight go down;
For, since Janiculum is lost,
   Naught else can save the town."

Just then a scout came flying,
   All wild with haste and fear:
"To arms! to arms! Sir Consul,—
   Lars Porsena is here."
On the low hills to westward
   The Consul fixed his eye,
And saw the swarthy storm of dust
   Rise fast along the sky.

And nearer fast and nearer
   Doth the red whirlwind come;
And louder still and still more loud,
From underneath that rolling cloud,
Is heard the trumpet's war-note proud,
   The trampling and the hum.
And plainly and more plainly
   Now through the gloom appears,
Far to left and far to right,
In broken gleams of dark-blue light,
The long array of helmets bright,
   The long array of spears. . . .

But the Consul's brow was sad,
   And the Consul's speech was low,
And darkly looked he at the wall,
   And darkly at the foe:
"Their van will be upon us
   Before the bridge goes down;
And if they once may win the bridge,
   What hope to save the town?"

Then out spake brave Horatius,
  The Captain of the Gate:
"To every man upon this earth
  Death cometh soon or late.
And how can man die better
  Than facing fearful odds
For the ashes of his fathers
  And the temples of his Gods?

"Hew down the bridge, Sir Consul,
  With all the speed ye may;
I, with two more to help me,
  Will hold the foe in play.
In yon straight path a thousand
  May well be stopped by three:
Now who will stand on either hand,
  And keep the bridge with me?"

Then out spake Spurius Lartius,—
  A Ramnian proud was he:
"Lo, I will stand at thy right hand,
  And keep the bridge with thee."
And out spake strong Herminius,—
  Of Titian blood was he:
"I will abide on thy left side,
  And keep the bridge with thee."

"Horatius," quoth the Consul,
  "As thou sayest so let it be."
And straight against that great array
  Forth went the dauntless Three.
For Romans in Rome's quarrel
  Spared neither land nor gold,
Nor son nor wife, nor limb nor life,
  In the brave days of old. . . .

Now while the Three were tightening
　　Their harness on their backs,
The Consul was the foremost man
　　To take in hand an axe;
And Fathers, mixed with Commons,
　　Seized hatchet, bar, and crow,
And smote upon the planks above,
　　And loosed the props below.

Meanwhile the Tuscan army,
　　Right glorious to behold,
Came flashing back the noonday light,
Rank behind rank, like surges bright
　　Of a broad sea of gold.
Four hundred trumpets sounded
　　A peal of warlike glee,
As that great host with measured tread,
And spears advanced, and ensigns spread,
Rolled slowly towards the bridge's head,
　　Where stood the dauntless Three.

The Three stood calm and silent,
　　And looked upon the foes,
And a great shout of laughter
　　From all the vanguard rose;
And forth three chiefs came spurring
　　Before that deep array;
To earth they sprang, their swords they drew,
And lifted high their shields, and flew
　　To win the narrow way:

Aunus, from green Tifernum,
　　Lord of the Hill of Vines;
And Seius, whose eight hundred slaves
　　Sicken in Ilva's mines;
And Picus, long to Clusium
　　Vassal in peace and war,

Who led to fight his Umbrian powers
From that gray crag where, girt with towers,
The fortress of Nequinum lowers
  O'er the pale waves of Nar.

Stout Lartius hurled down Aunus
  Into the stream beneath;
Herminius struck at Seius;
  And clove him to the teeth;
At Picus brave Horatius
  Darted one fiery thrust,
And the proud Umbrian's gilded arms
  Clashed in the bloody dust.

Then Ocnus of Falerii
  Rushed on the Roman Three;
And Lausulus of Urgo,
  The rover of the sea;
And Aruns of Volsinium,
  Who slew the great wild boar,—
The great wild boar that had his den
Amidst the reeds of Cosa's fen,
And wasted fields, and slaughtered men,
  Along Albinia's shore.

Herminius smote down Aruns;
  Lartius laid Ocnus low;
Right to the heart of Lausulus
  Horatius sent a blow:
"Lie there," he cried, "fell pirate!
  No more, aghast and pale,
From Ostia's walls the crowd shall mark
The track of thy destroying bark;
No more Campania's hinds shall fly
To woods and caverns, when they spy
  Thy thrice-accursed sail!"

But now no sound of laughter
  Was heard among the foes;
A wild and wrathful clamor
  From all the vanguard rose.
Six spears' lengths from the entrance,
  Halted that deep array,
And for a space no man came forth
  To win the narrow way. . . .

But meanwhile axe and lever
  Have manfully been plied;
And now the bridge hangs tottering
  Above the boiling tide.
"Come back, come back, Horatius!"
  Loud cried the Fathers all.—
"Back, Lartius! back, Herminius!
  Back, ere the ruin fall!"

Back darted Spurius Lartius;—
  Herminius darted back;
And, as they passed, beneath their feet
  They felt the timbers crack.
But when they turned their faces,
  And on the farther shore
Saw brave Horatius stand alone,
  They would have crossed once more;

But with a crash like thunder
  Fell every loosened beam,
And, like a dam, the mighty wreck
  Lay right athwart the stream:
And a long shout of triumph
  Rose from the walls of Rome,
As to the highest turret-tops
  Was splashed the yellow foam.

And, like a horse unbroken,
    When first he feels the rein,
The furious river struggled hard,
    And tossed his tawny mane,
And burst the curb, and bounded,
    Rejoicing to be free;
And whirling down, in fierce career,
Battlement, and plank, and pier,
    Rushed headlong to the sea.

Alone stood brave Horatius,
    But constant still in mind,—
Thrice thirty thousand foes before,
    And the broad flood behind.
"Down with him!" cried false Sextus,
    With a smile on his pale face;
"Now yield thee," cried Lars Porsena,
    "Now yield thee to our grace."

Round turned he, as not deigning
    Those craven ranks to see;
Naught spake he to Lars Porsena,
    To Sextus naught spake he;
But he saw on Palatinus
    The white porch of his home;
And he spake to the noble river
    That rolls by the towers of Rome:

"O Tiber! Father Tiber!
    To whom the Romans pray,
A Roman's life, a Roman's arms,
    Take thou in charge this day!"
So he spake, and, speaking, sheathèd
    The good sword by his side,
And, with his harness on his back,
    Plunged headlong in the tide.

No sound of joy or sorrow
   Was heard from either bank,
But friends and foes in dumb surprise,
With parted lips and straining eyes,
   Stood gazing where he sank;
And when above the surges
   They saw his crest appear,
All Rome sent forth a rapturous cry,
And even the ranks of Tuscany
   Could scarce forbear to cheer.

But fiercely ran the current,
   Swollen high by months of rain;
And fast his blood was flowing,
   And he was sore in pain,
And heavy with his armor,
   And spent with changing blows;
And oft they thought him sinking,
   But still again he rose.

Never, I ween, did swimmer,
   In such an evil case,
Struggle through such a raging flood
   Safe to the landing-place;
But his limbs were borne up bravely
   By the brave heart within,
And our good Father Tiber
   Bore bravely up his chin.

"Curse on him!" quoth false Sextus;—
   "Will not the villain drown?
But for this stay, ere close of day
   We should have sacked the town!"
"Heaven help him!" quoth Lars Porsena,
   "And bring him safe to shore;
For such a gallant feat of arms
   Was never seen before."

And now he feels the bottom;
  Now on dry earth he stands;
Now round him throng the Fathers
  To press his gory hands;
And now, with shouts and clapping,
  And noise of weeping loud,
He enters through the River-Gate,
  Borne by the joyous crowd.

They gave him of the corn-land,
  That was of public right,
As much as two strong oxen
  Could plough from morn till night;
And they made a molten image,
  And set it up on high,
And there it stands unto this day
  To witness if I lie.

It stands in the Comitium,
  Plain for all folk to see,—
Horatius in his harness,
  Halting upon one knee;
And underneath is written,
  In letters all of gold,
How valiantly he kept the bridge
  In the brave days of old.

And still his name sounds stirring
  Unto the men of Rome,
As the trumpet-blast that cries to them
  To charge the Volscian home;
And wives still pray to Juno
  For boys with hearts as bold
As his who kept the bridge so well
  In the brave days of old. . . .

                    Thomas Babington Macaulay

THE BATTLE OF BLENHEIM

[AUGUST 13, 1704]

It was a summer evening;
   Old Kaspar's work was done,
And he before his cottage-door
   Was sitting in the sun;
And by him sported on the green
His little grandchild, Wilhelmine.

She saw her brother Peterkin
   Roll something large and round,
That he beside the rivulet,
   In playing there, had found:
She ran to ask what he had found,
That was so large and smooth and round.

Old Kaspar took it from the boy,
   Who stood expectant by;
And then the old man shook his head,
   And with a natural sigh,
"'Tis some poor fellow's skull," said he,
"Who fell in the great victory.

"I find them in my garden,
   For there's many here about;
And often, when I go to plough,
   The ploughshare turns them out;
For many thousand men," said he,
"Were slain in that great victory."

"Now tell us what 'twas all about,"
   Young Peterkin he cries;
And little Wilhelmine looks up
   With wonder-waiting eyes;

"Now tell us all about the war,
And what they fought each other for."

"It was the English," Kaspar cried,
    "Who put the French to rout;
But what they fought each other for
    I could not well make out;
But everybody said," quoth he,
"That 'twas a famous victory.

"My father lived at Blenheim then,
    Yon little stream hard by;
They burned his dwelling to the ground,
    And he was forced to fly;
So with his wife and child he fled,
Nor had he where to rest his head.

"With fire and sword the country round
    Was wasted far and wide,
And many a childing mother then,
    And new-born baby died;
But things like that, you know, must be
At every famous victory.

"They say it was a shocking sight
    After the field was won;
For many thousand bodies here
    Lay rotting in the sun:
But things like that, you know, must be
After a famous victory.

"Great praise the Duke of Marlborough won
    And our good Prince Eugene."
"Why, 'twas a very wicked thing!"
    Said little Wilhelmine.
"Nay, nay, my little girl," quoth he,
"It was a famous victory.

"And everybody praised the Duke,
　Who this great fight did win."
"But what good came of it at last?"
　Quoth little Peterkin.
"Why, that I cannot tell," said he;
"But 'twas a famous victory."

Robert Southey

THE WRECK OF THE HESPERUS

[DECEMBER 17, 1839]

It was the schooner Hesperus,
　That sailed the wintry sea;
And the skipper had taken his little daughtèr,
　To bear him company.

Blue were her eyes as the fairy-flax,
　Her cheeks like the dawn of day,
And her bosom white as the hawthorn buds
　That ope in the month of May.

The skipper he stood beside the helm,
　His pipe was in his mouth,
And he watched how the veering flaw did blow
　The smoke now West, now South.

Then up and spake an old Sailòr,
　Had sailed to the Spanish Main,
"I pray thee, put into yonder port,
　For I fear a hurricane.

"Last night, the moon had a golden ring,
　And to-night no moon we see!"
The skipper, he blew a whiff from his pipe,
　And a scornful laugh laughed he.

Colder and louder blew the wind,
   A gale from the Northeast,
The snow fell hissing in the brine,
   And the billows frothed like yeast.

Down came the storm, and smote amain
   The vessel in its strength;
She shuddered and paused, like a frighted steed,
   Then leaped her cable's length.

"Come hither! come hither! my little daughtèr,
   And do not tremble so;
For I can weather the roughest gale
   That ever wind did blow."

He wrapped her warm in his seaman's coat
   Against the stinging blast;
He cut a rope from a broken spar,
   And bound her to the mast.

"O father! I hear the church-bells ring,
   Oh say, what may it be?"
" 'Tis a fog-bell on a rock-bound coast!"—
   And he steered for the open sea.

"O father! I hear the sound of guns,
   Oh say, what may it be?"
"Some ship in distress, that cannot live
   In such an angry sea!"

"O father! I see a gleaming light,
   Oh say, what may it be?"
But the father answered never a word,
   A frozen corpse was he.

Lashed to the helm, all stiff and stark,
   With his face turned to the skies,

The lantern gleamed through the gleaming snow
  On his fixed and glassy eyes.

Then the maiden clasped her hands and prayed
  That savèd she might be;
And she thought of Christ, who stilled the wave,
  On the Lake of Galilee.

And fast through the midnight dark and drear,
  Through the whistling sleet and snow,
Like a sheeted ghost, the vessel swept
  Towards the reef of Norman's Woe.

And ever the fitful gusts between
  A sound came from the land;
It was the sound of the trampling surf
  On the rocks and the hard sea-sand.

The breakers were right beneath her bows,
  She drifted a dreary wreck,
And a whooping billow swept the crew
  Like icicles from her deck.

She struck where the white and fleecy waves
  Looked soft as carded wool,
But the cruel rocks, they gored her side
  Like the horns of an angry bull.

Her rattling shrouds, all sheathed in ice,
  With the masts, went by the board;
Like a vessel of glass, she stove and sank,
  Ho! ho! the breakers roared!

At daybreak, on the bleak sea-beach,
  A fisherman stood aghast,
To see the form of a maiden fair,
  Lashed close to a drifting mast.

The salt sea was frozen on her breast,
  The salt tears in her eyes;
And he saw her hair, like the brown sea-weed,
  On the billows fall and rise.

Such was the wreck of the Hesperus,
  In the midnight and the snow!
Christ save us all from a death like this,
  On the reef of Norman's Woe!

Henry Wadsworth Longfellow

THE PIPES AT LUCKNOW

[SEPTEMBER 26, 1857]

Pipes of the misty moorlands,
  Voice of the glens and hills;
The droning of the torrents,
  The treble of the rills!
Not the braes of broom and heather,
  Nor the mountains dark with rain,
Nor maiden bower, nor border tower,
  Have heard your sweetest strain!

Dear to the Lowland reaper,
  And plaided mountaineer,—
To the cottage and the castle
  The Scottish pipes are dear;—
Sweet sounds the ancient pibroch
  O'er mountain, loch, and glade;
But the sweetest of all music
  The pipes at Lucknow played.

Day by day the Indian tiger
  Louder yelled, and nearer crept;
Round and round, the jungle-serpent
  Near and nearer circles swept.

"Pray for rescue, wives and mothers,—
    Pray to-day!" the soldier said;
"To-morrow, death's between us
    And the wrong and shame we dread."

Oh, they listened, looked, and waited,
    Till their hope became despair;
And the sobs of low bewailing
    Filled the pauses of their prayer.
Then up spake a Scottish maiden,
    With her ear unto the ground:
"Dinna ye hear it?—dinna ye hear it?
    The pipes o' Havelock sound!"

Hushed the wounded man his groaning;
    Hushed the wife her little ones;
Alone they heard the drum-roll
    And the roar of Sepoy guns.
But to sounds of home and childhood
    The Highland ear was true;—
As her mother's cradle-crooning
    The mountain pipes she knew.

Like the march of soundless music
    Through the vision of the seer,
More of feeling than of hearing,
    Of the heart than of the ear,
She knew the droning pibroch,
    She knew the Campbell's call:
"Hark! hear ye no' MacGregor's,
    The grandest o' them all!"

Oh, they listened, dumb and breathless,
    And they caught the sound at last;
Faint and far beyond the Goomtee
    Rose and fell the piper's blast!

Then a burst of wild thanksgiving
  Mingled woman's voice and man's;
"God be praised!—the march of Havelock!
  The piping of the clans!"

Louder, nearer, fierce as vengeance,
  Sharp and shrill as swords at strife,
Came the wild MacGregor's clan-call,
  Stinging all the air to life.
But when the far-off dust-cloud
  To plaided legions grew,
Full tenderly and blithesomely
  The pipes of rescue blew!

Round the silver domes of Lucknow,
  Moslem mosque and Pagan shrine,
Breathed the air to Britons dearest,
  The air of Auld Lang Syne.
O'er the cruel roll of war-drums
  Rose that sweet and homelike strain;
And the tartan clove the turban
  As the Goomtee cleaves the plain.

Dear to the corn-land reaper
  And plaided mountaineer,—
To the cottage and the castle
  The piper's song is dear.
Sweet sounds the Gaelic pibroch
  O'er mountain, glen, and glade;
But the sweetest of all music
  The pipes at Lucknow played!

              John Greenleaf Whittier

THE HIGHWAYMAN

PART ONE

The wind was a torrent of darkness among the gusty trees,
The moon was a ghostly galleon tossed upon cloudy seas,
The road was a ribbon of moonlight over the purple moor,
And the highwayman came riding—
   Riding—riding—
The highwayman came riding, up to the old inn-door.

He'd a French cock-hat on his forehead, a bunch of lace
   at his chin,
A coat of the claret velvet, and breeches of brown doe-
   skin;
They fitted with never a wrinkle: his boots were up to the
   thigh!
And he rode with a jeweled twinkle,
   His pistol butts a-twinkle,
His rapier hilt a-twinkle, under the jeweled sky.

Over the cobbles he clattered and clashed in the dark inn-
   yard,
And he tapped with his whip on the shutters, but all was
   locked and barred;
He whistled a tune to the window, and who should be
   waiting there
But the landlord's black-eyed daughter,
   Bess, the landlord's daughter,
Plaiting a dark red love-knot into her long black hair.

And dark in the dark old inn-yard a stable-wicket creaked
Where Tim the ostler listened; his face was white and
   peaked;
His eyes were hollows of madness, his hair like mouldy hay,
But he loved the landlord's daughter,

The landlord's red-lipped daughter,
Dumb as a dog he listened, and he heard the robber say—

"One kiss, my bonny sweetheart, I'm after a prize to-night,
But I shall be back with the yellow gold before the morn-
    ing light;
Yet, if they press me sharply, and harry me through the
    day,
Then look for me by moonlight,
    Watch for me by moonlight,
I'll come to thee by moonlight, though hell should bar the
    way."

He rose upright in the stirrups; he scarce could reach her
    hand,
But she loosened her hair i' the casement! His face burnt
    like a brand
As the black cascade of perfume came tumbling over his
    breast;
And he kissed its waves in the moonlight,
    (Oh, sweet black waves in the moonlight!)
Then he tugged at his rein in the moonlight, and galloped
    away to the West.

PART TWO

He did not come in the dawning; he did not come at noon;
And out o' the tawny sunset, before the rise o' the moon,
When the road was a gipsy's ribbon, looping the purple
    moor,
A red-coat troop came marching—
    Marching—marching—
King George's men came marching, up to the old inn-door.

They said no word to the landlord, they drank his ale in-
    stead,
But they gagged his daughter and bound her to the foot
    of her narrow bed;

Two of them knelt at her casement, with muskets at their
    side!
There was death at every window;
  And hell at one dark window;
For Bess could see, through her casement, the road that
    he would ride.

They had tied her up to attention, with many a sniggering
    jest;
They had bound a musket beside her, with the barrel be-
    neath her breast!
"Now keep good watch!" and they kissed her.
  She heard the dead man say—
Look for me by moonlight;
  Watch for me by moonlight;
I'll come to thee by moonlight, though hell should bar the
    way!

She twisted her hands behind her; but all the knots held
    good!
She writhed her hands till her fingers were wet with sweat
    or blood!
They stretched and strained in the darkness, and the hours
    crawled by like years,
Till, now, on the stroke of midnight,
  Cold, on the stroke of midnight,
The tip of one finger touched it! The trigger at least was
    hers!

The tip of one finger touched it; she strove no more for
    the rest!
Up, she stood up to attention, with the barrel beneath
    her breast,
She would not risk their hearing; she would not strive
    again;

For the road lay bare in the moonlight;
  Blank and bare in the moonlight;
And the blood of her veins in the moonlight throbbed to
  her love's refrain.

Tlot-tlot; tlot-tlot! Had they heard it? The horse-hoofs
  ringing clear;
Tlot-tlot, tlot-tlot, in the distance? Were they deaf that
  they did not hear?
Down the ribbon of moonlight, over the brow of the hill,
The highwayman came riding,
  Riding, riding!
The red-coats looked to their priming! She stood up,
  straight and still!

Tlot-tlot, in the frosty silence! *Tlot-tlot*, in the echoing
  night!
Nearer he came and nearer! Her face was like a light!
Her eyes grew wide for a moment; she drew one last deep
  breath,
Then her finger moved in the moonlight,
  Her musket shattered the moonlight,
Shattered her breast in the moonlight and warned him—
  with her death.

He turned; he spurred to the West; he did not know who
  stood
Bowed, with her head o'er the musket, drenched with her
  own red blood!
Not till the dawn he heard it, his face grew gray to hear
How Bess, the landlord's daughter,
  The landlord's black-eyed daughter,
Had watched for her love in the moonlight, and died in
  the darkness there.

Back, he spurred like a madman, shrieking a curse to the
    sky,
With the white road smoking behind him and his rapier
    brandished high!
Blood-red were his spurs i' the golden noon: wine-red was
    his velvet coat,
When they shot him down on the highway,
    Down like a dog in the highway,
And he lay in his blood on the highway, with the bunch of
    lace at his throat.

   .   .   .   .

And still of a winter's night, they say, when the wind is
    in the trees,
When the moon is a ghostly galleon tossed upon cloudy
    seas,
When the road is a ribbon of moonlight over the purple
    moor,
A highwayman comes riding—
    Riding—riding—
A highwayman comes riding, up to the old inn-door.

Over the cobbles he clatters and clangs in the dark inn-
    yard;
He taps with his whip on the shutters, but all is locked
    and barred;
He whistles a tune at the window, and who should be wait-
    ing there
But the landlord's black-eyed daughter,
    Bess, the landlord's daughter,
Plaiting a dark red love-knot into her long black hair.

Alfred Noyes

ɪx. My Country

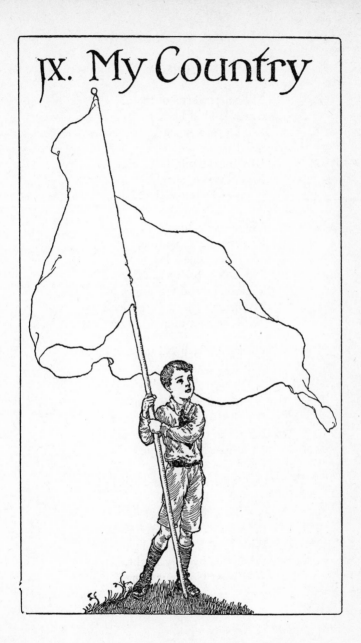

AMERICA

My country, 'tis of thee,
Sweet land of liberty,
    Of thee I sing;
Land where my fathers died,
Land of the pilgrims' pride,
From every mountain-side
    Let Freedom ring.

My native country, thee,
Land of the noble free,—
    Thy name I love;
I love thy rocks and rills,
Thy woods and templed hills;
My heart with rapture thrills
    Like that above.

Let music swell the breeze,
And ring from all the trees
    Sweet Freedom's song;
Let mortal tongues awake,
Let all that breathe partake,
Let rocks their silence break,
    The sound prolong.

Our fathers' God, to Thee,
Author of liberty,
    To Thee we sing;
Long may our land be bright
With Freedom's holy light;
Protect us by Thy might,
    Great God, our King.

Samuel Francis Smith

MY COUNTRY

THE STAR-SPANGLED BANNER

O say, can you see, by the dawn's early light,
    What so proudly we hailed at the twilight's last gleam-
      ing?
Whose broad stripes and bright stars, through the peri-
    lous fight,
    O'er the ramparts we watched, were so gallantly stream-
      ing!
And the rockets' red glare, the bombs bursting in air,
Gave proof through the night that our flag was still there:
    O say, does that star-spangled banner yet wave
    O'er the land of the free and the home of the brave?

On the shore, dimly seen through the mists of the deep,
    Where the foe's haughty host in dread silence reposes,
What is that which the breeze, o'er the towering steep,
    As it fitfully blows, now conceals, now discloses?
Now it catches the gleam of the morning's first beam,
In full glory reflected now shines on the stream:
    'Tis the star-spangled banner! O long may it wave
    O'er the land of the free and the home of the brave!

And where is that band who so vauntingly swore
    That the havoc of war and the battle's confusion
A home and a country should leave us no more?
    Their blood has washed out their foul footsteps' pollu-
      tion.
No refuge could save the hireling and slave
From the terror of flight, or the gloom of the grave:
    And the star-spangled banner in triumph doth wave
    O'er the land of the free and the home of the brave!

Oh! thus be it ever, when freemen shall stand
  Between their loved homes and the war's desolation!
Blest with victory and peace, may the heaven-rescued
    land
  Praise the Power that hath made and preserved us a
    nation.
Then conquer we must, for our cause it is just,
And this be our motto: "In God is our trust."
  And the star-spangled banner in triumph shall wave
  O'er the land of the free and the home of the brave!

                                          Francis Scott Key

THE AMERICAN FLAG

I

When Freedom, from her mountain height,
  Unfurled her standard to the air,
She tore the azure robe of night,
  And set the stars of glory there;
She mingled with its gorgeous dyes
The milky baldric of the skies,
And striped its pure, celestial white
With streakings of the morning light;
Then, from his mansion in the sun,
She called her eagle bearer down,
And gave into his mighty hand
The symbol of her chosen land.

II

Majestic monarch of the cloud!
  Who rear'st aloft thy regal form,
To hear the tempest-trumpings loud,
And see the lightning-lances driven,
  When strive the warriors of the storm,
And rolls the thunder-drum of heaven—
Child of the sun! to thee 'tis given

To guard the banner of the free,
To hover in the sulphur smoke,
To ward away the battle-stroke,
And bid its blendings shine afar,
Like rainbows on the cloud of war,
  The harbingers of victory!

III

Flag of the brave! thy folds shall fly,
The sign of hope and triumph high,
When speaks the signal-trumpet tone,
And the long line comes gleaming on:
Ere yet the life-blood, warm and wet,
Has dimmed the glistening bayonet,
Each soldier eye shall brightly turn
To where thy sky-born glories burn,
And, as his springing steps advance,
Catch war and vengeance from the glance;
And when the cannon-mouthings loud
Heave in wild wreaths the battle-shroud,
And gory sabres rise and fall,
Like shoots of flame on midnight's pall;
  Then shall thy meteor-glances glow,
And cowering foes shall sink beneath
  Each gallant arm that strikes below
That lovely messenger of death.

IV

Flag of the seas! on ocean wave
Thy stars shall glitter o'er the brave;
When death, careering on the gale,
Sweeps darkly round the bellied sail,
And frighted waves rush wildly back
Before the broadside's reeling rack,
Each dying wanderer of the sea
Shall look at once to heaven and thee,

And smile to see thy splendors fly
In triumph o'er his closing eye.

v

Flag of the free heart's hope and home,
    By angel hands to valor given;
Thy stars have lit the welkin dome,
    And all thy hues were born in heaven.
Forever float that standard sheet!
    Where breathes the foe but falls before us,
With Freedom's soil beneath our feet,
    And Freedom's banner streaming o'er us?

Joseph Rodman Drake

THE FLOWER OF LIBERTY

What flower is this that greets the morn,
Its hues from Heaven so freshly born?
With burning star and flaming band
It kindles all the sunset land:
Oh tell us what its name may be,—
Is this the Flower of Liberty?
    It is the banner of the free,
    The starry Flower of Liberty!

In savage nature's far abode
Its tender seed our fathers sowed;
The storm-winds rocked its swelling bud,
Its opening leaves were streaked with blood,
Till lo! earth's tyrants shook to see
The full-blown Flower of Liberty!

Behold its streaming rays unite,
One mingling flood of braided light,—
The red that fires the Southern rose,
With spotless white from Northern snows,

And, spangled o'er its azure, see
The sister Stars of Liberty

The blades of heroes fence it round,
Where'er it springs is holy ground;
From tower and dome its glories spread;
It waves where lonely sentries tread;
It makes the land as ocean free,
And plants an empire on the sea!

Thy sacred leaves, fair Freedom's flower,
Shall ever float on dome and tower,
To all their heavenly colors true,
In blackening frost or crimson dew.—
And God love us as we love thee,
Thrice holy Flower of Liberty!
    Then hail the banner of the free,
    The starry Flower of Liberty!

Oliver Wendell Holmes

THE FLAG GOES BY

Hats off!
Along the street there comes
A blare of bugles, a ruffle of drums,
A flash of color beneath the sky:
Hats off!
The flag is passing by!

Blue and crimson and white it shines,
Over the steel-tipped, ordered lines.
Hats off!
The colors before us fly;
But more than the flag is passing by:

Sea-fights and land-fights, grim and great,
Fought to make and to save the State:
Weary marches and sinking ships;
Cheers of victory on dying lips;

Days of plenty and years of peace;
March of a strong land's swift increase;
Equal justice, right and law,
Stately honor and reverend awe;

Sign of a nation, great and strong
To ward her people from foreign wrong:
Pride and glory and honor,—all
Live in the colors to stand or fall.

Hats off!
Along the street there comes
A blare of bugles, a ruffle of drums;
And loyal hearts are beating high:
Hats off!
The flag is passing by!

Henry Holcomb Bennett

AMERICA THE BEAUTIFUL

O beautiful for spacious skies,
　　For amber waves of grain,
For purple mountain majesties
　　Above the fruited plain!
　　　　America! America!
　　God shed His grace on thee
And crown thy good with brotherhood
　　From sea to shining sea!

O beautiful for pilgrim feet,
　　Whose stern, impassioned stress

A thoroughfare for freedom beat
 Across the wilderness!
  America! America!
 God mend thine every flaw,
Confirm thy soul in self-control,
 Thy liberty in law!

O beautiful for heroes proved
 In liberating strife,
Who more than self their country loved,
 And mercy more than life!
  America! America!
 May God thy gold refine
Till all success be nobleness,
 And every gain divine!

O beautiful for patriot dream
 That sees beyond the years
Thine alabaster cities gleam
 Undimmed by human tears!
  America! America!
 God shed His grace on thee
And crown thy good with brotherhood
 From sea to shining sea!

    Katharine Lee Bates

OH MOTHER OF A MIGHTY RACE

Oh mother of a mighty race,
Yet lovely in thy youthful grace!
The elder dames, thy haughty peers,
Admire and hate thy blooming years.
 With words of shame
And taunts of scorn they join thy name.

For on thy cheeks the glow is spread
That tints thy morning hills with red;

Thy step—the wild deer's rustling feet
Within thy woods are not more fleet;
  Thy hopeful eye
Is bright as thine own sunny sky.

Ay, let them rail—those haughty ones,
While safe thou dwellest with thy sons.
They do not know how loved thou art,
How many a fond and fearless heart
  Would rise to throw
Its life between thee and the foe.

They know not, in their hate and pride,
What virtues with thy children bide;
How true, how good, thy graceful maids
Make bright, like flowers, the valley-shades;
  What generous men
Spring, like thine oaks, by hill and glen;—

What cordial welcomes greet the guest
By thy lone rivers of the West;
How faith is kept, and truth revered,
And man is loved, and God is feared,
  In woodland homes,
And where the ocean border foams.

There's freedom at thy gates and rest
For Earth's down-trodden and oppressed,
A shelter for the hunted head,
For the starved laborer toil and bread,
  Power, at thy bounds,
Stops and calls back his baffled hounds.

Oh, fair young mother! on thy brow
Shall sit a nobler grace than now.

Deep in the brightness of the skies
The thronging years in glory rise,
　　And, as they fleet,
Drop strength and riches at thy feet.

　　　　　　　　　　William Cullen Bryant

DEAR LAND OF ALL MY LOVE

From "The Centennial Meditation of Columbia"

Long as thine Art shall love true love,
Long as thy Science truth shall know,
Long as thine Eagle harms no Dove,
Long as thy law by law shall grow,
Long as thy God is God above,
Thy brother every man below,
So long, dear Land of all my love,
Thy name shall shine, thy fame shall glow!

　　　　　　　　　　　　Sidney Lanier

BATTLE-HYMN OF THE REPUBLIC

Mine eyes have seen the glory of the coming of the Lord;
He is trampling out the vintage where the grapes of wrath
　　are stored;
He hath loosed the fateful lightning of His terrible swift
　　sword;
　　　His truth is marching on.

I have seen Him in the watch-fires of a hundred circling
　　camps;
They have builded Him an altar in the evening dews and
　　damps;
I can read His righteous sentence by the dim and flaring
　　lamps;
　　　His day is marching on.

I have read a fiery gospel, writ in burnished rows of steel:
"As ye deal with my contemners, so with you my grace
shall deal;
Let the Hero, born of woman, crush the serpent with his
heel,
Since God is marching on."

He has sounded forth the trumpet that shall never call re-
treat;
He is sifting out the hearts of men before His judgment-
seat:
Oh, be swift, my soul, to answer Him! be jubilant, my feet!
Our God is marching on.

In the beauty of the lilies Christ was born across the sea,
With a glory in His bosom that transfigures you and me:
As He died to make men holy, let us die to make men free,
While God is marching on.

Julia Ward Howe

AMERICA FOR ME

'Tis fine to see the Old World, and travel up and down
Among the famous palaces and cities of renown,
To admire the crumbly castles and the statues of the
kings,—
But now I think I've had enough of antiquated things.

So it's home again, and home again, America for me!
My heart is turning home again, and there I long to be,
In the land of youth and freedom beyond the ocean bars,
Where the air is full of sunlight and the flag is full of stars.

Oh, London is a man's town, there's power in the air;
And Paris is a woman's town, with flowers in her hair;

And it's sweet to dream in Venice, and it's great to study
    Rome;
But when it comes to living, there is no place like home.

I like the German fir-woods, in green battalions drilled;
I like the gardens of Versailles, with flashing fountains
    filled;
But oh, to take your hand, my dear, and ramble for a day
In the friendly Western woodland where Nature has her
    way!

I know that Europe's wonderful, yet something seems to
    lack:
The Past is too much with her, and the people looking back.
But the glory of the Present is to make the Future free,—
We love our land for what she is and what she is to be.

Oh, it's home again, and home again, America for me!
I want a ship that's westward bound to plow the rolling sea,
To the blessed Land of Room Enough beyond the ocean bars,
Where the air is full of sunlight and the flag is full of stars.
                      Henry Van Dyke

THE LANDING OF THE PILGRIM FATHERS

[NOVEMBER 19, 1620]

The breaking waves dashed high
    On a stern and rock-bound coast,
And the woods, against a stormy sky,
    Their giant branches tossed;

And the heavy night hung dark
    The hills and waters o'er,
When a band of exiles moored their bark
    On the wild New England shore.

Not as the conquerer comes,
   They, the true-hearted came:
Not with the roll of the stirring drums,
   And the trumpet that sings of fame;

Not as the flying come,
   In silence and in fear,—
They shook the depths of the desert's gloom
   With their hymns of lofty cheer.

Amidst the storm they sang,
   And the stars heard, and the sea;
And the sounding aisles of the dim woods rang
   To the anthem of the free!

The ocean-eagle soared
   From his nest by the white waves' foam,
And the rocking pines of the forest roared;
   This was their welcome home!

There were men with hoary hair
   Amidst that pilgrim-band;
Why had they come to wither there,
   Away from their childhood's land?

There was woman's fearless eye,
   Lit by her deep love's truth;
There was manhood's brow, serenely high,
   And the fiery heart of youth.

What sought they thus afar?
   Bright jewels of the mine?
The wealth of seas, the spoils of war?—
   They sought a faith's pure shrine!

Aye, call it holy ground,
   The soil where first they trod!

They have left unstained what there they found—
Freedom to worship God!

Felicia Dorothea Hemans

PAUL REVERE'S RIDE

"The Landlord's Tale" from "Tales of a Wayside Inn"

[APRIL 18–19, 1775]

Listen my children, and you shall hear
Of the midnight ride of Paul Revere,
On the eighteenth of April, in seventy-five;
Hardly a man is now alive
Who remembers that famous day and year.

He said to his friend, "If the British march
By land or sea from the town to-night,
Hang a lantern aloft in the belfry arch
Of the North Church tower as a signal light,—
One, if by land, and two, if by sea;
And I on the opposite shore will be,
Ready to ride and spread the alarm
Through every Middlesex village and farm,
For the country folk to be up and to arm."

Then he said, "Good night!" and with muffled oar
Silently rowed to the Charlestown shore,
Just as the moon rose over the bay,
Where swinging wide at her moorings lay
The Somerset, British man-of-war;
A phantom ship, with each mast and spar
Across the moon like a prison bar,
And a hugh black hulk, that was magnified
By its own reflection in the tide.

Meanwhile, his friend, through alley and street,
Wanders and watches with eager ears,

Till in the silence around him he hears
The muster of men at the barrack door,
The sound of arms, and the tramp of feet,
And the measured tread of the grenadiers,
Marching down to their boats on the shore.

Then he climbed the tower of the old North Church,
By the wooden stairs, with stealthy tread,
To the belfry-chamber overhead,
And startled the pigeons from their perch
On the sombre rafters, that round him made
Masses and moving shapes of shade,—
By the trembling ladder, steep and tall,
To the highest window in the wall,
Where he paused to listen and look down
A moment on the roofs of the town,
And the moonlight flowing over all.

Beneath, in the churchyard, lay the dead,
In their night-encampment on the hill,
Wrapped in silence so deep and still
That he could hear, like a sentinel's tread,
The watchful night-wind, as it went
Creeping along from tent to tent,
And seeming to whisper, "All is well!"
A moment only he feels the spell
Of the place and the hour, and the secret dread
Of the lonely belfry and the dead;
For suddenly all his thoughts are bent
On a shadowy something far away,
Where the river widens to meet the bay,—
A line of black that bends and floats
On the rising tide, like a bridge of boats.

Meanwhile, impatient to mount and ride,
Booted and spurred, with a heavy stride

On the opposite shore walked Paul Revere.
Now he patted his horse's side,
Now gazed at the landscape far and near,
Then, impetuous, stamped the earth,
And turned and tightened his saddle-girth;
But mostly he watched with eager search
The belfry-tower of the Old North Church,
As it rose above the graves on the hill,
Lonely and spectral and sombre and still.
And lo! as he looks, on the belfry's height
A glimmer, and then a gleam of light!
He springs to the saddle, the bridle he turns,
But lingers and gazes, till full on his sight
A second lamp in the belfry burns!

A hurry of hoofs in a village street,
A shape in the moonlight, a bulk in the dark,
And beneath, from the pebbles, in passing, a spark
Struck out by a steed flying fearless and fleet:
That was all! And yet, through the gloom and the light,
The fate of a nation was riding that night;
And the spark struck out by that steed, in his flight,
Kindled the land into flame with its heat.

He has left the village and mounted the steep,
And beneath him, tranquil and broad and deep,
Is the Mystic, meeting the ocean tides;
And under the alders that skirt its edge,
Now soft on the sand, now loud on the ledge,
Is heard the tramp of his steed as he rides.

It was twelve by the village clock,
When he crossed the bridge into Medford town.
He heard the crowing of the cock,
And the barking of the farmer's dog,
And felt the damp of the river fog,
That rises after the sun goes down.

It was one by the village clock,
When he galloped into Lexington.
He saw the gilded weathercock
Swing in the moonlight as he passed.
And the meeting-house windows, blank and bare,
Gaze at him with a spectral glare,
As if they already stood aghast
At the bloody work they would look upon.

It was two by the village clock,
When he came to the bridge in Concord town.
He heard the bleating of the flock,
And the twitter of birds among the trees,
And felt the breath of the morning breeze
Blowing over the meadows brown.
And one was safe and asleep in his bed
Who at the bridge would be first to fall,
Who that day would be lying dead,
Pierced by a British musket-ball.

You know the rest. In the books you have read,
How the British Regulars fired and fled,—
How the farmers gave them ball for ball,
From behind each fence and farmyard wall,
Chasing the red-coats down the lane,
Then crossing the fields to emerge again
Under the trees at the turn of the road,
And only pausing to fire and load.

So through the night rode Paul Revere;
And so through the night went his cry of alarm
To every Middlesex village and farm,—
A cry of defiance and not of fear,
A voice in the darkness, a knock at the door,
And a word that shall echo forevermore!

For, borne on the night-wind of the Past,
Through all our history, to the last,
In the hour of darkness and peril and need,
The people will waken and listen to hear
The hurrying hoof-beats of that steed,
And the midnight message of Paul Revere.

Henry Wadsworth Longfellow

NEW ENGLAND'S CHEVY CHASE

[APRIL 19, 1775]

'Twas the dead of the night. By the pineknot's red light
  Brooks lay, half-asleep, when he heard the alarm,—
Only this, and no more, from a voice at the door:
  "The Red-Coats are out, and have passed Phips's farm."

Brooks was booted and spurred; he said never a word:
  Took his horn from its peg, and his gun from the rack;
To the cold midnight air he led out his white mare,
  Strapped the girths and the bridle, and sprang to her
    back.

Up the North County road at her full pace she strode,
  Till Brooks reined her up at John Tarbell's to say,
"We have got the alarm,—they have left Phips's farm;
  You rouse the East Precinct, and I'll go this way."

John called his hired man, and they harnessed the span;
  They roused Abram Garfield, and Abram called me:
"Turn out right away; let no minute-man stay;
  The Red-Coats have landed at Phips's," says he.

By the Powder-House Green seven others fell in;
  At Nahum's the men from the Saw-Mill came down;
So that when Jabez Bland gave the word of command,
  And said, "Forward, march!" there marched forward
  THE TOWN.

Parson Wilderspin stood by the side of the road,
   And he took off his hat, and he said, "Let us pray!
O Lord, God of might, let thine angels of light
   Lead thy children to-night to the glories of day!
And let thy stars fight all the foes of the Right
   As the stars fought of old against Sisera."

And from heaven's high arch those stars blessed our march,
   Till the last of them faded in twilight away;
And with morning's bright beam, by the banks of the stream
   Half the county marched in, and we heard Davis say:

"On the King's own highway I may travel all day,
   And no man hath warrant to stop me," says he;
"I've no man that's afraid, and I'll march at their head."
   Then he turned to the boys, "Forward, march! Follow
     me."

And we marched as he said, and the Fifer he played
   The old "White Cockade," and he played it right well.
We saw Davis fall dead, but no man was afraid;
   That bridge we'd have had, though a thousand men fell.

This opened the play, and it lasted all day.
   We made Concord too hot for the Red-Coats to stay;
Down the Lexington way we stormed, black, white, and
     gray
   We were first in the feast, and were last in the fray.

They would turn in dismay, as red wolves turn at bay.
   They levelled, they fired, they charged up the road.
Cephas Willard fell dead; he was shot in the head
   As he knelt by Aunt Prudence's well-sweep to load.

John Danforth was hit just in Lexington Street,
   John Bridge at that lane where you cross Beaver Falls,

And Winch and the Snows just above John Munroe's—
  Swept away by one swoop of the big cannon-balls.

I took Bridge on my knee, but he said, "Don't mind me;
Fill your horn from mine,—let me lie where I be.
Our fathers," says he, "that their sons might be free,
Left their king on his throne, and came over the sea;
And that man is a knave, or a fool who, to save
His life for a minute, would live like a slave."

Well, all would not do! There were men good as new,—
  From Rumford, from Saugus, from towns far away,—
Who filled up quick and well for each soldier that fell;
  And we drove them, and drove them, and drove them,
    all day.
We knew, every one, it was war that begun,
When that morning's marching was only half done.

In the hazy twilight, at the coming of night,
  I crowded three buckshot and one bullet down.
'Twas my last charge of lead; and I aimed her and said,
  "Good luck to you, lobsters, in old Boston Town."

In a barn at Milk Row, Ephraim Bates and Munroe,
  And Baker, and Abram, and I made a bed.
We had mighty sore feet, and we'd nothing to eat;
  But we'd driven the Red-Coats, and Amos, he said:
"It's the first time," says he, "that it's happened to me
  To march to the sea by this road where we've come;
But confound this whole day, but we'd all of us say
  We'd rather have spent it this way than to home."

The hunt had begun with the dawn of the sun,
  And night saw the wolf driven back to his den.
And never since then, in the memory of men,
  Has the Old Bay State seen such a hunting again.

Edward Everett Hale

CONCORD HYMN

SUNG AT THE COMPLETION OF THE BATTLE MONUMENT,
APRIL 19, 1836

By the rude bridge that arched the flood,
　Their flag to April's breeze unfurled,
Here once the embattled farmers stood,
　And fired the shot heard round the world.

The foe long since in silence slept;
　Alike the conquerer silent sleeps;
And Time the ruined bridge has swept
　Down the dark stream which seaward creeps.

On this green bank, by this soft stream,
　We set to-day a votive stone;
That memory may their deed redeem,
　When, like our sires, our sons are gone.

Spirit, that made those heroes dare
　To die, and leave their children free,
Bid Time and Nature gently spare
　The shaft we raise to them and thee.

Ralph Waldo Emerson

WARREN'S ADDRESS AT BUNKER HILL

[JUNE 16–17, 1775]

Stand! the ground's your own, my braves!
Will ye give it up to slaves?
Will ye look for greener graves?
　Hope ye mercy still?
What's the mercy despots feel?
Hear it in that battle-peal!
Read it on yon bristling steel!
　Ask it,—ye who will.

Fear ye foes who kill for hire?
Will ye to your homes retire?
Look behind you!—they're afire!
　And, before you, see
Who have done it! From the vale
On they come—and will ye quail?
Leaden rain and iron hail
　Let their welcome be!

In the God of battles trust!
Die we may,—and die we must:
But, O, where can dust to dust
　Be consigned so well,
As where heaven its dews shall shed
On the martyred patriot's bed,
And the rocks shall raise their head,
　Of his deeds to tell?

John Pierpont

SONG OF MARION'S MEN

[1780–1781]

Our band is few, but true and tried,
　Our leader frank and bold;
The British soldier trembles
　When Marion's name is told.
Our fortress is the good greenwood,
　Our tent the cypress-tree;
We know the forest round us
　As seamen know the sea.
We know its walls of thorny vines,
　Its glades of reedy grass,
Its safe and silent islands
　Within the dark morass.

Woe to the English soldiery
　That little dread us near!

On them shall light at midnight
  A strange and sudden fear:
When, waking to their tents on fire,
  They grasp their arms in vain,
And they who stand to face us
  Are beat to earth again;
And they who fly in terror deem
  A mighty host behind,
And hear the tramp of thousands
  Upon the hollow wind.

Then sweet the hour that brings release
  From danger and from toil;
We talk the battle over,
  We share the battle's spoil.
The woodland rings with laugh and shout
  As if a hunt were up,
And woodland flowers are gathered
  To crown the soldier's cup.
With merry songs we mock the wind
  That in the pine-top grieves,
And slumber long and sweetly
  On beds of oaken leaves.

Well knows the fair and friendly moon
  The band that Marion leads—
The glitter of their rifles,
  The scampering of their steeds.
'Tis life to guide the fiery barb
  Across the moonlight plain;
'Tis life to feel the night-wind
  That lifts his tossing mane.
A moment in the British camp—
  A moment—and away,
Back to the pathless forest
  Before the peep of day.

Grave men there are by broad Santee,
  Grave men with hoary hairs;
Their hearts are all with Marion,
  For Marion are their prayers.
And lovely ladies greet our band
  With kindliest welcoming,
With smiles like those of summer,
  And tears like those of spring.
For them we wear these trusty arms,
  And lay them down no more
Till we have driven the Briton,
  Forever, from our shore.

William Cullen Bryant

OLD IRONSIDES

[SEPTEMBER 14, 1830]

Ay, tear her tattered ensign down!
  Long has it waved on high,
And many an eye has danced to see
  That banner in the sky;
Beneath it rung the battle shout,
  And burst the cannon's roar;—
The meteor of the ocean air
  Shall sweep the clouds no more.

Her deck, once red with heroes' blood,
  Where knelt the vanquished foe,
When winds were hurrying o'er the flood,
  And waves were white below,
No more shall feel the victor's tread,
  Or know the conquered knee;—
The harpies of the shore shall pluck
  The eagle of the sea!

Oh, better that her shattered hulk
    Should sink beneath the wave;
Her thunders shook the mighty deep,
    And there should be her grave;
Nail to the mast her holy flag,
    Set every threadbare sail,
And give her to the god of storms,
    The lightning and the gale!

                 Oliver Wendell Holmes

KEARNY AT SEVEN PINES

[MAY 31, 1862]

So that soldierly legend is still on its journey,—
    That story of Kearny who knew not to yield!
'Twas the day when with Jameson, fierce Berry, and
    Birney,
    Against twenty thousand he rallied the field.
Where the red volleys poured, where the clamor rose high-
    est,
    Where the dead lay in clumps through the dwarf oak
    and pine,
Where the aim from the thicket was surest and nighest,—
    No charge like Phil Kearny's along the whole line.

When the battle went ill, and the bravest were solemn,
    Near the dark Seven Pines, where we still held our
    ground,
He rode down the length of the withering column,
    And his heart at our war-cry leapt up with a bound;
He snuffed, like his charger, the wind of the powder,—
    His sword waved us on and we answered the sign;
Loud our cheer as we rushed, but his laugh rang the louder,
    "There's the devil's own fun, boys, along the whole
    line!"

How he strode his brown steed! How we saw his blade
   brighten
  In the one hand still left,—and the reins in his teeth!
He laughed like a boy when the holidays heighten,
  But a soldier's glance shot from his visor beneath.
Up came the reserves to the mellay infernal,
  Asking where to go in,—through the clearing or pine?
"Oh, anywhere! Forward! 'Tis all the same, Colonel:
  You'll find lovely fighting along the whole line!"

Oh, evil the black shroud of night at Chantilly,
  That hid him from sight of his brave men and tried!
Foul, foul sped the bullet that clipped the white lily,
  The flower of our knighthood, the whole army's pride!
Yet we dream that he still,—in that shadowy region
  Where the dead form their ranks at the wan drummer's
    sign,—
Rides on, as of old, down the length of his legion,
  And the word still is "Forward!" along the whole line.
Edmund Clarence Stedman

BARBARA FRIETCHIE

[SEPTEMBER 13, 1862]

Up from the meadows rich with corn,
Clear in the cool September morn,

The clustered spires of Frederick stand
Green-walled by the hills of Maryland.

Round about them orchards sweep,
Apple and peach tree fruited deep,

Fair as the garden of the Lord
To the eyes of the famished rebel horde,

On that pleasant morn of the early fall
When Lee marched over the mountain-wall;

Over the mountains winding down,
Horse and foot, into Frederick town.

Forty flags with their silver stars,
Forty flags with their crimson bars,

Flapped in the morning wind: the sun
Of noon looked down, and saw not one.

Up rose old Barbara Frietchie then,
Bowed with her fourscore years and ten;

Bravest of all in Frederick town,
She took up the flag the men hauled down;

In her attic window the staff she set,
To show that one heart was loyal yet.

Up the street came the rebel tread,
Stonewall Jackson riding ahead.

Under his slouched hat left and right
He glanced; the old flag met his sight.

"Halt!"—the dust-brown ranks stood fast.
"Fire!"—out blazed the rifle-blast.

It shivered the window, pane and sash;
It rent the banner with seam and gash.

Quick, as it fell, from the broken staff
Dame Barbara snatched the silken scarf.

She leaned far out on the window-sill,
And shook it forth with a royal will.

"Shoot, if you must, this old gray head,
But spare your country's flag," she said.

A shade of sadness, a blush of shame,
Over the face of the leader came;

The nobler nature within him stirred
To life at that woman's deed and word;

"Who touches a hair of yon gray head
Dies like a dog! March on!" he said.

All day long through Frederick street
Sounded the tread of marching feet:

All day long that free flag tossed
Over the heads of the rebel host.

Ever its torn folds rose and fell
On the loyal winds that loved it well;

And through the hill-gaps sunset light
Shone over it with a warm good-night.

Barbara Frietchie's work is o'er,
And the Rebel rides on his raids no more.

Honor to her! and let a tear
Fall, for her sake, on Stonewall's bier.

Over Barbara Frietchie's grave,
Flag of Freedom and Union, wave!

Peace and order and beauty draw
Round thy symbol of light and law;

And ever the stars above look down
On thy stars below in Frederick town!

John Greenleaf Whittier

FARRAGUT

[MOBILE BAY, AUGUST 5, 1864]

Farragut, Farragut,
Old Heart of Oak,
Daring Dave Farragut,
Thunderbolt stroke,
Watches the hoary mist
Lift from the bay,
Till his flag, glory-kissed,
Greets the young day.

Far, by gray Morgan's walls,
Looms the black fleet.
Hark, deck to rampart calls
With the drums' beat!
Buoy your chains overboard,
While the steam hums;
Men! to the battlement,
Farragut comes.

See, as the hurricane
Hurtles in wrath
Squadrons of clouds amain
Back from its path!
Back to the parapet,
To the guns' lips,
Thunderbolt Farragut
Hurls the black ships.

Now through the battle's roar
    Clear the boy sings,
"By the mark fathoms four,"
    While his lead swings.
Steady the wheelmen five
    "Nor' by East keep her,"
"Steady," but two alive:
    How the shells sweep her!

Lashed to the mast that sways
    Over red decks,
Over the flame that plays
    Round the torn wrecks,
Over the dying lips
    Framed for a cheer,
Farragut leads his ships,
    Guides the line clear.

On by heights cannon-browed,
    While the spars quiver;
Onward still flames the cloud
    Where the hulks shiver.
See, yon fort's star is set,
    Storm and fire past.
Cheer him, lads—Farragut,
    Lashed to the mast!

Oh! while Atlantic's breast
    Bears a white sail,
While the Gulf's towering crest
    Tops a green vale,
Men thy bold deeds shall tell,
    Old Heart of Oak,
Daring Dave Farragut,
    Thunderbolt stroke!

William Tuckey Meredith

CRAVEN

[MOBILE BAY, AUGUST 5, 1864]

Over the turret, shut in his ironclad tower,
  Craven was conning his ship through smoke and flame;
Gun to gun he had battered the fort for an hour,
  Now was a time for a charge to end the game.

There lay the narrowing channel, smooth and grim,
  A hundred deaths beneath it, and never a sign:
There lay the enemy's ships, and sink or swim
  The flag was flying, and he was head of the line.

The fleet behind was jamming: the monitor hung
  Beating the stream; the roar for a moment hushed;
Craven spoke to the pilot; slow she swung;
  Again he spoke, and right for the foe she rushed

Into the narrowing channel, between the shore
  And the sunk torpedoes lying in treacherous rank;
She turned but a yard too short; a muffled roar,
  A mountainous wave, and she rolled, righted, and sank.

Over the manhole, up in the ironclad tower,
  Pilot and captain met as they turned to fly:
The hundredth part of a moment seemed an hour,
  For one could pass to be saved, and one must die.

They stood like men in a dream; Craven spoke,—
  Spoke as he lived and fought, with a captain's pride:
"After you, Pilot." The pilot woke,
  Down the ladder he went, and Craven died.

All men praise the deed and the manner; but we—
  We set it apart from the pride that stoops to the proud,

The strength that is supple to serve the strong and free,
  The grave of the empty hands and promises loud;

Sidney thirsting a humbler need to slake,
  Nelson waiting his turn for the surgeon's hand,
Lucas crushed with chains for a comrade's sake,
  Outram coveting right before command,

These were paladins, these were Craven's peers,
  These with him shall be crowned in story and song,
Crowned with the glitter of steel and the glimmer of tears,
  Princes of courtesy, merciful, proud, and strong.

Henry Newbolt

SHERIDAN'S RIDE

[OCTOBER 19, 1864]

Up from the South, at break of day,
Bringing to Winchester fresh dismay,
The affrighted air with a shudder bore,
Like a herald in haste, to the chieftain's door,
The terrible grumble, and rumble, and roar,
Telling the battle was on once more,
    And Sheridan twenty miles away.

And wider still those billows of war
Thundered along the horizon's bar;
And louder yet into Winchester rolled
The roar of that red sea uncontrolled,
Making the blood of the listener cold,
As he thought of the stake in that fiery fray,
    And Sheridan twenty miles away.

But there is a road from Winchester town,
A good, broad highway leading down:

And there, through the flush of the morning light,
A steed as black as the steeds of night
Was seen to pass, as with eagle flight;
As if he knew the terrible need,
He stretched away with his utmost speed;
Hills rose and fell, but his heart was gay,
    With Sheridan fifteen miles away.

Still sprang from those swift hoofs, thundering south,
The dust, like smoke from the cannon's mouth,
Or the trail of a comet, sweeping faster and faster,
Foreboding to traitors the doom of disaster.
The heart of the steed and the heart of the master
Were beating like prisoners assaulting their walls,
Impatient to be where the battle-field calls;
Every nerve of the charger was strained to full play,
    With Sheridan only ten miles away.

Under his spurning feet, the road
Like an arrowy Alpine river flowed,
And the landscape sped away behind
Like an ocean flying before the wind;
And the steed, like a bark fed with furnace ire,
Swept on, with its wild eye full of fire;
But, lo! he is nearing his heart's desire;
He is snuffing the smoke of the roaring fray,
    With Sheridan only five miles away.

The first that the general saw were the groups
Of stragglers, and then the retreating troops;
What was done? what to do? a glance told him both,
Then, striking his spurs, with a terrible oath,
He dashed down the line, 'mid a storm of huzzas,
And the wave of retreat checked its course there, because
The sight of the master compelled it to pause.

With foam and with dust the black charger was gray;
By the flash of his eye, and the red nostril's play,
He seemed to the whole great army to say:
"I have brought you Sheridan all the way
    From Winchester town to save the day!"

Hurrah! hurrah for Sheridan!
Hurrah! hurrah for horse and man!
And when their statues are placed on high,
Under the dome of the Union sky,
The American soldier's Temple of Fame,
There, with the glorious general's name,
Be it said, in letters both bold and bright:
"Here is the steed that saved the day
By carrying Sheridan into the fight,
    From Winchester—twenty miles away!"

Thomas Buchanan Read

O CAPTAIN! MY CAPTAIN!

[ABRAHAM LINCOLN, 1809–1865]

O Captain! my Captain! our fearful trip is done,
The ship has weathered every rack, the prize we sought is
    won,
The port is near, the bells I hear, the people all exulting,
While follow eyes the steady keel, the vessel grim and dar-
    ing;
    But O heart! heart! heart!
        O the bleeding drops of red,
    Where on the deck my Captain lies,
        Fallen cold and dead.

O Captain! my Captain!—rise up and hear the bells;
Rise up—for you the flag is flung—for you the bugle trills,

For you bouquets and ribboned wreaths—for you the shores
      a-crowding,
For you they call, the swaying mass, their eager faces turn-
      ing;
      Here Captain! dear father!
      This arm beneath your head!
      It is some dream that on the deck
        You've fallen cold and dead.

My Captain does not answer, his lips are pale and still,
My father does not feel my arm, he has no pulse nor will,
The ship is anchored safe and sound, its voyage closed and
      done,
From fearful trip the victor ship comes in with object won;
      Exult, O shores, and ring, O bells!
      But I with mournful tread,
      Walk the deck my Captain lies,
        Fallen cold and dead.

Walt Whitman

LINCOLN

From the "Commemoration Ode"

Nature, they say, doth dote,
    And cannot make a man
    Save on some worn-out plan,
    Repeating us by rote:
For him her Old-World moulds aside she threw,
    And, choosing sweet clay from the breast
    Of the unexhausted West,
With stuff untainted shaped a hero new,
Wise, steadfast in the strength of God, and true.
    How beautiful to see
Once more a shepherd of mankind indeed,
Who loved his charge, but never loved to lead;
One whose meek flock the people joyed to be,

Not lured by any cheat of birth,
But by his clear-grained human worth,
And brave old wisdom of sincerity!
They knew that outward grace is dust;
They could not choose but trust
In that sure-footed mind's unfaltering skill,
And supple-tempered will
That bent like perfect steel to spring again and thrust.
His was no lonely mountain-peak of mind,
Thrusting to thin air o'er our cloudy bars,
A sea-mark now, now lost in vapors blind;
Broad prairie rather, genial, level-lined,
Fruitful and friendly for all human kind,
Yet also nigh to heaven and loved of loftiest stars.
Nothing of Europe here,
Or, then, of Europe fronting mornward still,
Ere any names of Serf and Peer
Could Nature's equal scheme deface
And thwart her genial will;
Here was the type of the true elder race,
And one of Plutarch's men talked with us face to face.
I praise him not; it were too late;
And some innative weakness there must be
In him who condescends to victory
Such as the Present gives, and cannot wait,
Safe in himself as in a fate.
So always firmly he:
He knew to bide his time,
And can his fame abide,
Still patient in his simple faith sublime,
Till the wise years decide.
Great captains, with their guns and drums,
Disturb our judgment for the hour,
But at last silence comes;
These all are gone, and, standing like a tower,

Our children shall behold his fame,
  The kindly-earnest, brave, foreseeing man,
Sagacious, patient, dreading praise, not blame,
  New birth of our new soil, the first American.

James Russell Lowell

THE EAGLE'S SONG

The lioness whelped, and the sturdy cub
Was seized by an eagle and carried up,
And homed for a while in an eagle's nest,
And slept for a while on an eagle's breast;
And the eagle taught it the eagle's song:
"To be staunch, and valiant, and free, and strong!"

The lion-whelp sprang from the eyrie nest,
From the lofty crag where the queen birds rest;
He fought the King on the spreading plain,
And drove him back o'er the foaming main.
He held the land as a thrifty chief,
And reared his cattle, and reaped his sheaf,
Nor sought the help of a foreign hand,
Yet welcomed all to his own free land!

Two were the sons that the country bore
To the Northern lakes and the Southern shore;
And Chivalry dwelt with the Southern son,
And Industry lived with the Northern one.
Tears for the time when they broke and fought!
Tears was the price of the union wrought!
And the land was red in a sea of blood,
Where brother for brother had swelled the flood!

And now that the two are one again,
Behold on their shield the word "Refrain!"

And the lion cubs twain sing the eagle's song:
"To be staunch, and valiant, and free, and strong!"
For the eagle's beak, and the lion's paw,
And the lion's fangs, and the eagle's claw,
And the eagle's swoop, and the lion's might,
And the lion's leap, and the eagle's sight,
Shall guard the flag with the word "Refrain!"
Now that the two are one again!

Richard Mansfield

THE SHIP OF STATE

From "The Building of the Ship"

Thou, too, sail on, O Ship of State!
Sail on, O Union, strong and great!
Humanity, with all its fears,
With all the hopes of future years,
Is hanging breathless on thy fate!
We know what Master laid thy keel,
What Workmen wrought thy ribs of steel,
Who made each mast, and sail, and rope;
What anvils rang, what hammers beat,
In what a forge and what a heat
Were forged the anchors of thy hope!
Fear not each sudden sound and shock—
'Tis of the wave, and not the rock;
'Tis but the flapping of the sail,
And not a rent made by the gale!
In spite of rock, and tempest's roar,
In spite of false lights on the shore,
Sail on, nor fear to breast the sea!
Our hearts, our hopes, are all with thee,
Our hearts, our hopes, our prayers, our tears,
Our faith triumphant o'er our fears,
Are all with thee,—are all with thee!

Henry Wadsworth Longfellow

UNMANIFEST DESTINY

To what new fates, my country, far
　And unforeseen of foe or friend,
Beneath what unexpected star,
　Compelled to what unchosen end,

Across the sea that knows no beach
　The Admiral of Nations guides
Thy blind obedient keels to reach
　The harbor where thy future rides!

The guns that spoke at Lexington
　Knew not that God was planning then
The trumpet word of Jefferson
　To bugle forth the rights of men.

To them that wept and cursed Bull Run,
　What was it but despair and shame?
Who saw behind the cloud the sun?
　Who knew that God was in the flame?

Had not defeat upon defeat,
　Disaster on disaster come,
The slave's emancipated feet
　Had never marched behind the drum.

There is a Hand that bends our deeds
　To mightier issues than we planned;
Each son that triumphs, each that bleeds,
　My country, serves Its dark command.

I do not know beneath what sky
　Nor on what seas shall be thy fate;
I only know it shall be high,
　I only know it shall be great.

Richard Hovey

THE FATHERLAND

Where is the true man's fatherland?
  Is it where he by chance is born?
  Doth not the yearning spirit scorn
In such scant borders to be spanned?
Oh yes! his fatherland must be
As the blue heaven wide and free!

Is it alone where freedom is,
  Where God is God and man is man?
  Doth he not claim a broader span
For the soul's love of home than this?
Oh yes! his fatherland must be
As the blue heaven wide and free!

Where'er a human heart doth wear
  Joy's myrtle-wreath or sorrow's gyves,
  Where'er a human spirit strives
After a life more true and fair,
There is the true man's birthplace grand,
His is a world-wide fatherland!

Where'er a single slave doth pine,
  Where'er one man may help another,—
  Thank God for such a birthright, brother,—
That spot of earth is thine and mine!
There is the true man's birthplace grand,
His is a world-wide fatherland!

James Russell Lowell

SONG OF THE NEW WORLD

I sing the song of a new Dawn waking,
  A new wind shaking the children of men.

I say the hearts that are nigh to breaking
　Shall leap with gladness and live again.
Over the woe of the world appalling,
　Wild and sweet as a bugle cry,
Sudden I hear a new voice calling—
　"Beauty is nigh!"

Beauty is nigh! Let the world believe it.
　Love has covered the fields of dead.
Healing is here! Let the earth receive it,
　Greeting the Dawn with lifted head.
I sing the song of the sin forgiven,
　The deed forgotten, the wrong undone.
Lo, in the East, where the dark is riven,
　Shines the rim of the rising sun.

Healing is here! O brother, sing it!
　Laugh, O heart, that has grieved so long.
Love will gather your woe and fling it
　Over the world in waves of song.
Hearken, mothers, and hear them coming—
　Heralds crying the day at hand.
Faint and far as the sound of drumming,
　Hear their summons across the land.

Look, O fathers! Your eyes were holden—
　Armies throng where the dead have lain.
Fiery steeds and chariots golden—
　Gone is the dream of soldiers slain.
Sing, O sing of a new world waking,
　Sing of creation just begun.
Glad is the earth when morn is breaking—
　Man is facing the rising sun!

Angela Morgan

X. The Happy Warrior

HOW SLEEP THE BRAVE

How sleep the brave, who sink to rest
By all their country's wishes blest!
When Spring, with dewy fingers cold,
Returns to deck their hallowed mould,
She there shall dress a sweeter sod
Than Fancy's feet have ever trod.

By fairy hands their knell is rung;
By forms unseen their dirge is sung;
There Honor comes, a pilgrim gray,
To bless the turf that wraps their clay;
And Freedom shall awhile repair
To dwell, a weeping hermit, there!

William Collins

THE HAPPY WARRIOR.

CHARACTER OF THE HAPPY WARRIOR

Who is the happy Warrior? Who is he
That every man in arms should wish to be?

It is the generous spirit, who, when brought
Among the tasks of real life, hath wrought
Upon the plan that pleased his boyish thought:
Whose high endeavors are an inward light
That makes the path before him always bright:
Who, with a natural instinct to discern
What knowledge can perform, is diligent to learn;
Abides by this resolve, and stops not there,
But makes his moral being his prime care;
Who, doomed to go in company with pain,
And fear, and bloodshed, miserable train!
Turns his necessity to glorious gain;
In face of these doth exercise a power
Which is our human nature's highest dower;
Controls them and subdues, transmutes, bereaves
Of their bad influence, and their good receives:
By objects which might force the soul to abate
Her feeling, rendered more compassionate;
Is placable—because occasions rise
So often that demand such sacrifice;
More skilful in self-knowledge, even more pure,
As tempted more; more able to endure,
As more exposed to suffering and distress;
Thence, also, more alive to tenderness.

'Tis he whose law is reason; who depends
Upon that law as on the best of friends;

Whence, in a state where men are tempted still
To evil for a guard against worse ill,
And what in quality or act is best
Doth seldom on a right foundation rest,
He labors good on good to fix, and owes
To virtue every triumph that he knows:
Who, if he rise to station of command,
Rises by open means; and there will stand
On honorable terms, or else retire,
And in himself possess his own desire;
Who comprehends his trust, and to the same
Keeps faithful with a singleness of aim;
And therefore does not stoop, nor lie in wait
For wealth, or honors, or for worldly state;
Whom they must follow; on whose head must fall,
Like showers of manna, if they come at all:
Whose powers shed round him in the common strife,
Or mild concerns of ordinary life,
A constant influence, a peculiar grace;
But who, if he be called upon to face
Some awful moment to which Heaven has joined
Great issues, good or bad for human kind,
Is happy as a lover; and attired
With sudden brightness, like a man inspired;
And, through the heat of conflict, keeps the law
In calmness made, and sees what he foresaw;
Or if an unexpected call succeed,
Come when it will, is equal to the need:
He who, though thus endued as with a sense
And faculty for storm and turbulence,
Is yet a soul whose master-bias leans
To homefelt pleasures and to gentle scenes;
Sweet images! which, whereso'er he be,
Are at his heart; and such fidelity
It is his darling passion to approve;
More brave for this, that he hath much to love.

'Tis, finally, the Man, who, lifted high,
Conspicuous object in a Nation's eye,
Or left unthought-of in obscurity,—
Who, with a toward or untoward lot,
Prosperous or adverse, to his wish or not—
Plays, in the many games of life, that one
Where what he most doth value must be won:
Whom neither shape of danger can dismay,
Nor thought of tender happiness betray;
Who, not content that former worth stand fast,

Looks forward, persevering to the last,
From well to better, daily self-surpassed:
Who, whether praise of him must walk the earth
For ever, and to noble deeds give birth,
Or he must fall, to sleep without his fame,
And leave a dead unprofitable name—
Finds comfort in himself and in his cause;
And, while the mortal mist is gathering, draws
His breath in confidence of Heaven's applause.

This is the happy Warrior; this is he
That every man in arms should wish to be.

William Wordsworth

COLUMBUS

Behind him lay the gray Azores,
    Behind the Gates of Hercules;
Before him not the ghost of shores,
    Before him only shoreless seas.
The good mate said: "Now must we pray,
    For lo! the very stars are gone.
Brave Admiral, speak, what shall I say?"
    "Why, say 'Sail on! sail on! and on!'"

"My men grow mutinous day by day;
   My men grow ghastly wan and weak."
The stout mate thought of home; a spray
   Of salt wave washed his swarthy cheek.
"What shall I say, brave Admiral, say,
   If we sight naught but seas at dawn?"
"Why, you shall say at break of day,
   'Sail on! sail on! sail on! and on!'"

They sailed and sailed, as winds might blow,
   Until at last the blanched mate said:
"Why, now not even God would know
   Should I and all my men fall dead.
These very winds forget their way,
   For God from these dread seas is gone.
Now speak, brave Admiral, speak and say"—
   He said: "Sail on! sail on! and on!"

They sailed. They sailed. Then spake the mate:
   "This mad sea shows his teeth to-night.
He curls his lip, he lies in wait,
   With lifted teeth, as if to bite!
Brave Admiral, say but one good word:
   What shall we do when hope is gone?"
The words leapt like a leaping sword:
   "Sail on! sail on! sail on! and on!"

Then, pale and worn, he kept his deck,
   And peered through darkness. Ah, that night
Of all dark nights! And then a speck—
   A light! a light! a light! a light!
It grew, a starlit flag unfurled!
   It grew to be Time's burst of dawn.
He gained a world; he gave that world
   Its grandest lesson: "On! sail on!"

Joaquin Miller

LEPANTO

[OCTOBER 7, 1571]

White founts falling in the Courts of the sun,
And the Soldan of Byzantium is smiling as they run;
There is laughter like the fountains in that face of all men
     feared,
It stirs the forest darkness, the darkness of his beard,
It curls the blood-red crescent, the crescent of his lips,
For the inmost sea of all the earth is shaken with his ships.
They have dared the white republics up the capes of Italy,
They have dashed the Adriatic round the Lion of the sea,
And the Pope has cast his arms abroad for agony and
     loss,
And called the kings of Christendom for swords about the
     Cross.
The cold queen of England is looking in the glass;
The shadow of the Valois is yawning at the Mass;
From evening isles fantastical rings faint the Spanish gun,
And the Lord upon the Golden Horn is laughing in the sun.

Dim drums throbbing, in the hills half heard,
Where only on a nameless throne a crownless prince has
     stirred,
Where, risen from a doubtful seat and half attainted stall,
The last knight of Europe takes weapons from the wall,
The last and lingering troubadour to whom the bird has
     sung,
That once went singing southward when all the world was
     young.
In that enormous silence, tiny and unafraid,
Comes up along a winding road the noise of the Crusade.

Strong gongs groaning as the guns boom far,
Don John of Austria is going to the war,

Stiff flags straining in the night-blast cold
In the gloom black-purple, in the glint old-gold,
Torchlight crimson on the copper kettle-drums,
Then the tuckets, then the trumpets, then the cannon,
    and he comes.
Don John laughing in the brave beard curled,
Spurning of his stirrups like the thrones of all the world,
Holding his head up for a flag of all the free.
Love-light of Spain—hurrah!
Death-light of Africa!
Don John of Austria
Is riding to the sea.

Mahound is in his paradise above the evening star,
(*Don John of Austria is going to the war.*)
He moves a mighty turban on the timeless houri's knees,
His turban that is woven of the sunsets and the seas.
He shakes the peacock gardens as he rises from his ease,
And he strides among the tree-tops and is taller than the
    trees,
And his voice through all the garden is a thunder sent to
    bring
Black Azrael and Ariel and Ammon on the wing.
Giants and the Genii,
Multiplex of wing and eye,
Whose strong obedience broke the sky
When Solomon was king.

They rush in red and purple from the red clouds of the
    morn,
From temples where the yellow gods shut up their eyes in
    scorn;
They rise in green robes roaring from the green hells of
    the sea
Where fallen skies and evil hues and eyeless creatures be;

On them the sea-valves cluster and the gray sea-forests
    curl,
Splashed with a splendid sickness, the sickness of the pearl;
They swell in sapphire smoke out of the blue cracks of the
    ground,—
They gather and they wonder and give worship to Ma-
    hound.
And he saith, "Break up the mountains where the hermit-
    folk can hide,
And sift the red and silver sands lest bone of saint abide,
And chase the Giaours flying night and day, not giving
    rest,
For that which was our trouble comes again out of the
    west.
We have set the seal of Solomon on all things under sun,
Of knowledge and of sorrow and endurance of things done,
But a noise is in the mountains, in the mountains, and I
    know
The voice that shook our palaces—four hundred years ago:
It is he that saith not 'Kismet'; it is he that knows not
    Fate;
It is Richard, it is Raymond, it is Godfrey in the gate!
It is he whose loss is laughter when he counts the wager
    worth,
Put down your feet upon him, that our peace be on the
    earth."
For he heard drums groaning and he heard guns jar,
(*Don John of Austria is going to the war.*)
Sudden and still—hurrah!
Bolt from Iberia!
Don John of Austria
Is gone by Alcalar.

St. Michael's on his Mountain in the sea-roads of the north
(*Don John of Austria is girt and going forth.*)

Where the gray seas glitter and the sharp tides shift
And the sea-folk labor and the red sails lift.
He shakes his lance of iron and he claps his wings of stone;
The noise is gone through Normandy; the noise is gone
    alone;
The North is full of tangled things and texts and aching eyes
And dead is all the innocence of anger and surprise,
And Christian killeth Christian in a narrow dusty room,
And Christian dreadeth Christ that hath a newer face of
    doom,
And Christian hateth Mary that God kissed in Galilee,
But Don John of Austria is riding to the sea.
Don John calling through the blast and the eclipse
Crying with the trumpet, with the trumpet of his lips,
Trumpet that sayeth ha!
   Domino gloria!
Don John of Austria
Is shouting to the ships.

King Philip's in his closet with the Fleece about his neck
(*Don John of Austria is armed upon the deck.*)
The walls are hung with velvet that is black and soft as sin,
And little dwarfs creep out of it and little dwarfs creep in.
He holds a crystal phial that has colors like the moon,
He touches, and it tingles, and he trembles very soon,
And his face is as a fungus of a leprous white and gray
Like plants in the high houses that are shuttered from the
    day,
And death is in the phial and the end of noble work,
But Don John of Austria has fired upon the Turk.
Don John's hunting, and his hounds have bayed—
Booms away past Italy the rumor of his raid.
Gun upon gun, ha! ha!
Gun upon gun, hurrah!
Don John of Austria
Has loosed the cannonade.

The Pope was in his chapel before day or battle broke,
(*Don John of Austria is hidden in the smoke.*)
The hidden room in man's house where God sits all the
    year,
The secret window whence the world looks small and very
    dear.
He sees as in a mirror on the monstrous twilight sea
The crescent of his cruel ships whose name is mystery;
They fling great shadows foe-wards, making Cross and
    Castle dark,
They veil the plumèd lions on the galleys of St. Mark;
And above the ships are palaces of brown, black-bearded
    chiefs,
And below the ships are prisons, where with multitudin-
    ous griefs,
Christian captives sick and sunless, all a laboring race re-
    pines
Like a race in sunken cities, like a nation in the mines.
They are lost like slaves that swat, and in the skies of
    morning hung
The stairways of the tallest gods when tyranny was young.
They are countless, voiceless, hopeless as those fallen or
    fleeing on
Before the high Kings' horses in the granite of Babylon.
And many a one grows witless in his quiet room in hell
Where a yellow face looks inward through the lattice of
    his cell,
And he finds his God forgotten, and he seeks no more a
    sign—
(*But Don John of Austria has burst the battle-line!*)
Don John pounding from the slaughter-painted poop,
Purpling all the ocean like a bloody pirate's sloop,
Scarlet running over on the silvers and the golds,
Breaking of the hatches up and bursting of the holds,
Thronging of the thousands up that labor under sea
White for bliss and blind for sun and stunned for liberty.

Vivat Hispania!
Domino Gloria!
Don John of Austria
Has set his people free!

Cervantes on his galley sets the sword back in the sheath
(*Don John of Austria rides homeward with a wreath.*)
And he sees across a weary land a straggling road in Spain,
Up which a lean and foolish knight for ever rides in vain,
And he smiles, but not as Sultans smile, and settles back
    the blade. . . .
(*But Don John of Austria rides home from the Crusade.*)
              Gilbert Keith Chesterton

SIR HUMPHREY GILBERT

[1583]

Southward with fleet of ice
    Sailed the corsair Death;
Wild and fast blew the blast,
    And the east-wind was his breath.

His lordly ships of ice
    Glisten in the sun;
On each side, like pennons wide,
    Flashing crystal streamlets run.

His sails of white sea-mist
    Dripped with silver rain;
But where he passed there was cast
    Leaden shadows o'er the main.

Eastward from Campobello
    Sir Humphrey Gilbert sailed;
Three days or more seaward he bore,
    Then, alas! the land-wind failed.

Alas! the land-wind failed,
   And ice-cold grew the night;
And nevermore, on sea or shore,
   Should Sir Humphrey see the light.

He sat upon the deck,
   The Book was in his hand;
"Do not fear! Heaven is as near,"
   He said, "by water as by land!"

In the first watch of the night,
   Without a signal's sound,
Out of the sea, mysteriously,
   The fleet of Death rose all around.

The moon and the evening star
   Were hanging in the shrouds;
Every mast, as it passed,
   Seemed to rake the passing clouds.

They grappled with their prize,
   At midnight black and cold!
As of a rock was the shock;
   Heavily the ground-swell rolled.

Southward through day and dark,
   They drift in close embrace,
With mist and rain, o'er the open main;
   Yet there seems no change of place.

Southward, forever southward,
   They drift through dark and day;
And like a dream, in the Gulf-Stream,
   Sinking, vanish all away.

               Henry Wadsworth Longfellow

IVRY

[MARCH 14, 1590]

Now glory to the Lord of Hosts, from whom all glories are!
And glory to our Sovereign Liege, King Henry of Navarre!
Now let there be the merry sound of music and of dance,
Through thy corn-fields green, and sunny vines, oh
    pleasant land of France!
And thou, Rochelle, our own Rochelle, proud city of the
    waters,
Again let rapture light the eyes of all thy mourning daugh-
    ters.
As thou wert constant in our ills, be joyous in our joy;
For cold, and stiff, and still are they who wrought thy
    walls annoy.
Hurrah! hurrah! a single field hath turned the chance of
    war.
Hurrah! hurrah! for Ivry, and Henry of Navarre.

Oh! how our hearts were beating, when, at the dawn of
    day,
We saw the army of the League drawn out in long array;
With all its priest-led citizens, and all its rebel peers,
And Appenzel's stout infantry, and Egmont's Flemish
    spears.
There rode the brood of false Lorraine, the curses of our
    land;
And dark Mayenne was in the midst, a truncheon in his
    hand;
And, as we looked on them, we thought of Seine's em-
    purpled flood,
And good Coligni's hoary hair all dabbled with his blood;
And we cried unto the living God, who rules the fate of war,
To fight for His own holy name, and Henry of Navarre.

The King is come to marshal us, in all his armor dressed;
And he has bound a snow-white plume upon his gallant
crest.
He looked upon his people, and a tear was in his eye;
He looked upon the traitors, and his glance was stern and
high.
Right graciously he smiled on us, as rolled from wing to
wing,
Down all our line, a deafening shout: "God save our Lord
the King!"
"And if my standard-bearer fall, as fall full well he may,
For never saw I promise yet of such a bloody fray,
Press where ye see my white plume shine, amidst the ranks
of war,
And be your oriflamme to-day the helmet of Navarre."

Hurrah! the foes are moving.   Hark to the mingled din,
Of fife, and steed, and trump, and drum, and roaring cul-
verin.
The fiery Duke is pricking fast across Saint André's plain,
With all the hireling chivalry of Guelders and Almayne.
Now by the lips of those ye love, fair gentlemen of France,
Charge for the golden lilies,—upon them with the lance!
A thousand spurs are striking deep, a thousand spears in
rest,
A thousand knights are pressing close behind the snow-
white crest;
And in they burst, and on they rushed, while, like a guid-
ing star,
Amidst the thickest carnage blazed the helmet of Navarre.

Now, God be praised, the day is ours.   Mayenne hath
turned his rein;
D'Aumale hath cried for quarter; the Flemish count is
slain.

Their ranks are breaking like thin clouds before a Biscay gale;
The field is heaped with bleeding steeds, and flags, and
    cloven mail.
And then we thought on vengeance, and, all along our van,
"Remember Saint Bartholomew!" was passed from man
    to man.
But out spake gentle Henry, "No Frenchman is my foe:
Down, down with every foreigner, but let your brethren go."
Oh! was there ever such a knight, in friendship or in war,
As our Sovereign Lord, King Henry, the soldier of Navarre?

Right well fought all the Frenchmen who fought for France
    to-day;
And many a lordly banner God gave them for a prey.
But we of the religion have borne us best in fight;
And the good Lord of Rosny hath ta'en the cornet white.
Our own true Maximilian the cornet white hath ta'en,
The cornet white with crosses black, the flag of false Lor-
    raine.
Up with it high; unfurl it wide; that all the host may know
How God hath humbled the proud house which wrought
    His Church such woe.
Then on the ground, while trumpets sound their loudest
    point of war,
Fling the red shreds, a footcloth meet for Henry of Navarre.

Ho! maidens of Vienna; ho! matrons of Lucerne,
Weep, weep, and rend your hair for those who never shall
    return.
Ho! Philip, send, for charity, thy Mexican pistoles,
That Antwerp monks may sing a mass for thy poor spear-
    men's souls.
Ho! gallant nobles of the League, look that your arms be
    bright;
Ho! burghers of St. Genevieve, keep watch and ward to-
    night;

For our God hath crushed the tyrant, our God hath raised
    the slave,
And mocked the counsel of the wise, and the valor of the
    brave.
Then glory to His holy name, from whom all glories are;
And glory to our Sovereign Lord, King Henry of Navarre!

Thomas Babington Macaulay

DRAKE'S DRUM

[SIR FRANCIS DRAKE, 1540?–1596]

Drake he's in his hammock an' a thousand mile away,
    (Capten, art tha sleepin' there below?),
Slung atween the round shot in Nombre Dios Bay,
    An' dreamin' arl the time o' Plymouth Hoe.
Yarnder lumes the Island, yarnder lie the ships,
    Wi' sailor lads a-dancin' heel-an'-toe,
An' the shore-lights flashin', an' the night-tide dashin',
    He sees et arl so plainly as he saw et long ago.

Drake he was a Devon man, an' ruled the Devon seas,
    (Capten, art tha sleepin' there below?),
Rovin' though his death fell, he went wi' heart at ease,
    An' dreamin' arl the time o' Plymouth Hoe.
"Take my drum to England, hang et by the shore,
    Strike et when your powder's runnin' low;
If the Dons sight Devon, I'll quit the port o' Heaven,
    An' drum them up the Channel as we drummed them
      long ago."

Drake he's in his hammock till the great Armadas come,
    (Capten, art tha sleepin' there below?),
Slung atween the round shot, listenin' for the drum,
    An' dreamin' arl the time o' Plymouth Hoe.
Call him on the deep sea, call him up the Sound,
    Call him when ye sail to meet the foe;

Where the old trade's plyin' an' the old flag flyin',
    They shall find him ware an' wakin', as they found him
      long ago!

Henry Newbolt

CASABIANCA

[BATTLE OF THE NILE, AUGUST, 1798]

The boy stood on the burning deck,
    Whence all but him had fled;
The flame that lit the battle's wreck
    Shone round him o'er the dead.

Yet beautiful and bright he stood,
    As born to rule the storm;
A creature of heroic blood,
    A proud, though child-like form.

The flames rolled on; he would not go
    Without his father's word;
That father, faint in death below,
    His voice no longer heard.

He called aloud, "Say, father, say,
    If yet my task be done!"
He knew not that the chieftain lay
    Unconscious of his son.

"Speak, father!" once again he cried,
    "If I may yet be gone!"
And but the booming shots replied,
    And fast the flames rolled on.

Upon his brow he felt their breath,
    And in his waving hair,

And looked from that lone post of death
   In still, yet brave despair;

And shouted but once more aloud,
   "My father! must I stay?"
While o'er him, fast, through sail and shroud,
   The wreathing fires made way.

They wrapped the ship in splendor wild,
   They caught the flag on high,
And streamed above the gallant child,
   Like banners in the sky.

There came a burst of thunder sound;
   The boy,—oh! where was he?
Ask of the winds, that far around
   With fragments strewed the sea,—

With mast, and helm, and pennon fair,
   That well had borne their part,—
But the noblest thing that perished there,
   Was that young, faithful heart.

                Felicia Dorothea Hemans

THE BURIAL OF SIR JOHN MOORE AFTER CORUNNA

[JANUARY 16, 1809]

Not a drum was heard, not a funeral note,
   As his corse to the rampart we hurried;
Not a soldier discharged his farewell shot
   O'er the grave where our hero we buried.

We buried him darkly at dead of night,
   The sods with our bayonets turning,
By the struggling moonbeam's misty light
   And the lanthorn dimly burning.

No useless coffin enclosed his breast,
　　Not in sheet or in shroud we wound him;
But he lay like a warrior taking his rest
　　With his martial cloak around him.

Few and short were the prayers we said,
　　And we spoke not a word of sorrow;
But we steadfastly gazed on the face that was dead,
　　And we bitterly thought of the morrow.

We thought, as we hollowed his narrow bed
　　And smoothed down his lonely pillow,
That the foe and the stranger would tread o'er his head,
　　And we far away on the billow!

Lightly they'll talk of the spirit that's gone,
　　And o'er his cold ashes upbraid him—
But little he'll reck, if they let him sleep on
　　In the grave where a Briton has laid him.

But half of our heavy task was done
　　When the clock struck the hour for retiring;
And we heard the distant and random gun
　　That the foe was sullenly firing.

Slowly and sadly we laid him down,
　　From the field of his fame fresh and gory;
We carved not a line, and we raised not a stone,
　　But we left him alone with his glory.

Charles Wolfe

INCIDENT OF THE FRENCH CAMP

[APRIL 23, 1809]

You know, we French stormed Ratisbon:
　　A mile or so away,

On a little mound, Napoleon
  Stood on our storming-day;
With neck out-thrust, you fancy how,
  Legs wide, arms locked behind,
As if to balance the prone brow
  Oppressive with its mind.

Just as perhaps he mused, "My plans
  That soar, to earth may fall,
Let once my army-leader Lannes
  Waver at yonder wall,"—
Out 'twixt the battery-smokes there flew
  A rider, bound on bound
Full-galloping; nor bridle drew
  Until he reached the mound.

Then off there flung in smiling joy,
  And held himself erect
By just his horse's mane, a boy:
  You hardly could suspect—
(So tight he kept his lips compressed,
  Scarce any blood came through),
You looked twice ere you saw his breast
  Was all but shot in two.

"Well," cried he, "Emperor, by God's grace
  We've got you Ratisbon!
The Marshal's in the market-place,
  And you'll be there anon
To see your flag-bird flap his vans
  Where I, to heart's desire,
Perched him!"   The chief's eye flashed; his plans
  Soared up again like fire.

The chief's eye flashed; but presently
  Softened itself, as sheathes

A film the mother-eagle's eye
   When her bruised eaglet breathes;
"You're wounded!"   "Nay," the soldier's pride
   Touched to the quick, he said:
"I'm killed, Sire!"   And his chief beside,
   Smiling the boy fell dead.

Robert Browning

THE LOST COLORS

[1843]

Frowning, the mountain stronghold stood,
Whose front no mortal could assail;
For more than twice three hundred years
The terror of the Indian vale.
By blood and fire the robber band
Answered the helpless village wail.

Hot was his heart and cool his thought,
When Napier from his Englishmen
Up to the bandits' rampart glanced,
And down upon his ranks again.
Summoned to dare a deed like that,
Which of them all would answer then?

What sullen regiment is this
That lifts its eyes to dread Cutchee?
Abased, its standard bears no flag.
For thus the punishment shall be
That England metes to Englishmen
Who shame her once by mutiny.

From out the disgraced Sixty-Fourth
There stepped a hundred men of might.
Cried Napier: "Now prove to me
I read my soldiers' hearts aright!

Form! Forward! Charge, my volunteers!
Your colors are on yonder height!"

So sad is shame, so wise is trust!
The challenge echoed bugle-clear.
Like fire along the Sixty-Fourth
From rank to file rang cheer on cheer.
In death and glory up the pass
They fought for all to brave men dear.

Old is the tale, but read anew
In every warring human heart,
What rebel hours, what coward shame,
Upon the aching memory start!
To find the ideal forfeited,
—What tears can teach the holy art?

Thou great Commander! leading on
Through weakest darkness to strong light;
By any anguish, give us back
Our life's young standard, pure and bright.
O fair, lost Colors of the soul!
For your sake storm we any height.

Elizabeth Stuart Phelps Ward

THE CHARGE OF THE LIGHT BRIGADE

[BALACLAVA, OCTOBER 25, 1852]

Half a league, half a league,
  Half a league onward,
All in the valley of Death
  Rode the six hundred.
"Forward, the Light Brigade!
Charge for the guns!" he said:
Into the valley of Death
  Rode the six hundred.

"Forward, the Light Brigade!"
Was there a man dismayed?
Not though the soldier knew
  Some one had blundered:
Theirs not to make reply,
Theirs not to reason why,
Theirs but to do and die:
Into the valley of Death
  Rode the six hundred.

Cannon to right of them,
Cannon to left of them,
Cannon in front of them
  Volleyed and thundered;
Stormed at with shot and shell,
Boldly they rode and well,
Into the jaws of Death,
Into the mouth of Hell
  Rode the six hundred.

Flashed all their sabres bare,
Flashed as they turned in air
Sabring the gunners there,
Charging an army, while
  All the world wondered:
Plunged in the battery-smoke
Right through the line they broke;
Cossack and Russian
Reeled from the sabre-stroke,
  Shattered and sundered.
Then they rode back, but not,
  Not the six hundred.

Cannon to right of them,
Cannon to left of them,
Cannon behind them
  Volleyed and thundered;

Stormed at with shot and shell,
While horse and hero fell,
They that had fought so well
Came through the jaws of Death,
Back from the mouth of Hell,
All that was left of them,
   Left of six hundred.

When can their glory fade?
O the wild charge they made!
   All the world wondered.
Honor the charge they made!
Honor the Light Brigade,
   Noble six hundred!

Alfred Tennyson

HE FELL AMONG THIEVES

"Ye have robbed," said he, "ye have slaughtered and made
   an end,
  Take your ill-got plunder, and bury the dead:
What will ye more of your guest and sometime friend?"
  "Blood for our blood," they said.

He laughed: "If one may settle the score for five,
  I am ready; but let the reckoning stand till day:
I have loved the sunlight as dearly as any alive."
  "You shall die at dawn," said they.

He flung his empty revolver down the slope,
  He climbed alone to the Eastward edge of the trees;
All night long in a dream untroubled of hope
  He brooded, clasping his knees.

He did not hear the monotonous roar that fills
  The ravine where the Yassîn river sullenly flows;

He did not see the starlight on the Laspur hills,
  Or the far Afghan snows.

He saw the April noon on his books aglow,
  The wistaria trailing in at the window wide;
He heard his father's voice from the terrace below
  Calling him down to ride.

He saw the gray little church across the park,
  The mounds that hid the loved and honored dead;
The Norman arch, the chancel softly dark,
  The brasses black and red.

He saw the School Close, sunny and green,
  The runner beside him, the stand by the parapet wall,
The distant tape, and the crowd roaring between,
  His own name over all.

He saw the dark wainscot and timbered roof,
  The long tables, and the faces merry and keen:
The College Eight and their trainer dining aloof,
  The Dons on the daïs serene.

He watched the liner's stem plowing the foam,
  He felt her trembling speed and the thrash of her screw;
He heard the passengers' voices talking of home,
  He saw the flag she flew.

And now it was dawn. He rose strong on his feet,
  And strode to his ruined camp below the wood;
He drank the breath of the morning cool and sweet;
  His murderers round him stood.

Light on the Laspur hills was broadening fast,
  The blood-red snow-peaks chilled to a dazzling white;
He turned, and saw the golden circle at last,
  Cut by the Eastern height.

"O glorious Life, Who dwellest in earth and sun,
  I have lived, I praise and adore Thee."
                            A sword swept.
Over the pass the voices one by one
  Faded, and the hill slept.

Henry Newboh

YOUNG WINDEBANK

They shot young Windebank just here,
  By Merton, where the sun
Strikes on the wall.   'Twas in a year
  Of blood the deed was done.

At morning from the meadows dim
  He watched them dig his grave.
Was this in truth the end for him,
  The well-beloved and brave?

He marched with soldier scarf and sword,
  Set free to die that day,
And free to speak once more the word
  That marshalled men obey.

But silent on the silent band
  That faced him stern as death,
He looked and on the summer land,
  And on the grave beneath.

Then with a sudden smile and proud
  He waved his plume and cried,
"The king! the king!" and laughed aloud,
  "The king! the king!" and died.

Let none affirm he vainly fell,
  And paid the barren cost

Of having loved and served too well
  A poor cause and a lost.

He in the soul's eternal cause
  Went forth as martyrs must—
The kings who make the spirit laws
  And rule us from the dust.

Whose wills unshaken by the breath
  Of adverse Fate endure,
To give us honor strong as death
  And loyal love as sure.

                                    Margaret L. Woods

THE SONG OF THE CAMP

"Give us a song!" the soldiers cried,
  The outer trenches guarding,
When the heated guns of the camps allied
  Grew weary of bombarding.

The dark Redan, in silent scoff,
  Lay, grim and threatening, under;
And the tawny mound of the Malakoff
  No longer belched its thunder.

There was a pause. A guardsman said,
  "We storm the forts to-morrow;
Sing while we may, another day
  Will bring enough of sorrow."

They lay along the battery's side,
  Below the smoking cannon:
Brave hearts, from Severn and from Clyde,
  And from the banks of Shannon.

They sang of love, and not of fame;
   Forgot was Britain's glory:
Each heart recalled a different name,
   But all sang "Annie Laurie."

Voice after voice caught up the song,
   Until its tender passion
Rose like an anthem, rich and strong,—
   Their battle-eve confession.

Dear girl, her name he dared not speak,
   But, as the song grew louder,
Something upon the soldier's cheek
   Washed off the stains of powder.

Beyond the darkening ocean burned
   The bloody sunset's embers,
While the Crimean valleys learned
   How English love remembers.

And once again a fire of hell
   Rained on the Russian quarters,
With scream of shot, and burst of shell,
   And bellowing of the mortars!

And Irish Nora's eyes are dim
   For a singer, dumb and gory;
And English Mary mourns for him
   Who sang of "Annie Laurie."

Sleep, soldiers! still in honored rest
   Your truth and valor wearing:
The bravest are the tenderest,—
   The loving are the daring.

Bayard Taylor

SOLDIER, REST! THY WARFARE O'ER

From "The Lady of the Lake"

Soldier, rest! thy warfare o'er,
 Sleep the sleep that knows not breaking;
Dream of battled fields no more,
 Days of danger, nights of waking.
In our isle's enchanted hall,
 Hands unseen thy couch are strewing,
Fairy strains of music fall,
 Every sense in slumber dewing.
Soldier, rest! thy warfare o'er,
Dream of fighting fields no more:
Sleep the sleep that knows not breaking,
Morn of toil, nor night of waking.

No rude sound shall reach thine ear,
 Armor's clang, or war-steed champing,
Trump nor pibroch summon here
 Mustering clan, or squadron tramping.
Yet the lark's shrill fife may come
 At the daybreak from the fallow,
And the bittern sound his drum,
 Booming from the sedgy shallow.
Ruder sounds shall none be near,
Guards nor warders challenge here,
Here's no war-steed's neigh and champing,
Shouting clans, or squadrons stamping.

Walter Scott

A BALLAD OF HEROES

Now all your victories are in vain—A. MARY F. ROBINSON

Because you passed, and now are not,—
 Because, in some remoter day,
Your sacred dust from doubtful spot
 Was blown of ancient airs away,—

Because you perished,—must men say
Your deeds were naught, and so profane
    Your lives with that cold burden? Nay,
The deeds you wrought are not in vain!

Though, it may be, above the plot
    That hid your once imperial clay,
No greener than o'er men forgot
    The unregarding grasses sway;—
    Though there no sweeter is the lay
From careless bird,—though you remain
    Without distinction of decay,—
The deeds you wrought are not in vain!

No. For while yet in tower or cot
    Your story stirs the pulses' play;
And men forget the sordid lot—
    The sordid care, of cities gray;
    While yet, beset in homelier fray,
They learn from you the lesson plain
    That Life may go, so Honor stay,—
The deeds you wrought are not in vain!

ENVOY

Heroes of old! I humbly lay
    The laurel on your graves again;
Whatever men have done, men may,—
    The deeds you wrought are not in vain!

Austin Dobson

EPILOGUE FROM "ASOLANDO"

At the midnight in the silence of the sleep-time,
    When you set your fancies free,

Will they pass to where—by death, fools think, impris-
    oned—
Low he lies who once so loved you, whom you loved so,
     —Pity me?

Oh to love so, be so loved, yet so mistaken!
   What had I on earth to do
With the slothful, with the mawkish, the unmanly?
Like the aimless, helpless, hopeless, did I drivel
     —Being—who?

One who never turned his back but marched breast for-
    ward,
   Never doubted clouds would break,
Never dreamed, though right were worsted, wrong would
    triumph,
Held we fall to rise, are baffled to fight better,
    Sleep to wake.

No, at noonday in the bustle of man's work-time
   Greet the unseen with a cheer!
Bid him forward, breast and back as either should be,
"Strive and thrive!" cry "Speed,—fight on, fare ever
    There as here!"

Robert Browning

xj. Life Lessons

THE NOBLE NATURE

From "To the Immortal Memory . . . of Sir Lucius Cary and
Sir Henry Morrison"

It is not growing like a tree
In bulk, doth make man better be;
Or standing long an oak, three hundred year,
To fall a log at last, dry, bald, and sear:
A lily of a day
Is fairer far in May,
Although it fall and die that night,—
It was the plant and flower of Light.
In small proportions we just beauties see,
And in short measures life may perfect be.

Ben Jonson

LIFE LESSONS

ABOU BEN ADHEM

Abou Ben Adhem (may his tribe increase!)
Awoke one night from a deep dream of peace,
And saw, within the moonlight in his room,
Making it rich, and like a lily in bloom,
An angel writing in a book of gold:—
Exceeding peace had made Ben Adhem bold,
And to the Presence in the room he said,
"What writest thou?"—The vision raised its head,
And with a look made of all sweet accord,
Answered, "The names of those who love the Lord."
"And is mine one?" said Abou. "Nay, not so,"
Replied the Angel. Abou spoke more low,
But cheerly still; and said, "I pray thee, then,
Write me as one that loves his fellow-men."

The angel wrote, and vanished. The next night
It came again with a great wakening light,
And showed the names whom love of God had blessed,
And lo! Ben Adhem's name led all the rest.

Leigh Hunt

THE HOUSE BY THE SIDE OF THE ROAD

There are hermit souls that live withdrawn
    In the place of their self-content;
There are souls like stars, that dwell apart,
    In a fellowless firmament;
There are pioneer souls that blaze their paths
    Where highways never ran—
But let me live by the side of the road
    And be a friend to man.

Let me live in a house by the side of the road
    Where the race of men go by—
The men who are good and the men who are bad,
    As good and as bad as I.
I would not sit in the scorner's seat
    Or hurl the cynic's ban—
Let me live in a house by the side of the road
    And be a friend to man.

I see from my house by the side of the road,
    By the side of the highway of life,
The men who press with the ardor of hope,
    The men who are faint with the strife,
But I turn not away from their smiles nor their tears,
    Both parts of an infinite plan—
Let me live in a house by the side of the road
    And be a friend to man.

I know there are brook-gladdened meadows ahead,
    And mountains of wearisome height;
That the road passes on through the long afternoon
    And stretches away to the night.
And still I rejoice when the travelers rejoice
    And weep with the strangers that moan,
Nor live in my house by the side of the road
    Like a man who dwells alone.

Let me live in my house by the side of the road,
    Where the race of men go by—
They are good, they are bad, they are weak, they are strong,
    Wise, foolish—so am I.
Then why should I sit in the scorner's seat,
    Or hurl the cynic's ban?
Let me live in my house by the side of the road
    And be a friend to man.

Sam Walter Foss

THE TUFT OF FLOWERS

I went to turn the grass once after one
Who mowed it in the dew before the sun.

The dew was gone that made his blade so keen
Before I came to view the levelled scene.

I looked for him behind an isle of trees;
I listened for his whetstone on the breeze.

But he had gone his way, the grass all mown,
And I must be, as he had been,—alone,

"As all must be," I said within my heart,
"Whether they work together or apart."

But as I said it, swift there passed me by
On noiseless wing a bewildered butterfly,

Seeking with memories grown dim over night
Some resting flower of yesterday's delight.

And once I marked his flight go round and round,
As where some flower lay withering on the ground.

And then he flew as far as eye could see,
And then on tremulous wing came back to me.

I thought of questions that have no reply,
And would have turned to toss the grass to dry;

But he turned first, and led my eye to look
At a tall tuft of flowers beside a brook,

A leaping tongue of bloom the scythe had spared
Beside a reedy brook the scythe had bared.

I left my place to know them by their name,
Finding them butterfly-weed when I came.

The mower in the dew had loved them thus,
By leaving them to flourish, not for us,

Nor yet to draw one thought of ours to him,
But from sheer morning gladness at the brim.

The butterfly and I had lit upon,
Nevertheless, a message from the dawn,

That made me hear the wakening birds around,
And hear his long scythe whispering to the ground,

And feel a spirit kindred to my own;
So that henceforth I worked no more alone;

But glad with him, I worked as with his aid,
And weary, sought at noon with him the shade;

And dreaming, as it were, held brotherly speech
With one whose thought I had not hoped to reach.

"Men work together," I told him from the heart,
"Whether they work together or apart."

Robert Frost

FOR A' THAT AND A' THAT

Is there, for honest Poverty,
   That hangs his head, and a' that!
The coward-slave, we pass him by,
   We dare be poor for a' that!
For a' that, and a' that,
   Our toils obscure, and a' that;
The rank is but the guinea's stamp,
   The Man's the gowd for a' that.

What though on hamely fare we dine,
  Wear hoddin-gray, and a' that;
Gie fools their silks, and knaves their wine,
  A Man's a Man for a' that.
For a' that, and a' that,
  Their tinsel show, and a' that;
The honest man, though e'er sae poor,
  Is king o' men for a' that.

Ye see yon birkie, ca'd a lord,
  Wha struts, and stares, and a' that;
Though hundreds worship at his word,
  He's but a coof for a' that;
For a' that, and a' that,
  His ribbon, star, and a' that;
The man of independent mind,
  He looks and laughs at a' that.

A prince can mak a belted knight,
  A marquis, duke and a' that;
But an honest man's aboon his might,
  Guid faith, he maunna fa' that!
For a' that, and a' that,
  Their dignities, and a' that,
The pith o' sense, and pride o' worth,
  Are higher rank than a' that.

Then let us pray that come it may,—
  As come it will for a' that,—
That Sense and Worth, o'er a' the earth,
  May bear the gree, and a' that.
For a' that, and a' that,
  It's coming yet, for a' that—
That Man to Man, the warld o'er,
  Shall brothers be for a' that!

Robert Burns

GOOD KING WENCESLAS

Good King Wenceslas looked out,
  On the Feast of Stephen,
When the snow lay round about,
  Deep, and crisp, and even:
Brightly shone the moon that night,
  Though the frost was cruel,
When a poor man came in sight,
  Gathering winter fuel.

"Hither, page, and stand by me,
  If thou know'st it, telling,
Yonder peasant, who is he?
  Where and what his dwelling?"
"Sire, he lives a good league hence,
  Underneath the mountain;
Right against the forest fence,
  By Saint Agnes' fountain."

"Bring me flesh, and bring me wine,
  Bring me pine logs hither;
Thou and I will see him dine,
  When we bear them thither."
Page and monarch forth they went,
  Forth they went together;
Through the rude wind's wild lament,
  And the bitter weather.

"Sire, the night is darker now,
  And the wind blows stronger;
Fails my heart, I know not how,
  I can go no longer."
"Mark my footsteps, good my page!
  Tread thou in them boldly;
Thou shalt find the winter's rage
  Freeze thy blood less coldly."

In his master's steps he trod,
   Where the snow lay dinted;
Heat was in the very sod
   Which the saint had printed.
Therefore, Christian men, be sure,
   Wealth or rank possessing,
Ye who now will bless the poor,
   Shall yourselves find blessing.

John Mason Neal

LITTLE AND GREAT

A traveler on a dusty road
   Strewed acorns on the lea;
And one took root and sprouted up,
   And grew into a tree.
Love sought its shade at evening-time,
   To breathe its early vows;
And Age was pleased, in heats of noon,
   To bask beneath its boughs.
The dormouse loved its dangling twigs,
   The birds sweet music bore—
It stood a glory in its place,
   A blessing evermore.

A little spring had lost its way
   Amid the grass and fern;
A passing stranger scooped a well
   Where weary men might turn;
He walled it in, and hung with care
   A ladle at the brink;
He thought not of the deed he did,
   But judged that Toil might drink.
He passed again; and lo! the well,
   By summer never dried,

Had cooled ten thousand parchèd tongues,
   And saved a life beside.

A dreamer dropped a random thought;
   'Twas old, and yet 'twas new;
A simple fancy of the brain,
   But strong in being true.
It shone upon a genial mind,
   And, lo! its light became
A lamp of life, a beacon ray,
   A monitory flame:
The thought was small; its issue great;
   A watch-fire on the hill,
It sheds its radiance far adown,
   And cheers the valley still.

A nameless man, amid the crowd
   That thronged the daily mart,
Let fall a word of hope and love,
   Unstudied from the heart;—
A whisper on the tumult thrown,
   A transitory breath,—
It raised a brother from the dust,
   It saved a soul from death.
O germ! O fount! O word of love!
   O thought at random cast!
Ye were but little at the first,
   But mighty at the last.

Charles Mackay

THE ARROW AND THE SONG

I shot an arrow into the air,
It fell to earth, I knew not where;
For, so swiftly it flew, the sight
Could not follow it in its flight.

I breathed a song into the air,
It fell to earth, I knew not where;
For who has sight so keen and strong,
That it can follow the flight of song?

Long, long afterward, in an oak
I found the arrow, still unbroke;
And the song, from beginning to end,
I found again in the heart of a friend.

Henry Wadsworth Longfellow

A LEGEND OF THE NORTHLAND

Away, away in the Northland,
  Where the hours of the day are few,
And the nights are so long in winter
  That they cannot sleep them through;

Where they harness the swift reindeer
  To the sledges, when it snows;
And the children look like bears' cubs
  In their funny, furry clothes:

They tell them a curious story—
  I don't believe 'tis true;
And yet you may learn a lesson
  If I tell the tale to you.

Once, when the good Saint Peter
  Lived in the world below,
And walked about it, preaching,
  Just as he did, you know,

He came to the door of a cottage,
  In traveling round the earth,
Where a little woman was making cakes,
  And baking them on the hearth;

And being faint with fasting,
    For the day was almost done,
He asked her, from her store of cakes,
    To give him a single one.

So she made a very little cake,
    But as it baking lay,
She looked at it, and thought it seemed
    Too large to give away.

Therefore she kneaded another,
    And still a smaller one;
But it looked, when she turned it over,
    As large as the first had done.

Then she took a tiny scrap of dough,
    And rolled and rolled it flat;
And baked it thin as a wafer—
    But she couldn't part with that.

For she said, "My cakes that seem too small
    When I eat of them myself,
Are yet too large to give away."
    So she put them on the shelf.

Then good Saint Peter grew angry,
    For he was hungry and faint;
And surely such a woman
    Was enough to provoke a saint.

And he said, "You are far too selfish
    To dwell in a human form,
To have both food and shelter,
    And fire to keep you warm.

"Now, you shall build as the birds do,
    And shall get your scanty food

By boring, and boring, and boring,
   All day in the hard, dry wood."

Then up she went through the chimney,
   Never speaking a word,
And out of the top flew a woodpecker,
   For she was changed to a bird.

She had a scarlet cap on her head,
   And that was left the same,
But all the rest of her clothes were burned
   Black as a coal in the flame.

And every country school-boy
   Has seen her in the wood,
Where she lives in the trees till this very day,
   Boring and boring for food.

And this is the lesson she teaches:
   Live not for yourself alone,
Lest the needs you will not pity
   Shall one day be your own.

Give plenty of what is given to you,
   Listen to pity's call;
Don't think the little you give is great,
   And the much you get is small.

Now, my little boy, remember that,
   And try to be kind and good,
When you see the woodpecker's sooty dress,
   And see her scarlet hood.

You mayn't be changed to a bird though you live
   As selfishly as you can;
But you will be changed to a smaller thing—
   A mean and selfish man.

Phœbe Cary

WHAT IS GOOD?

"What is the real good?"
I asked in musing mood.

Order, said the law court;
Knowledge, said the school;
Truth, said the wise man;
Pleasure, said the fool;
Love, said the maiden;
Beauty, said the page;
Freedom, said the dreamer;
Home, said the sage;
Fame, said the soldier;
Equity, the seer;—

Spake my heart full sadly,
"The answer is not here."

Then within my bosom
Softly this I heard:
"Each heart holds the secret;
Kindness is the word."

John Boyle O'Reilly

THE CRICKET'S STORY

The high and mighty lord of Glendare,
The owner of acres both broad and fair,
Searched, once on a time, his vast domains,
His deep, green forest, and yellow plains,
For some rare singer, to make complete
The studied charms of his country-seat;
But found, for all his pains and labors,
No sweeter songster than had his neighbors.

Ah, what shall my lord of the manor do?
He pondered the day and the whole night through.
He called on the gentry of hill-top and dale;
And at last on Madame the Nightingale,—
Inviting, in his majestical way,
Her pupils to sing at his grand soirée,
That perchance among them my lord might find
Some singer to whom his heart inclined.
What wonder, then, when the evening came,
And the castle gardens were all aflame
With the many curious lights that hung
O'er the ivied porches, and flared among
The grand old trees and the banners proud,
That many a heart beat high and loud,
While the famous choir of Glendare Bog,
Established and led by the Brothers Frog,
Sat thrumming as hoarsely as they were able,
In front of the manager's mushroom table!

The overture closed with a crash—then, hark!
Across the stage comes the sweet-voiced Lark.
She daintily sways, with an airy grace,
And flutters a bit of gossamer lace,
While the leafy alcove echoes and thrills
With her liquid runs and lingering trills.
Miss Goldfinch came next, in her satin gown,
And shaking her feathery flounces down,
With much expression and feeling sung
Some "Oh's" and "Ah's" in a foreign tongue;
While to give the affair a classic tone,
Miss Katydid rendered a song of her own,
In which each line closed as it had begun,
With some wonderful deed which she had done.
Then the Misses Sparrow, so prim and set,
Twittered and chirped through a long duet;

And poor little Wren, who tried with a will,
But who couldn't tell "Heber" from "Ortonville,"
Unconscious of sarcasm, piped away
And courtesied low o'er a huge bouquet
Of crimson clover-heads, culled by the dozen,
By some brown-coated, plebeian cousin.

But you should have heard the red Robin sing
His English ballad, "Come, beautiful Spring!"
And Master Owlet's melodious tune,
"O, meet me under the silvery moon!"
Then, as flighty Miss Humming-bird didn't care
To sing for the high and mighty Glendare,
The close of the evening's performance fell
To the fair young Nightingale, Mademoiselle.
Ah! the wealth of each wonderful note
That came from the depths of her tiny throat!
She carolled, she trilled, and she held her breath,
Till she seemed to hang at the point of death:
She ran the chromatics through every key,
And ended triumphant on upper C;
Airing the graces her mother had taught her
In a manner quite worthy of Madame's daughter.

But his lordship glared down the leafy aisle
With never so much as a nod or smile,
Till, out in the shade of a blackberry thicket,
He all of a sudden spied little Miss Cricket;
And, roused from his gloom, like an angry bat,
He sternly demanded, "Who is that?"
"Miss Cricket, my lord, may it please you so,
A charity scholar—ahem!—you know—
Quite worthy, of course, but we couldn't bring"—
Thundered His Mightiness, "Let her sing!"
The Nightingale opened her little eyes
Extremely wide in her blank surprise;

But catching a glimpse of his lordship's rage,
Led little Miss Cricket upon the stage,
Where she modestly sang, in her simple measures,
Of "Home, sweet Home," and its humble pleasures.
And the lord of Glendare cried out in his glee,
"This little Miss Cricket shall sing for me!"

Of course, of comment there was no need;
But the world said, "Really!" and "Ah, indeed!"
Yet, notwithstanding, we find it true
As his lordship does will the neighbors do;
So this is the way, as the legends tell,
In the very beginning it befell
That the Crickets came, in the evening's gloom,
To sing at our hearths of "Home, sweet Home."

Emma Huntington Nason

SIR LARK AND KING SUN: A PARABLE

From "Adela Cathcart"

"Good morrow, my lord!" in the sky alone,
Sang the lark, as the sun ascended his throne.
"Shine on me, my lord; I only am come,
Of all your servants, to welcome you home.
I have flown for an hour, right up, I swear,
To catch the first shine of your golden hair."

"Must I thank you, then," said the king, "Sir Lark,
For flying so high and hating the dark?
You ask a full cup for half a thirst:
Half is love of me, and half love to be first.
There's many a bird makes no such haste,
But waits till I come: that's as much to my taste."

And King Sun hid his head in a turban of cloud,
And Sir Lark stopped singing, quite vexed and cowed;
But he flew up higher, and thought, "Anon
The wrath of the king will be over and gone;

And his crown, shining out of its cloudy fold,
Will change my brown feathers to a glory of gold."

So he flew—with the strength of a lark he flew;
But, as he rose, the cloud rose too;
And not one gleam of the golden hair
Came through the depths of the misty air;
Till, weary with flying, with sighing sore,
The strong sun-seeker could do no more.

His wings had had no chrism of gold:
And his feathers felt withered and worn and old;
He faltered, and sank, and dropped like a stone.
And there on her nest, where he left her, alone
Sat his little wife on her little eggs,
Keeping them warm with wings and legs.

Did I say alone? Ah, no such thing!
Full in her face was shining the king.
"Welcome, Sir Lark! You look tired," said he;
"*Up* is not always the best way to me.
While you have been singing so high and away,
I've been shining to your little wife all day."

He had set his crown all about the nest,
And out of the midst shone her little brown breast;
And so glorious was she in russet gold,
That for wonder and awe Sir Lark grew cold.
He popped his head under her wing, and lay
As still as a stone, till King Sun was away.

George Macdonald

FABLE

The mountain and the squirrel
Had a quarrel,

And the former called the latter "Little Prig";
Bun replied,
"You are doubtless very big;
But all sorts of things and weather
Must be taken in together,
To make up a year
And a sphere.
And I think it no disgrace
To occupy my place.
If I'm not so large as you,
You are not so small as I,
And not half so spry.
I'll not deny you make
A very pretty squirrel track;
Talents differ; all is well and wisely put;
If I cannot carry forests on my back,
Neither can you crack a nut."

Ralph Waldo Emerson

HOW THE LITTLE KITE LEARNED TO FLY

"I never can do it," the little kite said,
As he looked at the others high over his head;
"I know I should fall if I tried to fly."
"Try," said the big kite; "only try!
Or I fear you never will learn at all."
But the little kite said, "I'm afraid I'll fall."

The big kite nodded: "Ah well, good-by;
I'm off"; and he rose toward the tranquil sky.
Then the little kite's paper stirred at the sight,
And trembling he shook himself free for flight.
First whirling and frightened, then braver grown,
Up, up he rose through the air alone,
Till the big kite looking down could see
The little one rising steadily.

Then how the little kite thrilled with pride,
As he sailed with the big kite side by side!
While far below he could see the ground,
And the boys like small spots moving round.
They rested high in the quiet air,
And only the birds and the clouds were there.
"Oh, how happy I am!" the little kite cried,
"And all because I was brave, and tried."

THE VILLAGE BLACKSMITH

Under a spreading chestnut-tree
    The village smithy stands;
The smith, a mighty man is he,
    With large and sinewy hands;
And the muscles of his brawny arms
    Are strong as iron bands.

His hair is crisp, and black, and long,
    His face is like the tan;
His brow is wet with honest sweat,
    He earns whate'er he can,
And looks the whole world in the face,
    For he owes not any man.

Week in, week out, from morn till night,
    You can hear his bellows blow;
You can hear him swing his heavy sledge
    With measured beat and slow,
Like a sexton ringing the village bell,
    When the evening sun is low.

And children coming home from school
    Look in at the open door;
They love to see the flaming forge,

And hear the bellows roar,
And catch the burning sparks that fly
  Like chaff from a threshing-floor.

He goes on Sunday to the church,
  And sits among his boys;
He hears the parson pray and preach,
  He hears his daughter's voice,
Singing in the village choir,
  And it makes his heart rejoice.

It sounds to him like her mother's voice,
  Singing in Paradise!
He needs must think of her once more,
  How in the grave she lies;
And with his hard, rough hand he wipes
  A tear out of his eyes.

Toiling,—rejoicing,—sorrowing,
  Onward through life he goes;
Each morning sees some task begin,
  Each evening sees it close;
Something attempted, something done,
  Has earned a night's repose.

Thanks, thanks to thee, my worthy friend,
  For the lesson thou hast taught!
Thus at the flaming forge of life
  Our fortunes must be wrought;
Thus on its sounding anvil shaped
  Each burning deed and thought!

Henry Wadsworth Longfellow

EXCELSIOR

The shades of night were falling fast,
As through an Alpine village passed

A youth, who bore, 'mid snow and ice,
A banner with the strange device,
            Excelsior!

His brow was sad; his eye beneath,
Flashed like a falchion from its sheath,
And like a silver clarion rung
The accents of that unknown tongue,
            Excelsior!

In happy homes he saw the light
Of household fires gleam warm and bright;
Above, the spectral glaciers shone,
And from his lips escaped a groan,
            Excelsior!

"Try not the Pass!" the old man said;
"Dark lowers the tempest overhead,
The roaring torrent is deep and wide!"
And loud that clarion voice replied,
            Excelsior!

"Oh stay," the maiden said, "and rest
Thy weary head upon this breast!"
A tear stood in his bright blue eye,
But still he answered, with a sigh,
            Excelsior!

"Beware the pine-tree's withered branch!
Beware the awful avalanche!"
This was the peasant's last Good-night,
A voice replied, far up the height,
            Excelsior!

At break of day, as heavenward
The pious monks of Saint Bernard

Uttered the oft-repeated prayer,
A voice cried through the startled air,
Excelsior!

A traveler, by the faithful hound,
Half buried in the snow was found,
Still grasping in his hand of ice
That banner with the strange device,
Excelsior!

There in the twilight cold and gray,
Lifeless, but beautiful, he lay,
And from the sky, serene and far,
A voice fell, like a falling star,
Excelsior!

Henry Wadsworth Longfellow

A PSALM OF LIFE

WHAT THE HEART OF THE YOUNG MAN SAID TO THE
PSALMIST

Tell me not, in mournful numbers,
Life is but an empty dream!—
For the soul is dead that slumbers,
And things are not what they seem.

Life is real! Life is earnest!
And the grave is not its goal;
Dust thou art, to dust returnest,
Was not spoken of the soul.

Not enjoyment, and not sorrow,
Is our destined end or way;
But to act, that each to-morrow
Find us farther than to-day.

Art is long, and Time is fleeting,
   And our hearts, though stout and brave,
Still, like muffled drums, are beating
   Funeral marches to the grave.

In the world's broad field of battle,
   In the bivouac of Life,
Be not like dumb, driven cattle!
   Be a hero in the strife!

Trust no Future, howe'er pleasant!
   Let the dead Past bury its dead!
Act,—act in the living Present!
   Heart within, and God o'erhead!

Lives of great men all remind us
   We can make our lives sublime,
And, departing, leave behind us
   Footprints on the sands of time;

Footprints, that perhaps another,
   Sailing o'er life's solemn main,
A forlorn and shipwrecked brother,
   Seeing, shall take heart again.

Let us, then, be up and doing,
   With a heart for any fate;
Still achieving, still pursuing,
   Learn to labor and to wait.

Henry Wadsworth Longfellow

TO-DAY

So here hath been dawning
   Another blue Day:
Think, wilt thou let it
   Slip useless away?

Out of Eternity
 This new Day is born;
Into Eternity,
 At night, will return.

Behold it aforetime
 No eye ever did:
So soon it for ever
 From all eyes is hid.

Here hath been dawning
 Another blue Day:
Think, wilt thou let it
 Slip useless away?

Thomas Carlyle

THE HERITAGE

The rich man's son inherits lands,
 And piles of brick and stone, and gold,
And he inherits soft white hands,
 And tender flesh that fears the cold,
 Nor dares to wear a garment old;
A heritage, it seems to me,
One scarce would wish to hold in fee.

The rich man's son inherits cares;
 The bank may break, the factory burn,
A breath may burst his bubble shares,
 And soft white hands could hardly earn
 A living that would serve his turn;
A heritage, it seems to me,
One scarce would wish to hold in fee.

The rich man's son inherits wants,
 His stomach craves for dainty fare;
With sated heart, he hears the pants

Of toiling hinds with brown arms bare,
  And wearies in his easy-chair;
A heritage, it seems to me,
One scarce would wish to hold in fee.

What doth the poor man's son inherit?
  Stout muscles and a sinewy heart,
A hardy frame, a hardier spirit,
  King of two hands, he does his part
  In every useful toil and art;
A heritage, it seems to me,
A king might wish to hold in fee.

What doth the poor man's son inherit?
  Wishes o'erjoyed with humble things,
A rank adjudged by toil-won merit,
  Content that from employment springs,
  A heart that in his labor sings;
A heritage, it seems to me,
A king might wish to hold in fee.

What doth the poor man's son inherit?
  A patience learned of being poor,
Courage, if sorrow come, to bear it,
  A fellow-feeling that is sure
  To make the outcast bless his door;
A heritage, it seems to me,
A king might wish to hold in fee.

O rich man's son! there is a toil
  That with all others level stands;
Large charity doth never soil,
  But only whiten, soft white hands;
  This is the best crop from thy lands,
A heritage, it seems to me,
Worth being rich to hold in fee.

O poor man's son! scorn not thy state;
   There is worse weariness than thine,
In merely being rich and great;
   Toil only gives the soul to shine,
   And makes rest fragrant and benign;
A heritage, it seems to me,
Worth being poor to hold in fee.

Both, heirs to some six feet of sod,
   Are equal in the earth at last;
Both, children of the same dear God,
   Prove title to your heirship vast
   By record of a well-filled past;
A heritage, it seems to me,
Well worth a life to hold in fee.

James Russell Lowell

FORBEARANCE

Hast thou named all the birds without a gun?
Loved the wood-rose, and left it on its stalk?
At rich men's tables eaten bread and pulse?
Unarmed, faced danger with a heart of trust?
And loved so well a high behavior,
In man or maid, that thou from speech refrained,
Nobility more nobly to repay?
O be my friend, and teach me to be thine!

Ralph Waldo Emerson

THE CELESTIAL SURGEON

If I have faltered more or less
In my great task of happiness;
If I have moved among my race
And shown no glorious morning face;

If beams from happy human eyes
Have moved me not; if morning skies,
Books, and my food, and summer rain
Knocked on my sullen heart in vain,—
Lord, Thy most pointed pleasure take,
And stab my spirit broad awake;
Or, Lord, if too obdurate I,
Choose Thou, before that spirit die,
A piercing pain, a killing sin,
And to my dead heart run them in!

Robert Louis Stevenson

DO YOU FEAR THE WIND?

Do you fear the force of the wind,
The slash of the rain?
Go face them and fight them,
Be savage again.
Go hungry and cold like the wolf,
　　Go wade like the crane:
The palms of your hands will thicken,
The skin of your cheek will tan,
You'll grow ragged and weary and swarthy,
　　But you'll walk like a man!

Hamlin Garland

AT THE END OF THE DAY

There is no escape by the river,
There is no flight left by the fen;
We are compassed about by the shiver
Of the night of their marching men.
Give a cheer!
For our hearts shall not give way.
Here's to a dark to-morrow,
And here's to a brave to-day!

The tale of their hosts is countless,
And the tale of ours a score;
But the palm is naught to the dauntless,
And the cause is more and more.
Give a cheer!
We may die, but not give way.
Here's to a silent morrow,
And here's to a stout to-day!

God has said: "Ye shall fail and perish;
But the thrill ye have felt to-night
I shall keep in my heart and cherish
When the worlds have passed in might."
Give a cheer!
For the soul shall not give way.
Here's to the greater to-morrow
That is born of a great to-day!

Now shame on the craven truckler
And the puling things that mope!
We've a rapture for our buckler
That outwears the wings of hope.
Give a cheer!
For our joy shall not give way.
Here's in the teeth of to-morrow
To the glory of to-day!

Richard Hovey

SACRIFICE

Though love repine and reason chafe,
There came a voice without reply:
" 'Tis man's perdition to be safe,
When for the truth he ought to die."

Ralph Waldo Emerson

THE SPLENDID SPUR

Not on the neck of prince or hound,
   Nor a woman's finger twined,
May gold from the deriding ground
   Keep sacred that we sacred bind:
         Only the heel
         Of splendid steel
   Shall stand secure on sliding fate,
   When golden navies weep their freight.

The scarlet hat, the laureled stave
   Are measures, not the springs, of worth;
In a wife's lap, as in a grave,
   Man's airy notions mix with earth.
         Seek other spur
         Bravely to stir
   The dust in this loud world, and tread
   Alp-high among the whispering dead.

Trust in thyself,—then spur amain:
   So shall Charybdis wear a grace,
Grim Ætna laugh, the Libyan plain
   Take roses to her shriveled face.
         This orb—this round
         Of sight and sound—
   Count it the lists that God hath built
   For haughty hearts to ride a-tilt.

              Arthur Quiller-Couch

INVICTUS

Out of the night that covers me,
   Black as the pit from pole to pole,
I thank whatever gods may be
   For my unconquerable soul.

In the fell clutch of circumstance
   I have not winced nor cried aloud:
Under the bludgeonings of chance
   My head is bloody, but unbowed.

Beyond this place of wrath and tears
   Looms but the Horror of the shade,
And yet the menace of the years
   Finds and shall find me unafraid.

It matters not how strait the gate,
   How charged with punishments the scroll,
I am the master of my fate:
   I am the captain of my soul.

              William Ernest Henley

IF—

If you can keep your head when all about you
   Are losing theirs and blaming it on you;
If you can trust yourself when all men doubt you,
   But make allowance for their doubting too;
If you can wait and not be tired by waiting,
   Or being lied about, don't deal in lies,
Or being hated, don't give way to hating,
   And yet don't look too good, nor talk too wise:

If you can dream—and not make dreams your master;
   If you can think—and not make thoughts your aim,
If you can meet with Triumph and Disaster
   And treat those two impostors just the same;
If you can bear to hear the truth you've spoken
   Twisted by knaves to make a trap for fools,
Or watch the things you've given your life to, broken,
   And stoop and build 'em up with worn-out tools:

If you can make one heap of all your winnings
   And risk it on one turn of pitch-and-toss,
And lose, and start again at your beginnings
   And never breathe a word about your loss;
If you can force your heart and nerve and sinew
   To serve your turn long after they are gone,
And so hold on when there is nothing in you
   Except the Will which says to them: "Hold on!"

If you can talk with crowds and keep your virtue,
   Or walk with Kings—nor lose the common touch,
If neither foes nor loving friends can hurt you,
   If all men count with you, but none too much;
If you can fill the unforgiving minute
   With sixty seconds' worth of distance run,
Yours is the Earth and everything that's in it,
   And—which is more—you'll be a Man, my son!

Rudyard Kipling

IMMORTALITY

Battles nor songs can from oblivion save,
   But Fame upon a white deed loves to build;
From out that cup of water Sidney gave,
   Not one drop has been spilled.

Lizette Woodworth Reese

MY PRAYER

Great God, I ask thee for no meaner pelf
Than that I may not disappoint myself;
That in my action I may soar as high
As I can now discern with this clear eye.

And next in value, which thy kindness lends,
That I may greatly disappoint my friends,

Howe'er they think or hope that it may be,
They may not dream how thou'st distinguished me.

That my weak hand may equal my firm faith,
And my life practise more than my tongue saith;
 That my low conduct may not show,
  Nor my relenting lines,
 That I thy purpose did not know,
  Or overrated thy designs.

Henry David Thoreau

DON QUIXOTE

Behind thy pasteboard, on thy battered hack,
Thy lean cheek striped with plaster to and fro,
Thy long spear leveled at the unseen foe,
And doubtful Sancho trudging at thy back,
Thou wert a figure strange enough, good lack!
To make Wiseacredom, both high and low,
Rub purblind eyes, and (having watched thee go),
Dispatch its Dogberrys upon thy track:
Alas! poor Knight!   Alas! poor soul possessed!
Yet would to-day, when Courtesy grows chill,
And life's fine loyalties are turned to jest,
Some fire of thine might burn within us still!
Ah! would but one might lay his lance in rest,
And charge in earnest—were it but a mill.

Austin Dobson

THE EFFECT OF EXAMPLE

We scatter seeds with careless hand,
  And dream we ne'er shall see them more;
   But for a thousand years
   Their fruit appears,
 In weeds that mar the land,
  Or healthful shore.

The deeds we do, the words we say,—
    Into still air they seem to fleet,
      We count them ever past;
      But they shall last,—
In the dread judgment they
    And we shall meet.

I charge thee by the years gone by,
    For the love's sake of brethren dear,
      Keep thou the one true way,
      In work and play,
Lest in that world their cry
    Of woe thou hear.

John Keble

THE CAPTAIN'S DAUGHTER

We were crowded in the cabin,
    Not a soul would dare to sleep,—
It was midnight on the waters,
    And a storm was on the deep.

'Tis a fearful thing in winter
    To be shattered by the blast,
And to hear the rattling trumpet
    Thunder, "Cut away the mast!"

So we shuddered there in silence,—
    For the stoutest held his breath,
While the hungry sea was roaring
    And the breakers talked with death.

As thus we sat in darkness,
    Each one busy with his prayers,
"We are lost!" the captain shouted,
    As he staggered down the stairs.

But his little daughter whispered,
    As she took his icy hand,
"Isn't God upon the ocean,
    Just the same as on the land?"

Then we kissed the little maiden,
    And we spake in better cheer,
And we anchored safe in harbor
    When the morn was shining clear.

                        James Thomas Fields

THE SHEPHERD OF KING ADMETUS

There came a youth upon the earth,
    Some thousand years ago,
Whose slender hands were nothing worth,
Whether to plough, or reap, or sow.

Upon an empty tortoise-shell
    He stretched some chords, and drew
Music that made men's bosoms swell
Fearless, or brimmed their eyes with dew.

Then King Admetus, one who had
    Pure taste by right divine,
Decreed his singing not too bad
To hear between the cups of wine:

And so, well pleased with being soothed
    Into a sweet half-sleep,
Three times his kingly beard he smoothed,
And made him viceroy o'er his sheep.

His words were simple words enough,
And yet he used them so,

That what in other mouths was rough
In his seemed musical and low.

Men called him but a shiftless youth,
    In whom no good they saw;
And yet, unwittingly, in truth,
They made his careless words their law.

They knew not how he learned at all,
    For idly, hour by hour,
He sat and watched the dead leaves fall,
Or mused upon a common flower.

It seemed the loveliness of things
    Did teach him all their use,
For, in mere weeds, and stones, and springs,
He found a healing power profuse.

Men granted that his speech was wise,
    But, when a glance they caught
Of his slim grace and woman's eyes,
They laughed, and called him good-for-naught.

Yet after he was dead and gone,
    And e'en his memory dim,
Earth seemed more sweet to live upon,
More full of love, because of him.

And day by day more holy grew
    Each spot where he had trod,
Till after-poets only knew
Their first-born brother as a god.

James Russell Lowell

THE BIRD IN THE ROOM

A robin skimmed into the room,
    And blithe he looked and jolly,

A foe to every sort of gloom,
  And, most, to melancholy.
He cocked his head, he made no sound,
  But gave me stare for stare back,
When, having fluttered round and round,
  He perched upon a chair-back.

I rose; ah, then, it seemed, he knew
  Too late his reckless error:
Away in eager haste he flew,
  And at his tail flew terror.
Now here, now there, from wall to floor,
  For mere escape appealing,
He fled and struck against the door
  Or bumped about the ceiling.

I went and flung each window wide,
  I drew each half-raised blind up;
To coax him out in vain I tried;
  He could not make his mind up.
He flew, he fell, he took a rest,
  And off again he scuffled
With parted beak and panting breast
  And every feather ruffled.

At length I lured him to the sill,
  All dazed and undivining;
Beyond was peace o'er vale and hill,
  And all the air was shining.
I stretched my hand and touched him; then
  He made no more resistance,
But left the cramped abode of men
  And flew into the distance.

· · · · · · ·

Is life like that? We make it so;
  We leave the sunny spaces,

And beat about, or high or low,
  In dark and narrow places;
Till, worn with failure, vexed with doubt,
  Our strength at last we rally,
And the bruised spirit flutters out
  To find the happy valley.

R. C. Lehmann

SO NIGH IS GRANDEUR

In an age of fops and toys,
Wanting wisdom, void of right,
Who shall nerve heroic boys
To hazard all in Freedom's fight,—
Break sharply off their jolly games,
Forsake their comrades gay
And quit proud homes and youthful dames
For famine, toil and fray?
Yet on the nimble air benign
Speed nimbler messages,
That waft the breath of grace divine
To hearts in sloth and ease.
So nigh is grandeur to our dust,
So near is God to man,
When Duty whispers low, *Thou must*,
The youth replies, *I can.*

Ralph Waldo Emerson

FOUR THINGS

Four things a man must learn to do
If he would make his record true:
To think without confusion clearly;
To love his fellow-men sincerely;
To act from honest motives purely;
To trust in God and Heaven securely.

Henry Van Dyke

OPPORTUNITY

Master of human destinies am I!
Fame, love, and fortune on my footsteps wait.
Cities and fields I walk; I penetrate
Deserts and seas remote, and passing by
Hovel and mart and palace—soon or late
I knock unbidden once at every gate!

If sleeping, wake—if feasting, rise before
I turn away.   It is the hour of fate,
And they who follow me reach every state
Mortals desire, and conquer every foe
Save death; but those who doubt or hesitate,
Condemned to failure, penury, and woe,
Seek me in vain and uselessly implore.
I answer not, and I return no more!

John James Ingalls

OPPORTUNITY

This I beheld, or dreamed it in a dream:—
There spread a cloud of dust along a plain;
And underneath the cloud, or in it, raged
A furious battle, and men yelled, and swords
Shocked upon swords and shields.   A prince's banner
Wavered, then staggered backward, hemmed by foes.
A craven hung along the battle's edge,
And thought, "Had I a sword of keener steel—
That blue blade that the king's son bears,—but this
Blunt thing!" he snapped and flung it from his hand,
And lowering crept away and left the field.
Then came the king's son, wounded, sore bestead,
And weaponless, and saw the broken sword,
Hilt-buried in the dry and trodden sand,

And ran and snatched it, and with battle-shout
Lifted afresh he hewed his enemy down,
And saved a great cause that heroic day.

Edward Rowland Sill

ARS VICTRIX

IMITATED FROM THÉOPHILE GAUTIER

Yes; when the ways oppose—
  When the hard means rebel,
Fairer the work out-grows,—
  More potent far the spell.

O Poet, then, forbear
  The loosely-sandalled verse,
Choose rather thou to wear
  The buskin—straight and terse;

Leave to the tyro's hand
  The limp and shapeless style;
See that thy form demand
  The labor of the file.

Sculptor, do thou discard
  The yielding clay,—consign
To Paros marble hard
  The beauty of thy line;—

Model thy Satyr's face
  For bronze of Syracuse;
In the veined agate trace
  The profile of thy Muse.

Painter, that still must mix
  But transient tints anew,

Thou in the furnace fix
    The firm enamel's hue;

Let the smooth tile receive
    Thy dove-drawn Erycine;
Thy Sirens blue at eve
    Coiled in a wash of wine.

All passes.   Art alone
    Enduring stays to us:
The Bust out-lasts the throne,—
    The Coin, Tiberius;

Even the gods must go;
    Only the lofty Rhyme
Not countless years o'erthrow,—
    Not long array of time.

Paint, chisel, then, or write;
    But, that the work surpass,
With the hard fashion fight,—
    With the resisting mass.

Austin Dobson

THE CALF-PATH

One day, through the primeval wood,
A calf walked home, as good calves should;
But made a trail all bent askew,
A crooked trail as all calves do.

Since then two hundred years have fled,
And, I infer, the calf is dead.
But still he left behind his trail,
And thereby hangs my moral tale.

The trail was taken up next day
By a lone dog that passed that way;
And then a wise bell-wether sheep
Pursued the trail o'er vale and steep,
And drew the flock behind him, too,
As good bell-wethers always do.

And from that day, o'er hill and glade,
Through those old woods a path was made;
And many men wound in and out,
And dodged, and turned, and bent about
And uttered words of righteous wrath
Because 'twas such a crooked path.

But still they followed—do not laugh—
The first migrations of that calf,
And through this winding wood-way stalked,
Because he wobbled when he walked.

This forest path became a lane,
That bent, and turned, and turned again;
This crooked lane became a road,
Where many a poor horse with his load
Toiled on beneath the burning sun,
And traveled some three miles in one.
And thus a century and a half
They trod the footsteps of that calf.

The years passed on in swiftness fleet,
The road became a village street;
And this, before men were aware,
A city's crowded thoroughfare;
And soon the central street was this
Of a renowned metropolis;
And men two centuries and a half
Trod in the footsteps of that calf.

Each day a hundred thousand rout
Followed the zigzag calf about;
And o'er his crooked journey went
The traffic of a continent.
A hundred thousand men were led
By one calf near three centuries dead.
They followed still his crooked way,
And lost one hundred years a day;
For thus such reverence is lent
To well-established precedent.

A moral lesson this might teach,
Were I ordained and called to preach:
For men are prone to go it blind
Along the calf-paths of the mind,
And work away from sun to sun
To do what other men have done.
They follow in the beaten track,
And out and in, and forth and back,
And still their devious course pursue,
To keep the path that others do.

But how the wise old wood-gods laugh,
Who saw the first primeval calf!
Ah! many things this tale might teach,—
But I am not ordained to preach.

Sam Walter Foss

THE HAPPIEST HEART

Who drives the horses of the sun
Shall lord it but a day;
Better the lowly deed were done,
And kept the humble way.

The rust will find the sword of fame,
The dust will hide the crown;

Ay, none shall nail so high his name
Time will not tear it down.

The happiest heart that ever beat
Was in some quiet breast
That found the common daylight sweet,
And left to Heaven the rest.

John Vance Cheney

DUTY

When Duty comes a-knocking at your gate,
Welcome him in; for if you bid him wait,
He will depart only to come once more
And bring seven other duties to your door.

Edwin Markham

STERN DAUGHTER OF THE VOICE OF GOD

From "Ode to Duty"

Stern Daughter of the Voice of God!
O Duty! if that name thou love,
Who art a light to guide, a rod
To check the erring and reprove;
Thou, who art victory and law
When empty terrors overawe;
From vain temptations dost set free;
And calm'st the weary strife of frail humanity!

Serene will be our days and bright,
And happy will our nature be,
When love is an unerring light,
And joy its own security.
And they a blissful course may hold
Even now, who, not unwisely bold,
Live in the spirit of this creed;
Yet seek thy firm support, according to their need.

I, loving freedom, and untried;
No sport of every random gust,
Yet being to myself a guide,
Too blindly have reposed my trust:
And oft, when in my heart was heard
Thy timely mandate, I deferred
The task, in smoother walks to stray;
But thee I now would serve more strictly, if I may.

To humbler functions, awful Power!
I call thee: I myself commend
Unto thy guidance from this hour;
O, let my weakness have an end!
Give unto me, made lowly wise,
The spirit of self-sacrifice;
The confidence of reason give;
And in the light of truth thy Bondman let me live!

William Wordsworth

RECESSIONAL

God of our fathers, known of old—
    Lord of our far-flung battle line—
Beneath whose awful Hand we hold
    Dominion over palm and pine—
Lord God of Hosts, be with us yet,
Lest we forget—lest we forget!

The tumult and the shouting dies—
    The Captains and the Kings depart—
Still stands Thine ancient sacrifice,
    An humble and a contrite heart.
Lord God of Hosts, be with us yet,
Lest we forget—lest we forget!

Far-called, our navies melt away—
    On dune and headland sinks the fire—

Lo, all our pomp of yesterday
   Is one with Nineveh and Tyre!
Judge of the Nations, spare us yet,
Lest we forget—lest we forget!

If, drunk with sight of power, we loose
   Wild tongues that have not Thee in awe—
Such boasting as the Gentiles use,
   Or lesser breeds without the Law—
Lord God of Hosts, be with us yet,
Lest we forget—lest we forget!

For heathen heart that puts her trust
   In reeking tube and iron shard—
All valiant dust that builds on dust,
   And guarding calls not Thee to guard,—
For frantic boast and foolish word,
Thy Mercy on Thy People, Lord! AMEN.

Rudyard Kipling

XII A Garland of Gold

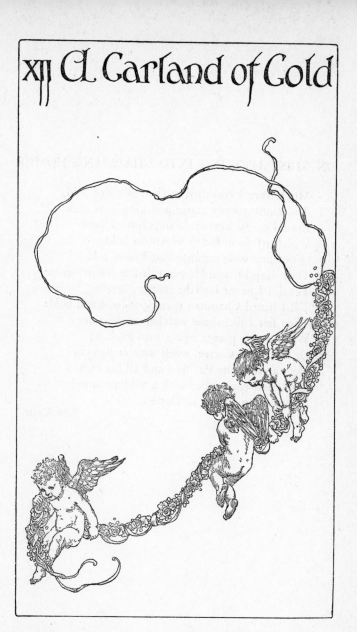

ON FIRST LOOKING INTO CHAPMAN'S HOMER

Much have I travelled in the realms of gold,
And many goodly states and kingdoms seen;
Round many western islands have I been
Which bards in fealty to Apollo hold.
Oft of one wide expanse had I been told
That deep-browed Homer ruled as his demesne:
Yet did I never breathe its pure serene
Till I heard Chapman speak out loud and bold:
Then felt I like some watcher of the skies
When a new planet swims into his ken;
Or like stout Cortez, when with eagle eyes
He stared at the Pacific—and all his men
Looked at each other with a wild surmise—
Silent, upon a peak in Darien.

John Keats

A GARLAND OF GOLD

I WANDERED LONELY AS A CLOUD

I wandered lonely as a cloud
That floats on high o'er vales and hills,
When all at once I saw a crowd,
A host, of golden daffodils;
Beside the lake, beneath the trees,
Fluttering and dancing in the breeze

Continuous as the stars that shine
And twinkle in the Milky Way,
They stretched in never-ending line
Along the margin of a bay:
Ten thousand saw I at a glance,
Tossing their heads in sprightly dance.

The waves beside them danced; but they
Out-did the sparkling waves in glee:
A poet could not but be gay,
In such a jocund company:
I gazed—and gazed—but little thought
What wealth the show to me had brought:

For oft, when on my couch I lie
In vacant or in pensive mood,
They flash upon that inward eye
Which is the bliss of solitude;
And then my heart with pleasure fills,
And dances with the daffodils.

William Wordsworth

THE WORLD IS TOO MUCH WITH US

The world is too much with us; late and soon,
Getting and spending, we lay waste our powers:
Little we see in Nature that is ours;
We have given our hearts away, a sordid boon!
This sea that bares her bosom to the moon,
The winds that will be howling at all hours,
And are up-gathered now like sleeping flowers;
For this, for everything, we are out of tune;
It moves us not.—Great God! I'd rather be
A Pagan suckled in a creed outworn;
So might I, standing on this pleasant lea,
Have glimpses that would make me less forlorn;
Have sight of Proteus rising from the sea;
Or hear old Triton blow his wreathèd horn.

William Wordsworth

THE RAINBOW

My heart leaps up when I behold
 A rainbow in the sky:
So was it when my life began;
So is it now I am a man;
So be it when I shall grow old,
 Or let me die!
The Child is father of the Man;
And I could wish my days to be
Bound each to each by natural piety.

William Wordsworth

THE SPACIOUS FIRMAMENT ON HIGH

The spacious firmament on high,
With all the blue ethereal sky,

And spangled heavens, a shining frame,
Their great Original proclaim.
The unwearied Sun, from day to day,
Does his Creator's power display;
And publishes to every land
The work of an Almighty hand.

Soon as the evening shades prevail,
The Moon takes up the wondrous tale;
And nightly to the listening Earth
Repeats the story of her birth:
Whilst all the stars that round her burn,
And all the planets in their turn,
Confirm the tidings as they roll
And spread the truth from pole to pole.

What though, in solemn silence, all
Move round the dark terrestrial ball?
What though nor real voice nor sound
Amidst their radiant orbs be found?
In Reason's ear they all rejoice,
And utter forth a glorious voice;
For ever singing as they shine,
"The Hand that made us is divine."

Joseph Addison

ODE ON SOLITUDE

Happy the man, whose wish and care
A few paternal acres bound,
Content to breathe his native air
                    In his own ground.

Whose herds with milk, whose fields with bread,
Whose flocks supply him with attire;
Whose trees in summer yield him shade,
                    In winter, fire.

Blest, who can unconcernedly find
Hours, days, and years, slide soft away
In health of body, peace of mind,
   Quiet by day;

Sound sleep by night; study and ease
Together mixed, sweet recreation,
And innocence, which most does please,
   With meditation.

Thus let me live, unseen, unknown;
Thus unlamented let me die;
Steal from the world, and not a stone
   Tell where I lie.
      Alexander Pope

THE SHEPHERD BOY SINGS

From "Pilgrim's Progress"

He that is down needs fear no fall,
 He that is low, no pride;
He that is humble ever shall
 Have God to be his guide.

I am content with what I have,
 Little be it or much:
And, Lord, contentment still I crave,
 Because Thou savest such.

Fullness to such a burden is
 That go on pilgrimage:
Here little, and hereafter bliss,
 Is best from age to age.

      John Bunyan

HE LIVETH LONG WHO LIVETH WELL

He liveth long who liveth well!
  All other life is short and vain;
He liveth longest who can tell
  Of living most for heavenly gain.

He liveth long who liveth well!
  All else is being flung away;
He liveth longest who can tell
  Of true things truly done each day.

Waste not thy being; back to Him
  Who freely gave it, freely give;
Else is that being but a dream;
  'Tis but to *be*, and not to *live*.

Be what thou seemest! live thy creed!
  Hold up to earth the torch divine;
Be what thou prayest to be made;
  Let the great Master's steps be thine.

Fill up each hour with what will last;
  Buy up the moments as they go;
The life above, when this is past,
  Is the ripe fruit of life below.

Sow truth, if thou the truth wouldst reap:
  Who sows the false shall reap the vain;
Erect and sound thy conscience keep;
  From hollow words and deeds refrain.

Sow love, and taste its fruitage pure;
  Sow peace, and reap its harvests bright;
Sow sunbeams on the rock and moor,
  And find a harvest-home of light.

Horatius Bonar

THE CHARACTER OF A HAPPY LIFE

How happy is he born and taught
    That serveth not another's will;
Whose armor is his honest thought,
    And simple truth his utmost skill!

Whose passions not his masters are;
    Whose soul is still prepared for death,
Not tied unto the world by care
    Of public fame or private breath;

Who envies none that chance doth raise,
    Nor vice; who never understood
How deepest wounds are given by praise;
    Nor rules of state, but rules of good;

Who hath his life from rumors freed;
    Whose conscience is his strong retreat;
Whose state can neither flatterers feed
    Nor ruin make oppressors great;

Who God doth late and early pray
    More of His grace than gifts to lend;
And entertains the harmless day
    With a well-chosen book or friend;

—This man is freed from servile bands
    Of hope to rise, or fear to fall:
Lord of himself, though not of lands,
    And having nothing, yet hath all.

Henry Wotton

THE LIFE UPRIGHT

(INTEGER VITÆ)

The man of life upright,
    Whose guiltless heart is free

From all dishonest deeds,
  Or thought of vanity;

The man whose silent days
  In harmless joys are spent,
Whom hope cannot delude,
  Nor sorrow discontent;

That man needs neither towers
  Nor armor for defense,
Nor secret vaults to fly
  From thunder's violence:

He only can behold
  With unaffrighted eyes
The horrors of the deep
  And terrors of the skies

Thus, scorning all the cares
  That fate or fortune brings,
He makes the heaven his book,
  His wisdom heavenly things;

Good thoughts his only friends,
  His wealth a well-spent age,
The earth his sober inn
  And quiet pilgrimage.

After Horace, by Thomas Campion

HONESTY

Thou must be true thyself,
If thou the truth wouldst teach;
Thy soul must overflow, if thou
Another's soul wouldst reach!
It needs the overflow of heart
To give the lips full speech.

Think truly, and thy thoughts
Shall the world's famine feed;
Speak truly, and each word of thine
Shall be a fruitful seed;
Live truly, and thy life shall be
A great and noble creed.

Horatius Bonar

ON HIS BLINDNESS

When I consider how my light is spent
Ere half my days in this dark world and wide,
And that one talent, which is death to hide,
Lodged with me useless, though my soul more bent
To serve therewith my Maker, and present
My true account, lest He returning chide;
"Doth God exact day-labor, light denied?"
I fondly ask.   But patience, to prevent
That murmur, soon replies, "God doth not need
Either man's work or his own gifts; who best
Bear his mild yoke, they serve him best; his state
Is kingly; thousands at his bidding speed,
And post o'er land and ocean without rest:
They also serve who only stand and wait."

John Milton

SAY NOT, THE STRUGGLE NAUGHT AVAILETH

Say not, the struggle naught availeth,
The labor and the wounds are vain,
The enemy faints not, nor faileth,
And as things have been they remain.

If hopes were dupes, fears may be liars;
It may be, in yon smoke concealed,
Your comrades chase e'en now the fliers,
And, but for you, possess the field.

For while the tired waves, vainly breaking,
  Seem here no painful inch to gain,
Far back, through creeks and inlets making,
  Comes silent, flooding in, the main.

And not by eastern windows only,
  When daylight comes, comes in the light;
In front, the sun climbs slow, how slowly!
  But westward, look, the land is bright!

Arthur Hugh Clough

TO A MOUSE

ON TURNING UP HER NEST WITH THE PLOW, NOVEMBER, 1785

Wee, sleekit, cow'rin', tim'rous beastie,
Oh, what a panic's in thy breastie!
Thou need na start awa' sae hasty,
    Wi' bickering brattle!
I wad be laith to rin an' chase thee,
    Wi' murd'ring pattle!

I'm truly sorry man's dominion
Has broken Nature's social union,
An' justifies that ill opinion,
    Which makes thee startle
At me, thy poor, earth-born companion,
    An' fellow-mortal!

I doubt na, whiles, but thou may thieve;
What then? poor beastie, thou maun live!
A daimen icker in a thrave
    'S a sma' request;
I'll get a blessin' wi' the laive,
    And never miss't!

Thy wee bit housie, too, in ruin!
Its silly wa's the win's are strewin'!
An' naething, now, to big a new ane,
        O' foggage green!
An' bleak December's winds ensuin',
        Baith snell an' keen!

Thou saw the fields laid bare an' waste,
An' weary winter comin' fast,
An' cozie here, beneath the blast,
        Thou thought to dwell,—
Till, crash! the cruel coulter passed
        Out through thy cell.

That wee bit heap o' leaves an' stibble
Has cost thee mony a weary nibble!
Now thou's turned out, for a' thy trouble,
        But house or hald,
To thole the winter's sleety dribble,
        An' cranreuch cauld!

But, Mousie, thou art no thy lane,
In proving foresight may be vain:
The best-laid schemes o' mice an' men,
        Gang aft a-gley,
An' lea'e us naught but grief an' pain,
        For promised joy!

Still thou art blest, compared wi' me!
The present only toucheth thee:
But, och! I backward cast my e'e
        On prospects drear!
An' forward, though I canna see,
        I guess an' fear!

                                    Robert Burns

THE RHODORA

ON BEING ASKED WHENCE IS THE FLOWER

In May, when sea-winds pierced our solitudes,
I found the fresh Rhodora in the woods,
Spreading its leafless blooms in a damp nook,
To please the desert and the sluggish brook.
The purple petals, fallen in the pool,
Made the black water with their beauty gay;
Here might the red-bird come his plumes to cool,
And court the flower that cheapens his array.
Rhodora! if the sages ask thee why
This charm is wasted on the earth and sky,
Tell them, dear, that if eyes were made for seeing,
Then Beauty is its own excuse for being:
Why thou wert there, O rival of the rose!
I never thought to ask, I never knew:
But, in my simple ignorance, suppose
The self-same Power that brought me there brought you.

Ralph Waldo Emerson

ODE ON A GRECIAN URN

Thou still unravished bride of quietness,
   Thou foster-child of Silence and slow Time,
Sylvan historian, who canst thus express
   A flowery tale more sweetly than our rhyme:
What leaf-fringed legend haunts about thy shape
   Of deities or mortals, or of both,
     In Tempe or the dales of Arcady?
   What men or gods are these?   What maidens loth?
What mad pursuit?   What struggle to escape?
     What pipes and timbrels?   What wild ecstasy?

Heard melodies are sweet, but those unheard
   Are sweeter; therefore, ye soft pipes, play on;

Not to the sensual ear, but, more endeared,
　　Pipe to the spirit ditties of no tone:
Fair youth, beneath the trees, thou canst not leave
　　Thy song, nor ever can those trees be bare;
　　　　Bold Lover, never, never canst thou kiss,
Though winning near the goal—yet, do not grieve;
　　　　She cannot fade, though thou hast not thy bliss,
For ever wilt thou love, and she be fair!

Ah, happy, happy boughs! that cannot shed
　　Your leaves, nor ever bid the Spring adieu;
And, happy melodist, unwearied,
　　For ever piping songs for ever new;
More happy love! more happy, happy love!
　　For ever warm and still to be enjoyed,
　　　　For ever panting and for ever young;
All breathing human passion far above,
　　That leaves a heart high-sorrowful and cloyed,
　　　　A burning forehead, and a parching tongue.

Who are these coming to the sacrifice?
　　To what green altar, O mysterious priest,
Lead'st thou that heifer lowing at the skies,
　　And all her silken flanks with garlands dressed?
What little town by river or sea-shore,
　　Or mountain-built with peaceful citadel,
　　　　Is emptied of its folk, this pious morn?
And, little town, thy streets for evermore
　　Will silent be; and not a soul, to tell
　　　　Why thou art desolate, can e'er return.

O Attic shape! fair attitude! with brede
　　Of marble men and maidens overwrought,
With forest branches and the trodden weed;
　　Thou, silent form! dost tease us out of thought
As doth eternity.　Cold Pastoral!

When old age shall this generation waste,
  Thou shalt remain, in midst of other woe
Than ours, a friend to man, to whom thou say'st,
"Beauty is truth, truth beauty,"—that is all
  Ye know on earth, and all ye need to know.

                                    John Keats

THE CHAMBERED NAUTILUS

This is the ship of pearl, which, poets feign,
    Sails the unshadowed main,—
    The venturous bark that flings
On the sweet summer wind its purpled wings
In gulfs enchanted, where the Siren sings,
    And coral reefs lie bare,
Where the cold sea-maids rise to sun their streaming hair.

Its webs of living gauze no more unfurl;
    Wrecked is the ship of pearl!
    And every chambered cell,
Where its dim dreaming life was wont to dwell,
As the frail tenant shaped his growing shell,
    Before thee lies revealed,—
Its irised ceiling rent, its sunless crypt unsealed!

Year after year beheld the silent toil
    That spread his lustrous coil;
    Still, as the spiral grew,
He left the past year's dwelling for the new,
Stole with soft step its shining archway through,
    Built up its idle door,
Stretched in his last-found home, and knew the old no
        more.

Thanks for the heavenly message brought by thee,
    Child of the wandering sea,

Cast from her lap, forlorn!
From thy dead lips a clearer note is born
Than ever Triton blew from wreathèd horn!
While on mine ear it rings,
Through the deep caves of thought I hear a voice that
sings—

Build thee more stately mansions, O my soul,
As the swift seasons roll!
Leave thy low-vaulted past!
Let each new temple, nobler than the last,
Shut thee from heaven with a dome more vast,
Till thou at length art free,
Leaving thine outgrown shell by life's unresting sea!

Oliver Wendell Holmes

TO A WATERFOWL

Whither, midst falling dew,
While glow the heavens with the last steps of day,
Far, through their rosy depths, dost thou pursue
Thy solitary way?

Vainly the fowler's eye
Might mark thy distant flight to do thee wrong,
As, darkly painted on the crimson sky,
Thy figure floats along.

Seek'st thou the plashy brink
Of weedy lake, or marge of river wide,
Or where the rocking billows rise and sink
On the chafed ocean-side?

There is a Power whose care
Teaches thy way along that pathless coast,—

The desert and illimitable air,—
    Lone wandering, but not lost.

All day thy wings have fanned
At that far height, the cold, thin atmosphere,
Yet stoop not, weary, to the welcome land,
    Though the dark night is near.

And soon that toil shall end;
Soon shalt thou find a summer home, and rest,
And scream among thy fellows; reeds shall bend,
    Soon, o'er thy sheltered nest.

Thou'rt gone, the abyss of heaven
Hath swallowed up thy form; yet, on my heart
Deeply hath sunk the lesson thou hast given,
    And shall not soon depart.

He who, from zone to zone,
Guides through the boundless sky thy certain flight,
In the long way that I must tread alone,
    Will lead my steps aright.

                  William Cullen Bryant

GRADATIM

Heaven is not reached at a single bound;
    But we build the ladder by which we rise
    From the lowly earth to the vaulted skies,
And we mount to its summit round by round.

I count this thing to be grandly true:
    That a noble deed is a step toward God,
    Lifting the soul from the common clod
To a purer air and a broader view.

We rise by the things that are under feet;
By what we have mastered of good and gain;
By the pride deposed and the passion slain,
And the vanquished ills that we hourly meet.

We hope, we aspire, we resolve, we trust,
When the morning calls us to life and light,
But our hearts grow weary, and, ere the night,
Our lives are trailing the sordid dust.

We hope, we resolve, we aspire, we pray,
And we think that we mount the air on wings
Beyond the recall of sensual things,
While our feet still cling to the heavy clay.

Wings for the angels, but feet for men!
We may borrow the wings to find the way—
We may hope, and resolve, and aspire, and pray;
But our feet must rise, or we fall again.

Only in dreams is a ladder thrown
From the weary earth to the sapphire walls;
But the dreams depart, and the vision falls,
And the sleeper wakes on his pillow of stone.

Heaven is not reached at a single bound;
But we build the ladder by which we rise
From the lowly earth to the vaulted skies,
And we mount to its summit, round by round.

Josiah Gilbert Holland

A TURKISH LEGEND

A certain Pasha, dead five thousand years,
Once from his harem fled in sudden tears,

And had this sentence on the city's gate
Deeply engraven, "Only God is great."

So these four words above the city's noise
Hung like the accents of an angel's voice,

And evermore, from the high barbican,
Saluted each returning caravan.

Lost is that city's glory.   Every gust
Lifts, with dead leaves, the unknown Pasha's dust,

And all is ruin,—save one wrinkled gate
Whereon is written, "Only God is great."

Thomas Bailey Aldrich

OZYMANDIAS OF EGYPT

I met a traveler from an antique land
Who said: Two vast and trunkless legs of stone
Stand in the desert.   Near them, on the sand,
Half sunk, a shattered visage lies, whose frown
And wrinkled lip and sneer of cold command
Tell that its sculptor well those passions read
Which yet survive, stamped on these lifeless things,
The hand that mocked them and the heart that fed;
And on the pedestal these words appear:
"My name is Ozymandias, king of kings:
Look on my works, ye Mighty, and despair!"
Nothing beside remains.   Round the decay
Of that colossal wreck, boundless and bare,
The lone and level sands stretch far away.

Percy Bysshe Shelley

TEARS

When I consider Life and its few years—
A wisp of fog betwixt us and the sun;

A call to battle, and the battle done
Ere the last echo dies within our ears;
A rose choked in the grass; an hour of fears;
The gusts that past a darkening shore do beat;
The burst of music down an unlistening street,—
I wonder at the idleness of tears.
Ye old, old dead, and ye of yesternight,
Chieftains, and bards, and keepers of the sheep,
By every cup of sorrow that you had,
Loose me from tears, and make me see aright
How each hath back what once he stayed to weep:
Homer his sight, David his little lad!

Lizette Woodworth Reese

I LOVE ALL BEAUTEOUS THINGS

I love all beauteous things,
I seek and adore them;
God hath no better praise,
And man in his hasty days
Is honored for them.

I too will something make
And joy in the making!
Although to-morrow it seem
Like the empty words of a dream
Remembered, on waking.

Robert Bridges

SAY NOT THAT BEAUTY

Say not that beauty is an idle thing
And gathered lightly as a wayside flower
That on the trembling verges of the spring
Knows but the sweet survival of an hour.
For 'tis not so.   Through dedicated days

And foiled adventure of deliberate nights
We lose and find and stumble in the ways
That lead to the far confluence of delights.
Not with the earthly eye and fleshly ear,
But lifted far above mortality,
We see at last the eternal hills, and hear
The sighing of the universal sea;
And kneeling breathless in the holy place
We know immortal Beauty face to face.

Robin Flower

THE STAR

Beauty had first my pride;
But now my heart she hath,
And all the whole world wide
   Is Beauty's path!
By mountain, field and flood
I walked in hardihood;
But now with delicate pace
   Her steps I trace.

Once did my spirit dare
In fond presumptuous dream
To make her ways more fair
   That fair did seem.
But all the world became
Her ways elect, to shame
With their least lovely lot
   My loftiest thought.

Her worshipful bright fire!
Ah! Whither will it lead
My burning faint desire
   And feet that bleed?
Far in my failing view,

A pure and blazing gem,
She lights on earth the New
Jerusalem!

Willoughby Weaving

HE WHOM A DREAM HATH POSSESSED

He whom a dream hath possessed knoweth no more of
doubting,
For mist and the blowing of winds and the mouthing of
words he scorns;
Not the sinuous speech of schools he hears, but a knightly
shouting,
And never comes darkness down, yet he greeteth a mil-
lion morns.

He whom a dream hath possessed knoweth no more of
roaming.
All roads and the flowing of waves and the speediest flight
he knows,
But wherever his feet are set, his soul is forever homing,
And going, he comes, and coming he heareth a call and
goes.

He whom a dream hath possessed knoweth no more of
sorrow.
At death and the dropping of leaves and the fading of suns
he smiles,
For a dream remembers no past and takes no thought of a
morrow,
And staunch amid seas of doom a dream sets the ultimate
isles.

He whom a dream hath possessed treads the impalpable
marches.
From the dust of the day's long road he leaps to a laughing
star,

And the ruin of worlds that fall he views from eternal
    arches,
And rides God's battle-field in a flashing and golden car.

Shaemas O'Sheel

THE LISTENERS

"Is there anybody there?" said the Traveller,
    Knocking on the moonlit door;
And his horse in the silence champed the grasses
    Of the forest's ferny floor:
And a bird flew up out of the turret,
    Above the Traveller's head:
And he smote upon the door again a second time;
    "Is there anybody there?" he said.
But no one descended to the Traveller;
    No head from the leaf-fringed sill
Leaned over and looked into his gray eyes,
    Where he stood perplexed and still.
But only a host of phantom listeners
    That dwelt in the lone house then
Stood listening in the quiet of the moonlight
    To that voice from the world of men:
Stood thronging the faint moonbeams on the dark
    stair,
    That goes down to the empty hall,
Hearkening in an air stirred and shaken
    By the lonely Traveller's call.
And he felt in his heart their strangeness,
    Their stillness answering his cry,
While his horse moved, cropping the dark turf,
    'Neath the starred and leafy sky;
For he suddenly smote on the door, even
    Louder, and lifted his head:—
"Tell them I came, and no one answered,
    That I kept my word," he said.

Never the least stir made the listeners,
   Though every word he spake
Fell echoing through the shadowiness of the still house
   From the one man left awake:
Ay, they heard his foot upon the stirrup,
   And the sound of iron on stone,
And how the silence surged softly backward,
   When the plunging hoofs were gone.

                    Walter de la Mare

A MUSICAL INSTRUMENT

What was he doing, the great god Pan,
   Down in the reeds by the river?
Spreading ruin and scattering ban,
Splashing and paddling with hoofs of a goat,
And breaking the golden lilies afloat
   With the dragon-fly on the river.

He tore out a reed, the great god Pan,
   From the deep cool bed of the river;
The limpid water turbidly ran,
And the broken lilies a-dying lay,
And the dragon-fly had fled away,
   Ere he brought it out of the river.

High on the shore sat the great god Pan,
   While turbidly flowed the river;
And hacked and hewed as a great god can,
With his hard bleak steel at the patient reed,
Till there was not a sign of a leaf indeed
   To prove it fresh from the river.

He cut it short, did the great god Pan,
   (How tall it stood in the river!)

Then drew the pith, like the heart of a man,
Steadily from the outside ring,
And notched the poor dry empty thing
    In holes, as he sat by the river.

"This is the way," laughed the great god Pan,
    (Laughed while he sat by the river,)
"The only way, since gods began
To make sweet music, they could succeed."
Then, dropping his mouth to a hole in the reed,
    He blew in power by the river.

Sweet, sweet, sweet, O Pan!
    Piercing sweet by the river!
Blinding sweet, O great god Pan!
The sun on the hill forgot to die,
And the lilies revived, and the dragon-fly
    Came back to dream on the river.

Yet half a beast is the great god Pan,
    To laugh as he sits by the river,
Making a poet out of a man:
The true gods sigh for the cost and pain,—
For the reed which grows nevermore again
    As a reed with the reeds in the river.

Elizabeth Barrett Browning

SHE WALKS IN BEAUTY

She walks in beauty, like the night
    Of cloudless climes and starry skies;
And all that's best of dark and bright
    Meet in her aspect and her eyes:
Thus mellowed to that tender light
    Which heaven to gaudy day denies.

One shade the more, one ray the less,
   Had half impaired the nameless grace
Which waves in every raven tress
   Or softly lightens o'er her face;
Where thoughts serenely sweet express
   How pure, how dear their dwelling-place.

And on that cheek, and o'er that brow
   So soft, so calm, yet eloquent,
The smiles that win, the tints that glow,
   But tell of days in goodness spent,
A mind at peace with all below,
   A heart whose love is innocent!

George Gordon Byron

THE SHEPHERDESS

She walks—the lady of my delight—
   A shepherdess of sheep.
Her flocks are thoughts. She keeps them white;
   She guards them from the steep.
She feeds them on the fragrant height,
   And folds them in for sleep.

She roams maternal hills and bright,
   Dark valleys safe and deep.
Into that tender breast at night
   The chastest stars may peep.
She walks—the lady of my delight—
   A shepherdess of sheep.

She holds her little thoughts in sight,
   Though gay they run and leap.
She is so circumspect and right;
   She has her soul to keep.
She walks—the lady of my delight—
   A shepherdess of sheep.

Alice Meynell

TO HELEN

Helen, thy beauty is to me
    Like those Nicæan barks of yore,
That gently, o'er a perfumed sea,
    The weary, wayworn wanderer bore
    To his own native shore.

On desperate seas long wont to roam,
    Thy hyacinth hair, thy classic face,
Thy Naiad airs, have brought me home
    To the glory that was Greece
    And the grandeur that was Rome.

Lo! in yon brilliant window-niche
    How statue-like I see thee stand,
The agate lamp within thy hand!
    Ah, Psyche, from the regions which
    Are Holy Land!

Edgar Allan Poe

AH, BE NOT FALSE

Ah, be not false, sweet Splendor!
    Be true, be good;
Be wise as thou art tender;
    Be all that Beauty should.

Not lightly be thy citadel subdued;
    Not ignobly, not untimely,
Take praise in solemn mood;
    Take love sublimely.

Richard Watson Gilder

SHE DWELT AMONG THE UNTRODDEN WAYS

She dwelt among the untrodden ways
    Beside the springs of Dove,

A Maid whom there were none to praise
  And very few to love:

A violet by a mossy stone
  Half hidden from the eye!
Fair as a star, when only one
  Is shining in the sky.

She lived unknown, and few could know
  When Lucy ceased to be;
But she is in her grave, and oh,
  The difference to me!

William Wordsworth

THREE YEARS SHE GREW

Three years she grew in sun and shower;
Then Nature said, "A lovelier flower
  On earth was never sown;
This child I to myself will take;
She shall be mine, and I will make
  A lady of my own.

"Myself will to my darling be
Both law and impulse; and with me
  The girl, in rock and plain,
In earth and heaven, in glade and bower,
Shall feel an overseeing power
  To kindle or restrain.

"She shall be sportive as the fawn
That wild with glee across the lawn
  Or up the mountain springs;
And hers shall be the breathing balm,
And hers the silence and the calm
  Of mute insensate things.

"The floating clouds their state shall lend
To her; for her the willow bend;
    Nor shall she fail to see
Even in the motions of the storm
Grace that shall mold the maiden's form
    By silent sympathy.

"The stars of midnight shall be dear
To her; and she shall lean her ear
    In many a secret place
Where rivulets dance their wayward round,
And beauty born of murmuring sound
    Shall pass into her face.

"And vital feelings of delight
Shall rear her form to stately height,
    Her virgin bosom swell;
Such thoughts to Lucy I will give
While she and I together live
    Here in this happy dell."

Thus Nature spake—The work was done—
How soon my Lucy's race was run!
    She died, and left to me
This heath, this calm and quiet scene;
The memory of what has been,
    And never more will be.

William Wordsworth

ANNABEL LEE

It was many and many a year ago,
    In a kingdom by the sea,
That a maiden there lived whom you may know
    By the name of Annabel Lee;
And this maiden she lived with no other thought
    Than to love and be loved by me.

I was a child and she was a child,
 In this kingdom by the sea,
But we loved with a love that was more than love,
 I and my Annabel Lee;
With a love that the wingèd seraphs of heaven
 Coveted her and me.

And this was the reason that, long ago,
 In this kingdom by the sea,
A wind blew out of a cloud, chilling
 My beautiful Annabel Lee;
So that her highborn kinsmen came
 And bore her away from me,
To shut her up in a sepulcher
 In this kingdom by the sea.

The angels, not half so happy in heaven,
 Went envying her and me;
Yes! that was the reason (as all men know,
 In this kingdom by the sea)
That the wind came out of the cloud by night,
 Chilling and killing my Annabel Lee.

But our love it was stronger by far than the love
 Of those who were older than we,
 Of many far wiser than we;
And neither the angels in heaven above,
 Nor the demons down under the sea,
Can ever dissever my soul from the soul
 Of the beautiful Annabel Lee:

For the moon never beams, without bringing me dreams
 Of the beautiful Annabel Lee;
And the stars never rise, but I feel the bright eyes
 Of the beautiful Annabel Lee;

And so, all the night-tide, I lie down by the side
Of my darling—my darling—my life and my bride,
   In the sepulcher there by the sea,
   In her tomb by the sounding sea.

                Edgar Allan Poe

LITTLE BOY BLUE

The little toy dog is covered with dust,
   But sturdy and stanch he stands;
And the little toy soldier is red with rust,
   And his musket moulds in his hands.
Time was when the little toy dog was new,
   And the soldier was passing fair;
And that was the time when our Little Boy Blue
   Kissed them and put them there.

"Now, don't you go till I come," he said,
   "And don't you make any noise!"
So, toddling off to his trundle-bed,
   He dreamt of the pretty toys;
And, as he was dreaming, an angel song
   Awakened our Little Boy Blue—
Oh! the years are many, the years are long,
   But the little toy friends are true!

Ay, faithful to Little Boy Blue they stand,
   Each in the same old place.
Awaiting the touch of a little hand,
   The smile of a little face;
And they wonder, as waiting the long years through
   In the dust of that little chair,
What has become of our Little Boy Blue,
   Since he kissed them and put them there.

                Eugene Field

ELEGY WRITTEN IN A COUNTRY CHURCHYARD

The curfew tolls the knell of parting day,
   The lowing herd winds slowly o'er the lea,
The plowman homeward plods his weary way,
   And leaves the world to darkness and to me.

Now fades the glimmering landscape on the sight,
   And all the air a solemn stillness holds,
Save where the beetle wheels his droning flight,
   And drowsy tinklings lull the distant folds:

Save that from yonder ivy-mantled tower
   The moping owl does to the moon complain
Of such as, wandering near her secret bower,
   Molest her ancient solitary reign.

Beneath those rugged elms, that yew-tree's shade,
   Where heaves the turf in many a moldering heap,
Each in his narrow cell for ever laid,
   The rude forefathers of the hamlet sleep.

The breezy call of incense-breathing morn,
   The swallow twittering from the straw-built shed,
The cock's shrill clarion, or the echoing horn,
   No more shall rouse them from their lowly bed.

For them no more the blazing hearth shall burn,
   Or busy housewife ply her evening care:
No children run to lisp their sire's return,
   Or climb his knees the envied kiss to share.

Oft did the harvest to their sickle yield,
   Their furrow oft the stubborn glebe has broke:
How jocund did they drive their team afield!
   How bowed the woods beneath their sturdy stroke!

Let not Ambition mock their useful toil,
  Their homely joys, and destiny obscure;
Nor Grandeur hear with a disdainful smile
  The short and simple annals of the poor.

The boast of heraldry, the pomp of power,
  And all that beauty, all that wealth e'er gave,
Awaits alike the inevitable hour:
  The paths of glory lead but to the grave.

Nor you, ye proud, impute to these the fault
  If Memory o'er their tomb no trophies raise,
Where through the long-drawn aisle and fretted vault
  The pealing anthem swells the note of praise.

Can storied urn or animated bust
  Back to its mansion call the fleeting breath?
Can Honor's voice provoke the silent dust,
  Or Flattery soothe the dull cold ear of death?

Perhaps in this neglected spot is laid
  Some heart once pregnant with celestial fire;
Hands, that the rod of empire might have swayed,
  Or waked to ecstasy the living lyre.

But Knowledge to their eyes her ample page
  Rich with the spoils of time did ne'er unroll;
Chill Penury repressed their noble rage,
  And froze the genial current of the soul.

Full many a gem of purest ray serene
  The dark unfathomed caves of ocean bear:
Full many a flower is born to blush unseen,
  And waste its sweetness on the desert air.

Some village Hampden that, with dauntless breast,
  The little tyrant of his fields withstood,

Some mute inglorious Milton here may rest,
   Some Cromwell guiltless of his country's blood.

The applause of listening senates to command,
   The threats of pain and ruin to despise,
To scatter plenty o'er a smiling land,
   And read their history in a nation's eyes,

Their lot forbade: nor circumscribed alone
   Their growing virtues, but their crimes confined;
Forbade to wade through slaughter to a throne,
   And shut the gates of mercy on mankind;

The struggling pangs of conscious truth to hide,
   To quench the blushes of ingenuous shame,
Or heap the shrine of Luxury and Pride
   With incense kindled at the Muse's flame.

Far from the madding crowd's ignoble strife,
   Their sober wishes never learned to stray;
Along the cool, sequestered vale of life
   They kept the noiseless tenor of their way.

Yet even these bones from insult to protect
   Some frail memorial still erected nigh,
With uncouth rhymes and shapeless sculpture decked,
   Implores the passing tribute of a sigh.

Their name, their years, spelt by the unlettered Muse,
   The place of fame and elegy supply:
And many a holy text around she strews,
   That teach the rustic moralist to die.

For who, to dumb Forgetfulness a prey,
   This pleasing anxious being e'er resigned,

Left the warm precincts of the cheerful day,
  Nor cast one longing lingering look behind?

On some fond breast the parting soul relies,
  Some pious drops the closing eye requires;
E'en from the tomb the voice of Nature cries,
  E'en in our ashes live their wonted fires.

For thee, who, mindful of the unhonored dead,
  Dost in these lines their artless tale relate;
If chance, by lonely contemplation led,
  Some kindred spirit shall inquire thy fate,—

Haply some hoary-headed swain may say,
  "Oft have we seen him at the peep of dawn
Brushing with hasty steps the dews away
  To meet the sun upon the upland lawn.

"There at the foot of yonder nodding beech
  That wreathes its old fantastic roots so high,
His listless length at noontide would he stretch,
  And pore upon the brook that babbles by.

"Hard by yon wood, now smiling as in scorn,
  Muttering his wayward fancies he would rove,
Now drooping, woeful-wan, like one forlorn,
  Or crazed with care, or crossed in hopeless love.

"One morn I missed him on the customed hill,
  Along the heath, and near his favorite tree;
Another came; nor yet beside the rill,
  Nor up the lawn, nor at the wood was he:

"The next, with dirges due in sad array,
  Slow through the church-way path we saw him borne.
Approach and read (for thou canst read) the lay
  Graved on the stone beneath yon aged thorn:"

THE EPITAPH

Here rests his head upon the lap of Earth
  A Youth, to Fortune and to Fame unknown.
Fair Science frowned not on his humble birth,
  And Melancholy marked him for her own.

Large was his bounty, and his soul sincere,
  Heaven did a recompense as largely send:
He gave to Misery (all he had) a tear,
  He gained from Heaven ('twas all he wished) a friend.

No farther seek his merits to disclose,
  Or draw his frailties from their dread abode,
(There they alike in trembling hope repose,)
  The bosom of his Father and his God.

Thomas Gray

THANATOPSIS

To him who in the love of Nature holds
Communion with her visible forms, she speaks
A various language; for his gayer hours
She has a voice of gladness, and a smile
And eloquence of beauty, and she glides
Into his darker musings, with a mild
And healing sympathy, that steals away
Their sharpness, ere he is aware.   When thoughts
Of the last bitter hour come like a blight
Over thy spirit, and sad images
Of the stern agony, and shroud, and pall,
And breathless darkness, and the narrow house,
Make thee to shudder and grow sick at heart;—
Go forth, under the open sky, and list
To Nature's teachings, while from all around—
Earth and her waters, and the depths of air—
Comes a still voice:—

Yet a few days, and thee
The all-beholding sun shall see no more
In all his course; nor yet in the cold ground,
Where thy pale form was laid, with many tears,
Nor in the embrace of ocean, shall exist
Thy image.   Earth, that nourished thee, shall claim
Thy growth, to be resolved to earth again,
And, lost each human trace, surrendering up
Thine individual being, shalt thou go
To mix forever with the elements,
To be a brother to the insensible rock
And to the sluggish clod, which the rude swain
Turns with his share, and treads upon.   The oak
Shall send his roots abroad, and pierce thy mold.

Yet not to thine eternal resting-place
Shalt thou retire alone, nor couldst thou wish
Couch more magnificent.   Thou shalt lie down
With patriarchs of the infant world—with kings,
The powerful of the earth—the wise, the good,
Fair forms, and hoary seers of ages past,
All in one mighty sepulcher.   The hills
Rock-ribbed and ancient as the sun,—the vale
Stretching in pensive quietness between;
The venerable woods—rivers that move
In majesty, and the complaining brooks
That make the meadows green; and, poured round all,
Old Ocean's gray and melancholy waste,—
Are but the solemn decorations all
Of the great tomb of man.   The golden sun,
The planets, all the infinite host of heaven,
Are shining on the sad abodes of death
Through the still lapse of ages.   All that tread
The globe are but a handful to the tribes
That slumber in its bosom.—Take the wings
Of morning, pierce the Barcan wilderness,

Or lose thyself in the continuous woods
Where rolls the Oregon, and hears no sound,
Save his own dashings—yet the dead are there:
And millions in those solitudes, since first
The flight of years began, have laid them down
In their last sleep—the dead reign there alone.
So shalt thou rest, and what if thou withdraw
In silence from the living, and no friend
Take note of thy departure?   All that breathe
Will share thy destiny.   The gay will laugh
When thou art gone, the solemn brood of care
Plod on, and each one as before will chase
His favorite phantom; yet all these shall leave
Their mirth and their employments, and shall come
And make their bed with thee.   As the long train
Of ages glides away, the sons of men—
The youth in life's fresh spring, and he who goes
In the full strength of years, matron and maid,
The speechless babe, and the gray-headed man—
Shall one by one be gathered to thy side,
By those, who in their turn shall follow them.

So live, that when thy summons comes to join
The innumerable caravan, which moves
To that mysterious realm, where each shall take
His chamber in the silent halls of death,
Thou go not, like the quarry-slave at night,
Scourged to his dungeon, but, sustained and soothed
By an unfaltering trust, approach thy grave
Like one who wraps the drapery of his couch
About him, and lies down to pleasant dreams.

William Cullen Bryant

CROSSING THE BAR

Sunset and evening star,
And one clear call for me!

And may there be no moaning of the bar,
   When I put out to sea,

But such a tide as moving seems asleep,
   Too full for sound and foam,
When that which drew from out the boundless deep
   Turns again home.

Twilight and evening bell,
   And after that the dark!
And may there be no sadness of farewell,
   When I embark;

For though from out our bourne of Time and Place
   The flood may bear me far,
I hope to see my Pilot face to face
   When I have crossed the bar.

Alfred Tennyson

REQUIEM

Under the wide and starry sky
Dig the grave and let me lie.
Glad did I live and gladly die,
   And I laid me down with a will.

This be the verse you grave for me:
Here he lies where he longed to be;
Home is the sailor, home from sea,
   And the hunter home from the hill.

Robert Louis Stevenson

SO BE MY PASSING

A late lark twitters from the quiet skies
And from the west,

Where the sun, his day's work ended,
Lingers as in content,
There falls on the old, gray city
An influence luminous and serene,
A shining peace.

The smoke ascends
In a rosy-and-golden haze.   The spires
Shine and are changed.   In the valley
Shadows rise.   The lark sings on.   The sun,
Closing his benediction,
Sinks, and the darkening air
Thrills with a sense of the triumphing night—
Night with her train of stars
And her great gift of sleep.

So be my passing!
My task accomplished and the long day done,
My wages taken, and in my heart
Some late lark singing,
Let me be gathered to the quiet west,
The sundown splendid and serene,
Death.

William Ernest Henley

PROSPICE

Fear death?—to feel the fog in my throat,
   The mist in my face,
When the snows begin, and the blasts denote
   I am nearing the place,
The power of the night, the press of the storm,
   The post of the foe;
Where he stands, the Arch Fear in a visible form,
   Yet the strong man must go:

For the journey is done and the summit attained,
 And the barriers fall,
Though a battle's to fight ere the guerdon be gained,
 The reward of it all.
I was ever a fighter, so—one fight more,
 The best and the last!
I would hate that death bandaged my eyes, and forbore,
 And bade me creep past.
No! let me taste the whole of it, fare like my peers
 The heroes of old,
Bear the brunt, in a minute pay glad life's arrears
 Of pain, darkness and cold.
For sudden the worst turns the best to the brave,
 The black minute's at end,
And the elements' rage, the fiend-voices that rave,
 Shall dwindle, shall blend,
Shall change, shall become first a peace out of pain,
 Then a light, then thy breast,
O thou soul of my soul! I shall clasp thee again,
 And with God be the rest!

Robert Browning

JOY, SHIPMATE, JOY!

Joy, shipmate, joy!
(Pleased to my soul at death I cry)
Our life is closed, our life begins,
The long, long anchorage we leave,
The ship is clear at last, she leaps!
She swiftly courses from the shore,
Joy, shipmate, joy!

Walt Whitman

INDEX OF AUTHORS

INDEX OF FIRST LINES

A

PAGE

G

H

O

P

R

PAGE

PAGE

Y

INDEX OF TITLES